LIGHT
PRINCIPLES AND EXPERIMENTS

LIGHT

PRINCIPLES AND EXPERIMENTS

BY

GEORGE S. MONK

Assistant Professor of Physics
University of Chicago

FIRST EDITION
FOURTH IMPRESSION

McGRAW-HILL BOOK COMPANY, INC.

NEW YORK AND LONDON

1937

THE MAPLE PRESS COMPANY, YORK, PA.

PREFACE

During thirteen years' teaching of the subject of light at an intermediate level, in classroom and laboratory, the author has had the usual experience of finding it necessary to refer students to several different textbooks for outside reading to supplement the lectures. Rarely has it been possible to find a single textbook in which the treatment of a given topic contained the degree of elaboration consistent with the purposes of an intermediate course. For this reason the author believed that a text covering the essentials of geometrical and physical optics, with the addition of several chapters covering the more recently developed subjects of modern optics, would serve a useful purpose.

The book is intended for students who have finished the equivalent of an ordinary sophomore college course in general physics. It is intended for both those for whom an intermediate course in the subject is the last, and those who expect to continue graduate study in the field of light or in associated fields in the physical or biological sciences. For this reason, while the emphasis is on physical optics, particularly interference, diffraction, and polarization, considerable space has also been devoted to geometrical optics, a subject which is only too often not a familiar one to students who will later use optical instruments whose principles they should understand. A working knowledge of elementary mathematics, including the fundamentals of the differential and integral calculus, is required, but so far as possible each topic has been treated so that abstract mathematical development is subordinated to the discussion of the physical concepts involved. This has required that in several instances where the mathematical theory is beyond the scope of the book only the results are set down, while in other cases mere algebraic development has been relegated to appendices. An experiment, not necessarily novel, has been tried in basing several of the problems upon illustrations in the book, thus supplying a degree of substitution for laboratory experience.

Other texts have been drawn upon freely in compiling this one, principally Drude, "Theory of Optics"; Wood, "Physical Optics"; Preston, "Theory of Light"; L. W. Taylor, "College Manual of Optics"; Mann, "Manual of Optics"; Born, "Optik"; Williams, "Applications of Interferometry"; Hardy and Perrin, "Principles of Optics"; and to a lesser extent many others. The author acknowledges with gratitude advice and criticism by his colleagues, especially Professors H. G. Gale, A. H. Compton, and Carl Eckart, each of whom read parts of the manuscript. Thanks are also due Dr. Rudolf Kingslake for valuable criticisms of an earlier draft of the chapters on geometrical optics, and Dr. J. S. Campbell for criticisms of an earlier draft of the chapters on interference, diffraction, and polarization. Helpful criticism by Dr. George E. Ziegler, Mr. Richard W. Hamming, and Mr. Alfred Kelcy is acknowledged, as well as comments and corrections by members of classes during the preparation of the manuscript. A great deal is due to the helpful and stimulating advice given by Professor F. K. Richtmyer, who suggested important changes and additions. Acknowledgments for illustrations copied or otherwise obtained from others are for the most part made at the point of insertion. Exceptions are: Fig. 7-8, which was copied from a cut kindly supplied by the Bausch and Lomb Optical Company; Fig. 11-17, which is a copy of a photograph made for the author some years ago by Dr. J. S. Campbell; Fig. 13-9, from a wash drawing made by Miss Libuse Lukas; Fig. 14-10a, from a spectrogram made by Mr. Leonard N. Liebermann; Fig. 16-1, supplied by the Mount Wilson Observatory; and Fig. 16-12, adapted from an illustration by F. E. Foster in the *Physical Review*, **23**, 669, 1924.

Finally, no words of the author can express the thanks due his wife, Ardis T. Monk, for criticisms of the manuscript, for reading and correcting the proof, and for the preparation of the index.

GEORGE S. MONK.

UNIVERSITY OF CHICAGO,
    September, 1937.

CONTENTS

vii

CONTENTS

LIGHT: PRINCIPLES AND EXPERIMENTS

CHAPTER I

FUNDAMENTAL CONCEPTS IN GEOMETRICAL OPTICS

1. Fundamental Postulates.—Optical phenomena may be divided into two classes. The most important of these in the light of modern experimental discovery is that which is included in the subject of *physical optics*, which deals with theories of the nature of light and of its interaction with material objects, together with experimental verification of these theories. Fundamental to the study of physical optics, however, is a knowledge of the principles of another class of optical phenomena which, after the introduction of a few fundamental experimental facts, may be described without taking into account any hypotheses concerning the nature of light or its interaction with material bodies. This division of optics, concerned with image formation by optical systems and with the laws of photometry, is called *geometrical optics*, since its description is founded almost entirely on geometrical relations. Because an understanding of the laws of image formation is fundamental, geometrical optics will be dealt with first.

There are certain experimental facts, sometimes regarded as postulates, upon which the study of geometrical optics may be based:

1. Light is propagated in straight lines in a homogeneous medium.

2. Two independent beams of light may intersect each other and thereafter be propagated as independent beams.

3. The angle of incidence of light upon a reflecting surface is equal to the angle of reflection.

4. On refraction, the ratio of the sine of the angle of incidence to the sine of the angle of refraction is a constant depending only on the nature of the media (Snell's law).

1

To these four facts may be added the concept of the ray and certain deduced laws which are subject to experimental verification.

2. The Ray.—The ray may be defined as the path along which light travels. Since for most purposes it is possible to consider the light to be a wave motion spreading out with the same velocity in all directions from the source (in a homogeneous and isotropic[1] medium), we may say that the ray is the direction in which this wave motion is propagated. Indeed, it is not necessary to specify the wave form of the light, but simply to consider it to be propagated in straight lines, since any consideration of the physical nature of the light takes us outside the realm of geometrical optics. While some exception may be taken to the use of the ray concept as not conforming to modern ideas of the nature of light, it is found most convenient in discussing the characteristics of optical systems to trace the paths of the rays from a source through succeeding media in accordance with the preceding four laws.

3. The Optical Length of a Ray.—It has been proved experimentally that light undergoes a change in velocity in passing from one medium to another, and that the index of refraction given by Snell's law, $n = \sin i / \sin r$, is also given by

$$n_{abs} = \frac{\text{velocity } in\ vacuo}{\text{velocity in the medium}}.$$

As given here, n_{abs} is the *absolute index* of the medium. Since the velocity of light in air is very little different from that in vacuo, for optical purposes the index of air is taken as unity. For example, the index of refraction of glass is commonly given by

$$n = \frac{\text{velocity in air}}{\text{velocity in glass}};$$

this is the ratio of the absolute index of glass to that of air.

The *optical length* of a ray of length l in a medium of index n is defined as the product nl. Light rays from a point source at

---

[1] A medium is said to be optically *isotropic* when it has the same optical properties in all directions. Thus, water, and glass free from strains, are isotropic. Glass with strains, and all crystals except cubic, are *anisotropic*. On the other hand, any one of these is *homogeneous* if different portions of its mass have the same characteristics.

O on the optical axis of a lens (Fig. 1-1) reach the lens at its vertex B sooner than at any other point, A. At the surfaces the rays will undergo refraction and, if the lens is free from aberrations, will converge to an image point I. If the distance BB' is greater than AA' the retardation along the axis in the glass will be more than between A and A'. While the *linear* path $OAA'I$ is greater than $OBB'I$, the *optical* paths are the same; *i.e.*, the times taken by the light to go from O to I over the two paths are the same.

Let the indices of refraction of air and glass be n_a and n_g, respectively. Then the optical paths

$$OA \cdot n_a + AA' \cdot n_g + A'I \cdot n_a \quad \text{and} \quad OB \cdot n_a + BB' \cdot n_g + B'I \cdot n_a$$

are the same. A more general statement is that $\Sigma n_i \cdot l_i$ is constant for all rays traversing a perfect optical system, where l_i

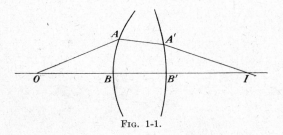

FIG. 1-1.

is the linear distance in each medium of index of refraction n_i. In ordinary lens systems the statement would be true only for two *adjacent* rays.

4. Fermat's Principle.—If, in Fig. 1-1, the angle made by the ray OA with the axis is θ, then

$$\frac{\partial(\Sigma n \cdot l)}{\partial \theta} = 0.$$

This is the mathematical statement of a principle first stated by Fermat, the *principle of least time*, which says that the path taken by light in passing between two points is that which it will traverse in the least time.

Sometimes the general law expressed by Fermat's principle is called the *law of extreme path*. Light reflected from a plane surface at P, in Fig. 1-2, travels from A to B by the shortest path

APB. To prove this, consider the distance of the virtual image *A'* from *B* through *P* as compared to the distance through any other point *P'* on the surface. According to the law of reflection, $i = i'$, hence *APB* is the actual path of the light, and is equal to *A'PB*, which is shorter than any other path *A'P'B*. In this case

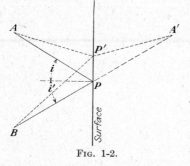

the "extreme" path is the shortest path; in other cases, however, "extreme" may mean either a maximum or a minimum.

Illustration may be simplified by introducing the *aplanatic surface.* A reflecting or refracting surface is aplanatic if it causes all rays incident upon it from an object to converge to a single image point. Thus, an ellipsoid

FIG. 1-2.

of revolution is an aplanatic surface by reflection for a point object placed at one focus, the image point being the other focus, since the sum of the distances from the two foci of the ellipsoid to any point on the surface is constant.

An aplanatic refracting surface is illustrated in Fig. 1-3 by the curve *SPS'*. The equation of such a surface is

$$n_1 \cdot AP + n_2 \cdot PB = constant,$$

where n_1 and n_2 are the indices of refraction of the two media and *AP* and *PB* are the linear distances, respectively, from the object point to the surface, and from the surface to the image point. The surface is concave toward the medium of greater index, n_2; consequently the optical path

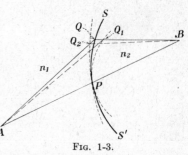

FIG. 1-3.

$$n_1 \cdot AQ + n_2 \cdot QB$$

is the same as that through the point *P.*

Now suppose the rays to be refracted, instead of at the surface *SPS'*, at another surface, through *P* and Q_1, of greater curvature than *SPS'*, and tangent to the first surface at *P*. Then

$$n_1 \cdot AP + n_2 \cdot PB = n_1 \cdot AQ + n_2 \cdot QB$$
$$= n_1 \cdot AQ + n_2 \cdot QQ_1 + n_2 \cdot Q_1B$$
$$> n_1 \cdot AQ + n_1 \cdot QQ_1 + n_2 \cdot Q_1B$$
$$\text{(since } n_2 > n_1)$$
$$> n_1 \cdot AQ_1 + n_2 \cdot Q_1B$$
$$\text{(since } n_1 \cdot AQ + n_1 \cdot QQ_1 > n_1 \cdot AQ_1).$$

Since the point Q_1 is any point on the second surface except P, the optical path of the light through P is a maximum for this surface.

On the other hand, consider the light to be refracted from a third surface, passing through P and Q_2, but of smaller curvature than SPS'. By an argument similar to the preceding one, the optical path of the ray refracted at P can be shown to be less than that of any other ray refracted at the third surface, and hence to be a minimum.

Thus the optical path of a ray by refraction may be either a maximum or a minimum.

5. The Principle of Reversibility.—By referring to Fig. 1-1 it will be seen also that a ray starting from I and traversing the path IA' must of necessity be subject to refraction through the lens which will make the ultimate path of the ray AO. The fact that the direction in which the light is propagated may be reversed without changing the *path* of a ray is known as the *principle of reversibility.*

6. The Law of Malus.—From the geometrical laws already stated, particularly from Fermat's principle, may be deduced another principle, the *law of Malus*, which states that an orthotomic system of rays remains orthotomic after any number of refractions and reflections. An *orthotomic system* is one which contains only rays which may be cut at right angles by a properly constructed surface. The geometrical proof will not be given here. It is evident that if we consider the light to be radiated from a point source in all directions, the surface of a sphere about the point will, in a homogeneous and isotropic medium, constitute the surface cutting the rays at right angles. The passage of the light into another medium will give rise to another surface which, although not a sphere having its center at the source, will nevertheless cut all the rays at right angles. An extended source may be considered as a multiplicity of point sources. From the standpoint of the wave theory, in which we may regard the ray as the direction of propagation of the wave, the law of Malus needs no proof.

7. The Focal Length of a Thin Lens.—A "thin" lens is one whose thickness is negligible compared to its focal length.

In a simple thin lens, the optical axis is the line through the center of the lens joining the centers of curvature of the surfaces. If the lens is used to form an image of an object, then the relation

$$\frac{1}{a} + \frac{1}{a'} = \frac{1}{f} \tag{1-1}$$

holds, when a, the distance from object to lens, a', the distance from image to lens, and f, the *principal focal length* of the lens, are measured along the optical axis. It will be shown in the following chapters that $1/f$, sometimes called the power of the lens, depends only on the radii of curvature r_1 and r_2 of the surfaces and the index of refraction n of the substance used, and is given by

$$\frac{1}{f} = (n - 1)\left(\frac{1}{r_1} - \frac{1}{r_2}\right). \tag{1-2}$$

If in eq. 1-1 a is put equal to infinity, $a' = f$. By definition, the focal length of a simple thin lens is the distance from the lens at which all incident rays parallel to the axis will meet after refraction. Similarly, if $a' = \infty$, $a = f$; the lens thus possessing two principal focal points.

8. Two Thin Lenses.—If two thin lenses are used coaxially, the focal length f of the combination depends upon their focal lengths f_1 and f_2 and the distance d between them and is given by

$$\frac{1}{f} = \frac{1}{f_1} + \frac{1}{f_2} - \frac{d}{f_1 f_2}. \tag{1-3}$$

This relationship will be developed in the following chapters.

9. The Concept of Principal Planes.—It is evident that the distance f in eq. 1-3 is not in general measured to any of the four surfaces of the lenses. Nevertheless, the principal focal length must be measured to some axial point. Only in the simplest cases of single thin lenses, or of combinations of thin lenses very close together is the principal focal length given even approximately by the distance to the lens from the point where incident parallel rays meet. For thick lenses and most combinations it is necessary to specify a pair of planes, perpendicular to the optical axis, to which the principal focal distances are measured. The positions of these *principal* or *unit planes*, determined by rules developed in the following chapters, depend upon the curvatures of the surfaces, the indices of refraction of the glass used, and the separation of the surfaces. Only in the case of a simple thin lens are the principal planes appreciably close to the refracting surfaces, compared to the other dimensions of the system.

10. Equivalent Focal Lengths.—The concept of principal planes may be further illustrated by a description of the equivalent focal length of a combination of two thin lenses. Let P_1 and P_2 in Fig. 1-4a be the positions of two thin lenses. Then a

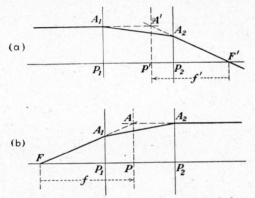

Fig. 1-4.—Illustrating the concept of principal planes.

ray parallel to the axis incident upon the first lens at A_1 and upon the second at A_2 will intersect the axis at the principal focus F' of the combination. But the effect will be that of a single thin lens placed at P' whose focal length f' on the emergent side is $F'P'$. Similarly, a ray from a point object on the axis at F (Fig. 1-4b) refracted at A_1 and A_2, will proceed as if refracted by a single thin lens placed at P, whose focal length f on the incident side is FP. The distances f and f' are the *equivalent focal lengths* of the combination, and for the case of two thin lenses in air can be shown to be the same. The planes at positions P and P' are the principal planes of the combination.

In the following chapters it will be shown that such a pair of principal planes exists for any optical system, such as a thick lens, a mirror, or combinations of lenses and mirrors.

CHAPTER II

THE LAWS OF IMAGE FORMATION

1. Ideal Optical Systems.—In Sec. **4** of the preceding chapter it was indicated that reflecting and refracting surfaces of only certain shapes will bring rays from a point object to a focus at an image point. The restrictions on image-forming systems are still greater if the object or the aperture of the system is of appreciable size. In any actual case, the laws of image formation become a series of approximations. There are, however, certain

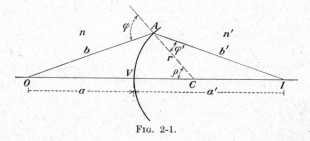

Fig. 2-1.

principles and concepts which may be established for all systems by considering ideal systems in which the effects of object size and aperture are ignored. The laws thus developed may be considered as a *first-order theory.*

2. Refraction at a Spherical Surface.—In Fig. 2-1 is shown an element of a single refracting surface. This element can be considered as the line generating the surface if rotated about the optical axis $OVCI$. The plane of the paper is called the plane of incidence containing all the rays under discussion. Obviously any plane containing the optical axis would serve the same purpose. The *object space,* of index of refraction n, is on the left of the surface and the *image space,* of index of refraction $n'(n' > n)$, is on the right. Distances along the rays are taken positively from O toward V in the object space, and from I toward V in the image space. The radius of curvature r of the spherical surface is considered positive when the surface is convex toward the object space.   A ray from an axial point O is refracted at A in accordance with Snell's law, and proceeds to the axial image point I.   Calling $OV = a$, $OA = b$, $IV = a'$, and $IA = b'$, there result from the law of sines

$$\frac{\sin \varphi}{\sin \rho} = \frac{a + r}{b} \quad \text{and} \quad \frac{\sin \varphi'}{\sin \rho} = \frac{a' - r}{b'}.$$

doesn't show 1st order approx.

Dividing the first of these equations by the second, and making the important assumption that the distance of A from the axis is so small compared to a and a' that to a sufficient degree of approximation $b = a$ and $b' = a'$,

$$\frac{\sin \varphi}{\sin \varphi'} = \frac{a + r}{a' - r} \cdot \frac{a'}{a} = \frac{n'}{n} \quad \text{(from Snell's law)}.$$

Clearing of fractions, rearranging, and dividing by $aa'r$,

$$\frac{n}{a} + \frac{n'}{a'} = \frac{n' - n}{r}. \tag{2-1}$$

When O is infinitely distant, I will by definition be the principal focus F' in the image space, and the corresponding value of a' is, from eq. 2-1,

$$f' = \frac{rn'}{n' - n}. \tag{2-2}$$

Similarly there will be a principal focal point F in the object space corresponding to an infinitely distant I, for which the value of a is, from eq. 2-1,

$$f = \frac{rn}{n' - n}. \tag{2-3}$$

From eqs. 2-2 and 2-3 it follows that for a system composed of a single refracting surface,

$$\frac{f'}{f} = \frac{n'}{n}. \tag{2-4}$$

Thus if an optical system consisted of a tube containing water, with a convex surface at one end, the ratio of the focal lengths in the water and in the air would be 1.33/1.

If eqs. 2-2 and 2-3 are divided by a' and a, respectively, the quotients added, and the result combined with eq. 2-1, it follows that

$$\frac{f}{a} + \frac{f'}{a'} = 1. \tag{2-5}$$

3. The Collinear Relation.—Most commonly, refracting optical systems have more than one surface. For these, it is possible to build up equations analogous to those just derived for a single surface by repeated applications of Snell's law at each succeeding surface. Both the method and the results, however, would be extremely cumbersome. In Sec. **3-2** by a method of particular elegance a general lens formula is developed with which the focal length of a system of any number of surfaces may be found. There are, however, certain concepts applicable to any optical system which may be best expounded by a consideration of the one to one relationship existing between object and image points in an ideal system. This relationship may be represented by making use of the so-called *collinear relation*. This relation is a development of projective geometry and is applicable in all cases where there is a one to one correspondence between points, lines, and planes in one coordinate system and points, lines, and planes in another. It is applicable to the optical case, since in any optical system to any point, line, or plane in the *object space*, there is a conjugate point, line, or plane in the *image space*. It is true that this relation holds rigorously only for ideal systems, *i.e.*, those in which there are no aberrations, but the concepts derived are most general and can properly be used for all systems, no matter how complex. The steps by which the general collinear relation is modified to fit the optical case are so largely algebraic that the development is given in Appendix I instead of in the text at this point. These steps lead to the following simplified collinear equations:

$$xx' = ff', \tag{2-6}$$

$$\frac{y'}{y} = \frac{f}{x} = \frac{x'}{f'}. \tag{2-7}$$

These equations, which *hold for all coaxial optical systems*, no matter how complex they may be, are illustrated in Fig. 2-2. A point O_1 in the object space has the coordinates (x, y). In the image space there is a point I_1, with coordinates (x', y'), conjugate to O_1. The point F is the principal focal point in the object space. If a point source of light is placed at F, all the rays which are emergent from the optical system will be parallel to the optical axis XX'. Similarly, the point F' is the principal focal point in the image space. Rays which are parallel to the optical axis in the object space will, after interception by the

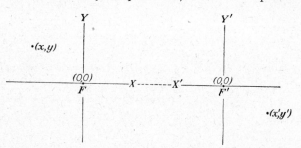

Fig. 2-2.—The coordinates in the object and image spaces.

optical system, meet at F'. In the figure y' is negative, illustrating the case for a real image formed by an ordinary double-convex lens. The rays proceed from left to right. By convention, distances in the object space are positive to the right of F, and in the image space to the left of F'.

4. Lateral Magnification.—The ratio y'/y in eq. 2-7 is known as the *lateral magnification* and is characterized by the symbol β.

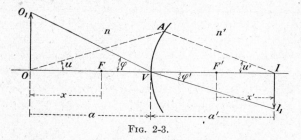

Fig. 2-3.

5. Collinear Equations for a Single Refracting Surface.—If the system is a single refracting surface, then, in eq. 2-1, $a = f - x$, and $a' = f' - x'$. Substituting these values in eq. 2-5, we obtain $xx' = ff'$, which is eq. 2-6. To obtain eq. 2-7 for a single surface we may proceed as follows: Consider an object OO_1 and its conjugate image II_1, as illustrated in Fig. 2-3. Putting

$OO_1 = y$ and $II_1 = y'$, and assuming that y and y' are small compared to OV and IV, we may write

$$\frac{\tan \varphi}{\tan \varphi'} = -\frac{y(f' - x')}{y'(f - x)} \cdot \frac{\sin \varphi}{\sin \varphi'} = \frac{n'}{n}.$$

From this it follows, using eq. 2-4, that

$$-\frac{y(f' - x')}{y'(f - x)} = \frac{f'}{f},$$

which by simplification becomes $y'/y = f/x = x'/f'$, which is eq. 2-7.

6. Principal Points and Planes.—It should be pointed out that the distances f and f' as obtained from the collinear relation are not necessarily the focal lengths in the object and image spaces; thus far this has only been shown to be true for a single refracting

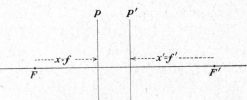

Fig. 2-4.—The principal (unit) planes are where $x = f$ and $x' = f'$.

surface. In coaxial systems in general they are *thus far* considered only as two numbers whose values depend upon the characteristics of the optical system, such as the radii of curvature of the surfaces, the indices of refraction of the media, and the distances between the surfaces. They can be given a more definite meaning for ideal systems by considering eq. 2-7. The value of the lateral magnification, β, will be unity when $f = x$ or when $f' = x'$. Since x and x' are the distances from the principal focal points to the object and image planes, respectively, the value $\beta = 1$ defines two planes perpendicular to the optical axis whose distances from F and F' are f $(= x)$ and f' $(= x')$. These planes are illustrated in Fig. 2-4 by the lines marked P and P' perpendicular to the optical axis. These planes are called the *unit* or *principal planes*. Their intersections with the axis are called the *principal points*. By eqs. 2-6 and 2-7, for these values of x and x', $y' = y$, and both are on the same side of the axis. Moreover, nothing in the development of the collinear eqs. 2-6 and 2-7 requires that the principal planes be located *between* the focal points F and F' as shown in Fig. 2-4, but only that the distances from F to P and from F' to P' have the same sign for the condition $\beta = 1$.

7. Conjugate Rays and Conjugate Points.—Although the concept of conjugate points has been introduced in Sec. **2-3,** some further discussion of it is worth while.   As a result of the one to one relation existing between points, lines, or planes in the object space and image space, it follows that corresponding to every ray originating at an object point and lying in the object space there is a second ray in the image space which is a continuation of the first.   These two rays constitute a pair of *conjugate rays.*   Moreover, corresponding to each point lying on a ray in the object space there is a point lying on the conjugate ray in the image space.   Any such two points constitute a pair of conjugate points.   In Fig. 2-3, O and I are conjugate points, as are also O_1 and I_1.   Similarly O_1V and I_1V are conjugate rays.

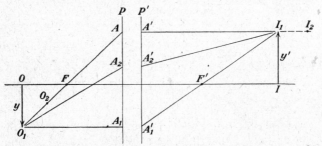

Fig. 2-5.—Illustrating conjugate rays and points. I_1 is conjugate to O_1; I_2 is conjugate to O_2; the conjugate to F is at infinity; A' is conjugate to A.

The principal planes of an optical system have the important property that a pair of conjugate rays will intersect the planes at equal distances from the axis.   The realization of this will be easier if it is considered that y and y' need not necessarily be the distances of points O_1 and I_1 from the axis, but may be the distances from the axis of another pair of points, provided these points are also conjugate one to the other.   For instance, in Fig. 2-5, the ray O_1FA must emerge from the system at A', since P and P' are defined as a pair of planes for which $f = x$ and $f' = x'$.   This ray, moreover, must, after leaving A', proceed parallel to the axis, since in the object space it passes through

F. If the object point were any other point on the line O_1FA except O_1, this would still be true. For any other point, such as O_2, however, the conjugate point in the image space would not be at I_1 but at some point such as I_2. Similarly, there will be a ray $A_1'F'I_1$ conjugate to the ray O_1A_1, and a ray $A_2'I_1$ conjugate to the ray O_1A_2. But for all such pairs of conjugate rays, there is only one pair of planes for which $\beta = 1$ and these are the principal planes of the system. In Fig. 2-5 we may see also that the distances f and f' of these planes from the principal focal points F and F' may be regarded as the *principal focal lengths* of the system. A comparison with the definitions of f and f' given in eqs. 2-2 and 2-3 shows that the principal planes of a single refracting surface coincide and cut the axis at the vertex of the surface. It is also evident that only in the case where the indices of the initial and final media are the same will $f = f'$.

8. Lagrange's Law.—Returning to a further consideration of Fig. 2-3, it follows that since $\tan \varphi' = y'/a'$ and $\tan \varphi = y/a$, the equation for the lateral magnification may be written

$$\beta = \frac{y'}{y} = \frac{a'\varphi'}{a\varphi} \tag{2-8}$$

provided the angles φ and φ' are small. If we consider in addition a *paraxial ray*, *i.e.*, one which makes a very small angle with the axis and lies close to the axis throughout its length, from O to I, then, putting $AV = h$, we have

$$h = au = a'u', \tag{2-9}$$

in which u and u' are the angles made by the ray in the object and image spaces, respectively. Also, for small angles, Snell's law may be written

$$\frac{\varphi'}{\varphi} = \frac{n}{n'}. \tag{2-10}$$

Combining eqs. 2-8 and 2-9, there results

$$\frac{y'}{y} = \frac{\varphi'u}{\varphi u'}, \tag{2-11}$$

and from eq. 2-10 it follows that

$$nyu = n'y'u', \tag{2-12}$$

which is known as *Lagrange's law*, and sometimes as the *Smith-Helmholtz law*. It may be shown that this law can be extended to the case of refraction at any number of successive surfaces, provided y and u are both very small. This is tantamount to an assumption that the rays under consideration are paraxial rays.

9. Longitudinal Magnification.—From elementary considerations, it is evident that for an object of any *depth* along the x-direction there will be a corresponding depth in the image. Indicating these distances by da and da', respectively, we may define the *longitudinal* magnification α as the ratio da'/da. By differentiation of eq. 2-5 it follows that

$$\alpha = \frac{da'}{da} = -\frac{a'^2}{a^2} \cdot \frac{f}{f'}. \tag{2-13}$$

10. Angular Magnification. Nodal Points.—Consider a ray from some point O_1, not on the axis, to intersect the axis at a

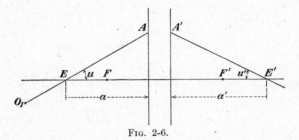

FIG. 2-6.

point E, as in Fig. 2-6, and the incident principal plane at A. There will be a ray conjugate to this emerging from A' and intersecting the axis at some point E'. It is evident that the axis constitutes another pair of conjugate rays passing through E and E'. Hence a point object at E will give rise to a point image at E'. If the angles made by EA and $E'A'$ with the axis are u and u', respectively, then the *angular magnification* γ may be represented by $\gamma = \tan u'/\tan u$. But this is equal to a/a', since $y = y'$. We have, however, established for all ideal optical systems the identity of f and f' with the focal lengths in the object and image spaces. In consequence, it follows that $a/a' = (f - x)/(f' - x')$, and from eqs. 2-6 and 2-7 we have finally that

$$\gamma = -\frac{f}{x'} = -\frac{x}{f'}. \tag{2-14}$$

When the angular magnification, γ, is equal to -1, $f' = x$ and $f = x'$; also $\tan u' = -\tan u$. In this case the conjugate rays are parallel and intersect the axis at two points N and N' called the *nodal points* of the system, as shown in Fig. 2-7.

The focal points F and F', the principal points P and P', and the nodal points N and N' are called the *cardinal points* of an optical system. From the character of their definitions they give a description of the system and its effect on the rays incident upon it.

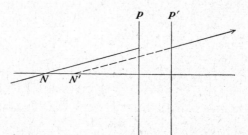

Fig. 2-7.—The nodal points (NN') are the (conjugate) intersections with the axis of a pair of conjugate parallel rays.

Disregarding the negative sign on the right-hand side of eq. 2-13, combining eqs. 2-7, 2-13, and 2-14 results in

$$\beta = \gamma \cdot \alpha. \tag{2-15}$$

Also, since $\gamma = a/a'$, it follows from eqs. 2-8, and 2-10 that

$$\beta \cdot \gamma = \frac{\varphi'}{\varphi} = \frac{n}{n'}.$$

By adopting the convention that in the case of a real image u and u' are of the same sign, while y and y' are of opposite sign, we obtain

$$\beta \cdot \gamma = \frac{f}{f'};$$

hence

$$\frac{f}{f'} = \frac{n}{n'}. \tag{2-16}$$

11. Mirror Systems.—The equations and concepts which have been developed in the preceding paragraphs for refracting surfaces can be used with slight modifications for mirrors. In Fig. 2-8,

$$\sin \varphi = \frac{(a - r) \sin \rho}{b} = \frac{(r - a') \sin \rho}{b'},$$

from which it follows that

$$\frac{(a - r)}{b} = \frac{(r - a')}{b'}.$$

For paraxial rays, $b = a$ and $b' = a'$ approximately, so that

$$\frac{1}{a} + \frac{1}{a'} = \frac{2}{r}. \qquad (2\text{-}17)$$

This is analogous to eq. 2-1. Since for small angles $r = 2f$, it follows that for a mirror

$$\frac{1}{a} + \frac{1}{a'} = \frac{1}{f}. \qquad (2\text{-}18)$$

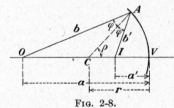

Fig. 2-8.

The conventions already adopted may be used for the case of mirrors also. In Fig. 2-8, r is negative, while in the case of a convex mirror, r would be positive.

Problems

1. Given a lens system for which $f = +10$, $f' = +8$, $x = -12$, $y = +6$. Using a diagram, find x' and y'.

2. Given an optical system for which $f = +10$, $f' = -16$, $x = 20$, $y = 2$. Using a diagram, find x'.

3. How far from a convergent mirror must an object be placed to give an image four times as large, if the focal length of the mirror is 50 cm.?

4. An object is 1 m. in front of a concave mirror whose radius of curvature is 30 cm. It is then required to move the image 15 cm. farther from the mirror. Through what distance must the object be moved, and which way?

5. An object is placed between two plane mirrors which are inclined at an angle of 60 deg. How many images are formed?

6. What must be the angle between two plane mirrors if a ray incident on one and parallel to the other becomes after two reflections parallel to the first?

7. A small bubble in a sphere of glass 5 cm. in diameter appears, when looked at along the radius of the sphere, to be 1.25 cm. from the surface nearer the eye.   What is its actual position?   If the image of the bubble is 1 mm. in height, what is its real diameter?   What will be the longitudinal magnification?   (Assume $n = 1.5$)

8. A spherical bowl of liquid has a radius of 10 cm.   For what index of refraction will the focus of the sun's rays be at one side, *i.e.*, at P_2P_2'?

9. A spherical bowl of 20 cm. radius is filled with water.   What will be the apparent position of a bubble, seen along a radius, which is 15 cm. from the side of the bowl?   What will be the lateral magnification?   The longitudinal magnification?

10. What must be the focal length of a lens which will give an image of the sun 6 in. across?

11. Derive the expression for the longitudinal magnification α from eq. 2-6, and show that it is the same as given in eq. 2-13.

12. An object lies 250 mm. in front of the incident nodal point of a lens whose focal length is $+60$ mm.   Where is the image with respect to the emergent nodal point?   Use a diagram in answering the question.

CHAPTER III

COMBINATIONS OF OPTICAL SYSTEMS

1. Equation for a Thin Lens.—In Sec. **2-2,** by considering the refraction of rays at a spherical surface, it was found that the distance a' of an image point on the axis from the vertex of the surface was related to the distance a of the conjugate object point from the same vertex by eq. 2-1:

$$\frac{n}{a} + \frac{n'}{a'} = \frac{n' - n}{r},$$

in which n is the index of refraction of the medium in the object space to the left of the surface r, and n' is the index of the medium of the image space to the right of the surface. Equation 2-1 is based upon the important hypothesis that the aperture of the optical system, in this case consisting of a single refracting surface, is small compared to the other dimensions involved. Two rays were considered, one constituting the optical axis, the other a paraxial ray OAI (Fig. 2-1) incident upon the surface at a relatively short distance from the axis. To continue this procedure and thus derive a lens formula for an ideal system of more than one surface, with a distance of any appreciable amount between the surfaces, would be extremely cumbersome. It is relatively easy, however, to obtain the formula for a thin lens. As the term is used here, a thin lens means one in which the distance between the surfaces is so small relative to other dimensions that it may be ignored.

In Fig. 3-1, the essential features of Fig. 2-1 are reproduced. The radius of curvature of the first surface is now called r_1 and there is added a second surface of radius r_2. Both r_1 and r_2 are by convention positive, and the medium to the right of the second surface has the index n''. As in eq. 2-1, the image distance obtained by refraction at the first surface only is

$$\frac{n}{a} + \frac{n'}{a_m'} = \frac{n' - n}{r_1}, \tag{3-1}$$

where a_m' is used for the image distance, to distinguish it from a', which will be reserved for the image distance for the entire lens.

With regard to the second surface, the conjugate points I_m and I have the relation of object and image. Hence we may write an equation analogous to eq. 3-1,

$$-\frac{n'}{a_m'} + \frac{n''}{a'} = \frac{n'' - n'}{r_2}, \qquad (3\text{-}2)$$

the object distance a_m' for the second surface being negative. Adding eqs. 3-2 and 3-1, we obtain

$$\frac{n}{a} + \frac{n''}{a'} = \frac{n' - n}{r_1} + \frac{n'' - n'}{r_2}. \qquad (3\text{-}3)$$

If the system is a thin lens in air, $n = n'' = 1$, and n' may be

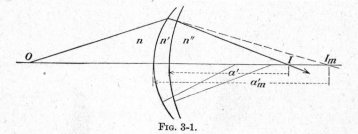

Fig. 3-1.

called n, the index of refraction of the glass, whereupon eq. 3-3 becomes

$$\frac{1}{a} + \frac{1}{a'} = (n - 1)\left(\frac{1}{r_1} - \frac{1}{r_2}\right). \qquad (3\text{-}4)$$

Since by definition the principal focus of a system is that point at which incident rays parallel to the axis will meet, by the substitution of ∞ for a in eq. 3-4, a' becomes f, the focal length of the lens, and the right-hand member of this equation is equal to $1/f$.

By comparison with eqs. 2-5 and 2-18 it will be seen that the focal length for any simple system in air is given by

$$\frac{1}{a} + \frac{1}{a'} = \frac{1}{f}.$$

In using eq. 3-4 it is important to remember that r_1 and r_2 are positive when the surfaces are convex toward the object. For a surface concave toward the object, the sign of r must be changed.

2. Combinations of Two Systems.—Since the equations developed in Chap. II apply to any ideal optical system, *i.e.*, one in which the sizes of the apertures and objects are limited, they can be used for an ideal system composed of two coaxial parts. These parts may consist of separate lenses placed coaxially, of lens and mirror combinations, or of several refracting surfaces placed coaxially so as to constitute an image-forming system. It is the purpose here to show how the cardinal points and equations for the focal length of the combination can be expressed in terms of the characteristics of the separate parts.

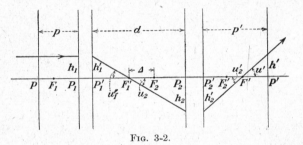

Fig. 3-2.

In Fig. 3-2 is shown a ray passing through two systems having a common axis. The subscript 1 refers to the first system, the subscript 2 to the second, and symbols with no subscript to the combination considered as a single system. As before, primed symbols refer to the image spaces for the systems, and unprimed symbols to the object spaces. In accordance with the procedure in Secs. **2-3** to **2-10,** inclusive, the origins of the systems will be the focal points. For example, the point F_1 is the origin in the object space in the first system, F_1' is the origin in the conjugate image space, and F' is the origin in the image space for the combination. The ray incident to the entire system is parallel to the optic axis and will consequently pass through F_1' and F'. Let $h_1 = h_1'$ represent the distance from the axis of the intersections of the ray with P_1' and P_1, and $h_2' = h_2$ represent the distance from the axis of its intersections with P_2' and P_2. Let Δ, the separation of the principal focal points F_1' and F_2, be positive when there is no overlapping of the inner focal distances $F_1'P_1'$ and F_2P_2 as shown in the figure, and negative when overlapping exists. Then the angular magnification γ_2 of the second system is given by

$$\gamma_2 = -\frac{x_2}{f_2'} = \frac{\Delta}{f_2'},$$

since x_2 is, by convention, negative to the left of F_2. But since $u' = u_2'$, and $u_2 = u_1'$, by eq. 2-14

$$\gamma_2 = \frac{\tan u_2'}{\tan u_2} = \frac{\tan u'}{\tan u_1'} = -\frac{h'/f'}{h_1'/f_1'} = -\frac{f_1'}{f'},$$

as h' for the entire system is equal to h_1', because the ray must cross P' for the entire system at the same distance from the axis at which it is incident upon P. The negative sign is used for f' since the principal focus F' lies to the left of P'. (If Δ is negative for a combination of two lenses, *i.e.*, if the focal distances f_1' and f_2 overlap, then f' will be positive.) Hence

$$f' = -\frac{f_1'f_2'}{\Delta}, \quad \text{and similarly,} \quad f = -\frac{f_1f_2}{\Delta}. \quad (3\text{-}5)$$

By the use of eq. 2-6 it is also possible to show that

$$F_2'F' = \frac{f_2f_2'}{\Delta}, \quad \text{and similarly,} \quad F_1F = \frac{f_1f_1'}{\Delta}. \quad (3\text{-}6)$$

The distance $p'(=P'P_2') = f_2' + F_2'F' + f'$, hence from eqs. 3-5 and 3-6,

$$p' = \frac{f_1'f_2' + f_2f_2' + f_2'\Delta}{\Delta},$$

$$p = \frac{f_1f_2 + f_1f_1' + f_1\Delta}{\Delta},$$

and since $d = f_1' + \Delta + f_2$, these can be reduced to

$$\left. \begin{aligned} p' &= \frac{f_2'd}{d - f_1' - f_2}, \\ p &= \frac{f_1d}{d - f_1' - f_2}. \end{aligned} \right\} \quad (3\text{-}7)$$

It is further evident that consideration of a ray passed through the system in the opposite direction will yield all the necessary relations in the object space,

For a combination in air of two thin lenses of focal lengths f_1 and f_2,

$$f = -\frac{f_1 f_2}{\Delta} = -\frac{f_1 f_2}{d - f_1 - f_2},$$

or

$$\frac{1}{f} = \frac{1}{f_1} + \frac{1}{f_2} - \frac{d}{f_1 f_2}. \tag{3-8}$$

3. A General Lens Formula.—Methods have been described for obtaining the characteristics of image formation by refracting surfaces, and it has been shown that the fundamental formulas of ideal lens systems may be obtained by applying the principles of projective geometry to the optical case. Often it is found desirable to introduce the concept of the *power* of a system in increasing the convergence of the rays incident upon it. A lens in air is said to have a power of 1 *diopter* when its focal length is 1 m.; one having a power of 10 diopters has a focal length of 0.1 m. Thus the power $\mathcal{P}$ of a lens in air is the reciprocal of its focal length in meters.

In a more general case, however, the index of refraction of the medium into which the rays emerge must be considered. For example, if light is incident in air upon a lens sealed to the end of a tube of water, the focal length f' in the water will be greater than the focal length f in air. A more extreme case would be that of a lens immersed in a medium of higher index than that of the glass. In this case the lens, convergent in air, would be divergent in the medium of higher index. In a divergent system, *i.e.*, one which decreases the convergence of the rays incident upon it, the power is a negative quantity.

Using the concept of power of convergence described above, a general lens formula may be obtained.[1] In Fig. 3-3 the shaded area bounded on the right by the surface S_1 represents a system upon which light is incident from the left. Let y be the distance from the axis of a ray parallel to it, and let h_0 be the distance from the axis at which the ray leaves S_1. If the surface S_2 were not present, such rays parallel to the axis would converge to F_0', and the focal length of the system A to the left of S_1 would be f_0'. The addition of S_2, cut by the ray under consideration at a distance h from the axis, will cause the ray to cross the optical

[1] The elegant method here described was originated by Professor C. W. Woodworth.

axis at F', and the focal length of the combination will be f'. The value of f_0' will depend upon the index of refraction of the medium between the surfaces S_1 and S_2, and the value of f' upon that to the right of S_2. Hence we may redefine the power of the system as the index of refraction divided by the focal length; *i.e.*, $\mathcal{P}_0 = n/f_0'$ and $\mathcal{P}_1 = n'/f'$. Assuming that the aperture is so small that h_0 and h may be considered to lie in the surfaces S_1

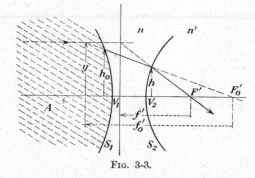

Fig. 3-3.

and S_2, we get, from similar triangles, to a sufficient degree of approximation,

$$V_2F_0' = \frac{h}{y} \cdot f_0' = \frac{h}{y} \cdot \frac{n}{\mathcal{P}_0}, \tag{3-9}$$

and

$$V_2F' = \frac{h}{y} \cdot f' = \frac{h}{y} \cdot \frac{n'}{\mathcal{P}}. \tag{3-10}$$

But by eq. 2-1 the object and image distances for a single refracting surface are given by

$$\frac{n'}{a'} + \frac{n}{a} = \frac{n' - n}{r}.$$

In the present case, $a' = V_2F'$, and $-a = V_2F_0'$, hence from eqs. 3-9 and 3-10

$$\mathcal{P} = \mathcal{P}_0 + \frac{h}{y}\left(\frac{n' - n}{r}\right). \tag{3-11}$$

The second term on the right-hand side gives the amount by which the power of the system will be changed by the addition of a refracting surface of radius r.   There will be a similar term for every such surface added, hence eq. 3-11 is a recurrent formula, and for any system may be written

$$\mathcal{P}_i = \sum \left(\frac{h_i}{y}\right)\left(\frac{n_i - n_{i-1}}{r_i}\right). \tag{3-12}$$

The value of the h at each added surface may be obtained as follows: In Fig. 3-3

$$t = V_1 V_2 = V_1 F_0{}' - V_2 F_0{}' = \frac{h_0 - h}{y} \cdot f_0{}',$$

where h_0 refers to the distance from the axis at which the rays

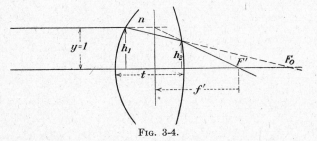

Fig. 3-4.

emerge from the system A.   Substituting in this the value of $f_0{}'$ from $\mathcal{P}_0 = n/f_0{}'$,

$$h = h_0 - \frac{ty\mathcal{P}_0}{n}. \tag{3-13}$$

If y is put equal to unity, eq. 3-11 can be simplified to

$$\mathcal{P}_i = \mathcal{P}_{i-1} + \frac{h_i}{r_i}(n_i - n_{i-1}), \tag{3-14}$$

and, using the general subscript i as before, eq. 3-13 becomes

$$h_i = h_{i-1} - \frac{t\mathcal{P}_{i-1}}{n}, \tag{3-15}$$

in which n is the index for the part of the system in which t lies.

The equation for a single lens may now be found.   In Fig. 3-4 a lens of index n in air has surfaces of radii r_1 and r_2, and a thickness between its vertices of t.   The power of the first surface is given by eq. 3-14

$$\mathcal{P}_1 = \mathcal{P}_0 + \frac{h_1}{r_1}(n - 1) = \frac{n - 1}{r_1}, \tag{3-16}$$

since for parallel light entering the lens $\mathcal{P}_0 = 0$, and $h_1 = y_1 = 1$. For the second surface, by eq. 3-15, $h_2 = h_1 - \dfrac{t\mathcal{P}_1}{n}$, or, substituting the value of $\mathcal{P}_1$ from eq. 3-16,

$$h_2 = 1 - \frac{t}{n} \cdot \frac{n-1}{r_1}. \tag{3-17}$$

Also, by eq. 3-14, $\mathcal{P}_2 = \mathcal{P}_1 + \dfrac{h_2}{r_2}(1 - n)$, which on substitution of h_2 from eq. 3-17 and $\mathcal{P}_1$ from eq. 3-16 becomes

$$\mathcal{P}_2 = \frac{n-1}{r_1} - \frac{n-1}{r_2} + \frac{t}{n} \cdot \frac{(n-1)^2}{r_1 r_2}.$$

This is the power of the entire lens, which may be written

$$\mathcal{P}_c = (n-1)\left(\frac{1}{r_1} - \frac{1}{r_2} + \frac{t}{n} \cdot \frac{n-1}{r_1 r_2}\right) = \frac{1}{f'}. \tag{3-18}$$

For a thin lens in air, t may be put equal to zero, and eq. 3-18 is reduced to the familiar form

$$\frac{1}{f} = (n-1)\left(\frac{1}{r_1} - \frac{1}{r_2}\right). \tag{3-19}$$

It is frequently desirable to know the distance from the back face of the lens to the emergent focal point F'. This is given by the ratio $h_2/h_1 = v'/f'$, from which, since $h_1 = 1$,

$$v' = h_2 f' = f' - \frac{f't}{n} \cdot \frac{n-1}{r_1}. \tag{3-20}$$

By means of eq. 3-18 v' can also be expressed in terms of r_2 instead of r_1.

By methods similar to that above, the equation analogous to eq. 3-18 for $1/f$, and one analogous to eq. 3-20 for v, may be found. If the lens system is in air, $f = f'$. It is evident that, in order to obtain the focal length of a system, eqs. 3-14 and 3-15 may be used successively for as many surfaces as there are in the combination.

4. Classification of Optical Systems.—Often a lens or mirror is designated as convex or concave, according to the shape of its surface. The difficulty in this usage is that simply the concavity or convexity of the surfaces is not enough to describe the character of the system. A more useful procedure is to describe a system by its effect upon the light incident on it, *i.e.*, the convergence or divergence imposed upon the rays.

Convergent systems can be characterized as *dioptric* or *katoptric*. The former are those in which the image moves to the right as the object moves to the right, *i.e.*, toward the lens system, while the latter are those in which the image moves to the left as the object moves to the right. Thus it will be seen that a "double-convex" lens, of index greater than unity, is convergent and dioptric, since no matter where the object is, as it moves to the right the image does likewise. On the other hand, a concave mirror, also convergent, is katoptric since the image moves to the left as the object moves to the right. A combination of two such mirrors is dioptric. Hence there is a general rule that a dioptric system is one composed of one or more refracting surfaces, or these combined with an *even* number of reflections, while a katoptric system is composed of an odd number of reflections, or combinations of these with refractions. Similarly, divergent systems may also be characterized as dioptric or katoptric.

Since the difference produced in a lens by changing from convex to concave refracting surfaces is a difference in the signs of the principal foci, we can classify optical systems as follows:

Convergent: Dioptric: f positive, f' positive
                Katoptric: f positive, f' negative
Divergent: Dioptric: f negative, f' negative
                Katoptric: f negative, f' positive

If a lens system is classified according to its power of increasing the convergence of the rays incident upon it, a convergent system is said to be *positive*, while a divergent lens is *negative*. A positive lens may also be defined as one which forms an inverted image of a distant object.

A simple lens which has a greater thickness between its vertices than at its rim is convergent, and one which is thinner is divergent.

5. Telescopic Systems.—In the strict sense of the word a telescope is a combination of two or more lenses, mirrors, or both, for the purpose of obtaining magnified images of objects which, because of their great distance, appear too small for distant

vision.   The term telescope is also employed, however, when a
single lens or mirror of great light-gathering power is used to
enable the observer to photograph images or spectra of distant
objects, such as celestial bodies.   In this case no ocular, or eyepiece, is needed.   By telescopic systems as discussed in this
section are meant those combinations of *objective* and *ocular* with
which distant objects are observed visually.   When the object
is very distant, it can be said to be an infinite distance away,
and the image formed by the objective will be at the emergent
principal focus.   For best vision this point should also be the
incident principal focus of the ocular, whereupon the rays will be
parallel upon reaching the eye.   Thus we have for consideration
a coaxial optical system of two parts for which, as shown in
Fig. 3-5, $\Delta = 0$.

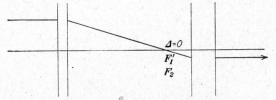

Fig. 3-5.—The principal planes of a telescopic system.

For such a system, the equation $xx' = ff'$ has no meaning,
since x and x' are both infinite, or at least very large compared
to the other dimensions of the system.   Consequently the focal
distances f and f' for the entire system are also infinite or very
large, and we may choose any pair of conjugate points on the axis
as origins in the object and image spaces.   But although the
focal positions of object and image may be distant, the relation
between them is still that of conjugate points.   In consequence,
the ratio between x and x' and the lateral magnification will be
finite and definite quantities, and we may write

$$x' = \alpha x, \qquad \text{and} \qquad y' = \beta y. \qquad (3\text{-}21)$$

From the first of these may be obtained by differentiation
$dx' = \alpha \, dx$, which says that the longitudinal magnification α
of a telescopic system is constant.   Since $\Delta = 0$, *i.e.*, since F_1'
and F_2 coincide,

$$\beta = \frac{y'}{y} = -\frac{f_2}{f_1'} = \text{constant.} \qquad (3\text{-}22)$$

Also, as Δ approaches zero, the limiting value of f/f' is, by eqs. 3-6, $f_1f_2/f_1'f_2'$; or, for a telescopic system with the same medium on both sides,

$$\frac{f}{f'} = 1.$$

Also, the limiting value of $\alpha(=x'/x = F_2F'/F_1F)$ is, by eq. 3-6, given by f_2f_2'/f_1f_1'; or, for a telescope in air,

$$\alpha = -\frac{f_2{}^2}{f_1{}^2}. \tag{3-23}$$

The angular magnification γ is also constant for a telescopic system. To show this, consider a pair of conjugate rays as shown in Fig. 3-6. Let (x,y) and (x',y') be any pair of conjugate points on these rays. Since any pair of points, A and A', on the axis

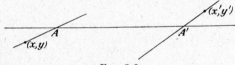

Fig. 3-6.

may serve as origins, the tangents of u and u' are respectively y/x and y'/x'. Thus, by eqs. 2-15, 3-22, and 3-23,

$$\gamma = \frac{\beta}{\alpha} = \frac{f_1}{f_2'}. \tag{3-24}$$

Also, $y'u'/yu = \beta^2/\alpha$. Since for any optical system this ratio is also equal to $-\dfrac{f}{f'}$, for a telescope in air $\alpha = -\beta^2$, from which it follows that $\gamma = -1/\beta$, or, the reciprocal of the lateral magnification has the same numerical value as the angular magnification. It should be noted that the *magnifying power* of a telescopic system, ordinarily obtained by dividing the principal focal length of the objective by that of the ocular, is the angular, and not the lateral, magnification.

Problems

1. Using diagrams, locate the principal planes of the lenses having the following characteristics:

    (a) $r_1 = +10$, $r_2 = -10$, $t = 2$, $n = 1.5$
    (b) $r_1 = -10$, $r_2 = +10$, $t = 2$, $n = 1.5$

(c) $r_1 = \infty$, $r_2 = +10$, $t = 2$, $n = 1.5$
(d) $r_1 = +10$, $r_2 = \infty$, $t = 1$, $n = 1.5$
(e) $r_1 = +5$, $r_2 = +10$, $t = 1.5$, $n = 1.5$
(f) $r_1 = +10$, $r_2 = +5$, $t = 1.5$, $n = 1.5$.
(Note that t is the d of Fig. 3-2)

2. A sphere of glass has a radius of 10 and an index of 1.5. Using a diagram, locate all the cardinal points for the separate refracting surfaces and for the whole sphere.

3. Repeat Prob. 2 above for a hemisphere of glass of the same radius and index of refraction.

4. An air-glass-water system has the following constants: $n_1 = 1$, $n_2 = 1.5$, $n_3 = 1.33$, $r_1 = +10$, $r_2 = -12$, $t = 2$. Using a diagram, locate all the cardinal points for the separate components and for the whole system.

5. Using a diagram to scale, locate all the cardinal points of the separate components and the whole system for the schematic eye given on page 323.

6. Obtain eq. 3-18 by the relations given in Sec. **3-2.** NOTE: make use of eqs. 2-2 and 2-3.

7. A luminous point source is on the axis of a convergent lens, and an image is formed 25 cm. from the lens on the other side. If a second lens is placed in contact with the first, the image is formed 40 cm. from the combination and on the same side as the first image. What is the focal length of the second lens? Consider both lenses to be thin.

8. A bowl of water, spherical in shape, has a radius of 10 cm. Where will the focus of the sun's rays be?

9. What is the focal length of a spherical bubble of air suspended in glycerin if the bubble has a diameter of 2 mm.?

10. What will be the focal length of a sheet of glass bent into cylindrical form, if the thickness of the glass is 2 cm., the index of refraction is 1.5, and the radius of the cylinder is 5 m.?

11. Is it possible to have two thin lenses, one divergent, the other convergent, for which $f_2 = -f_1$, used together to give an image at a finite distance? If so, will the image be real or virtual? Discuss all cases, and illustrate them with diagrams.

12. Using the power formulas of Sec. **3-3,** find the focal length of a doublet made of a double-convex lens of index n_1, and a concavo-plane lens of index n_2, which are in contact. Let $r_1 = r_2$, $r_3 = r_2$. Call the thicknesses of the two lenses t_1 and t_2, respectively.

13. Using the formula derived in the preceding problem, find the actual focal length of the achromatic doublet calculated in Sec. **6-16,** if instead of being a thin lens, the values of t_1 and t_2 are 5 and 3 mm., respectively.

CHAPTER IV

APERTURES IN OPTICAL SYSTEMS

1. The Stop.—If an object is placed before a simple converging lens the rays which combine to form the image will be only those which pass through the lens. The rim of the lens thus constitutes the *aperture* or *stop* of the optical system. Should the image be formed by a simple lens and the eye, it is not certain whether the rays which combine to form the image on the retina are limited by the rim of the lens or by the iris of the eye. Most compound systems, such as photographic objectives, telescopes, microscopes, etc., are provided with circular openings which act as stops in addition to those which may be due to lens apertures. In general an optical system has one stop which is in such a position that it will, by limiting the rays, improve image formation as well as provide a restriction on the aperture of the instrument.

The use of stops is not necessarily to reduce the effects of faults or aberrations. Even if perfect imagery be assumed, with coaxial surfaces as in the ideal optical system, restrictions on aperture may be necessary. For the image must be formed on a single plane, even if the object has considerable depth. With most lens systems, only for points in a given object plane will there be sensibly point images in a chosen image plane. Points in object planes nearer to, or farther from, the lens will be represented by *circles of confusion* whose dimensions will depend upon the longitudinal magnification and upon the size of the cone of rays from the object point through the lens system. Limiting the extent of this bundle will in general tend to reduce the size of the circles of confusion and thus improve the performance of the system.

Another effect of stops in certain positions is to limit the extent of the object field for which an image may be obtained.

2. The Aperture Stop.—Consider a simple convergent lens, thin enough so that it may be represented by a pair of principal

31

planes superposed as in Fig. 4-1.   Let groups of rays be drawn as shown.   From the laws of image formation it is evident that rays from the object space crossing at E, the edge of the stop S, will give a virtual image of E at E'.   It will be seen that E' need

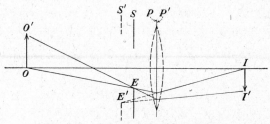

Fig. 4-1.—A front stop as aperture stop.

not necessarily be between the object and the lens; its position along the axis will depend on the character of the image formation and the position of E.   While S limits the bundle of rays passing to the lens from any point on the object, the rays after refraction proceed to any point on the image as if limited by stop S'.   The actual stop S is called the *aperture stop* of the system, and in the case described is called a *front stop*.

3. Entrance and Exit Pupils.—A more general case is that of a combination of systems which may be represented by two thin convergent lenses as in Fig. 4-2.   Here the first lens L_1 represents all the component parts lying on the side of the aperture stop S toward O, and the second lens L_2, all the components on the side toward I.   Also, L_1 will give an image of S at some position S_1. This image is called the *entrance pupil*.   Its position may be found by the ordinary laws of image formation.   For instance, if O in Fig. 4-2, is an object position for which S is the aperture stop of the system, and L_1 a simple lens, then the equation

$$\frac{1}{a} + \frac{1}{a'} = \frac{1}{f}$$ gives the position of the entrance pupil.   Here a

is the distance from L_1 to S, a' is the distance from L_1 to S_1, and f is the focal length of L_1.   Similarly, there will be at some position S_2 an image of S produced by L_2; this image is called the *exit pupil*.   If an observer looks through the optical system with his eye in the vicinity of O, he will see the image of S at a position S_1, and if he looks through the system with his eye at I, he will see the image of S at a position S_2.   For an extended object, the entrance pupil may be defined as the common base of all the cones of rays entering the lens from all the points in the extended object. A similar definition may be made of the exit pupil. In many cases the position of the aperture stop is not restricted to a single place in the system. It might be placed anywhere within a considerable range and still be the aperture stop. For every such position there will be an entrance pupil and an exit pupil corresponding to given object and image positions. The stop which performs the duty of aperture stop for

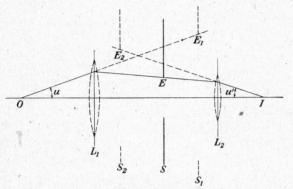

Fig. 4-2.—Entrance and exit pupils.

one position of the object may not do so for another; hence the locations of the entrance and exit pupils will depend on the position of the object. In general a good optical system is so constructed that a fixed stop performs the duty of aperture stop for object positions over a certain prescribed range.

Since the entrance and exit pupils are separately conjugate to the aperture stop, they are conjugate to each other. For instance, in Fig. 4-2, E_1 and E_2 are conjugate, since they are both conjugate to E, and have the usual relations of object and image.

4. The Chief Ray.—The ray which passes through the system so as to intersect the axis at the plane of the aperture stop is called the *chief ray*. It is represented in Fig. 4-3 by the solid line OI'. The conjugate rays OA and $I'A'$ will also intersect the axis at the planes of the two pupils, but will not necessarily intersect the axis at the centers of any of the lenses. The chief ray may be regarded as an axis of symmetry for the bundle of rays from a point which are restricted by an aperture. If the aperture is small, the chief ray may be used as a representative ray.

5. Telecentric Systems.—In case the aperture stop is placed at the principal focal point F of the lens, the chief ray after refraction is parallel to the optical axis and the exit pupil is at infinity. This system, illustrated in Fig. 4-4, is then said to be

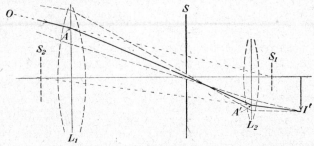

Fig. 4-3.—The chief ray of a bundle cuts the axis at the aperture stop.

telecentric on the side of the image. Similarly, if the aperture stop is placed at the second focus F' of the system, it will be *telecentric on the side of the object.* The former system has certain advantages if the size of I is to be measured accurately, for the y-position of I' will not depend upon its distance from the lens. Slight inaccuracy of focusing will result in blurring of the image point,

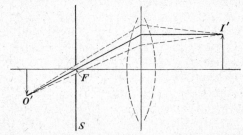

Fig. 4-4.—A system telecentric on the image side.

but the center of the image will be the same distance from the axis as if it were accurately focused. This arrangement is of particular advantage in micrometer microscopes.

6. Field Stop, Entrance Window, Exit Window.—As distinguished from those stops which merely limit the cone of rays from an object, there is always one stop which limits the field of view. This is called the *field stop.* Its image as formed by the front lens is called the *entrance window*. Since all chief rays intersect the axis at the entrance pupil, it follows that the angular dimensions of the entrance window are given by the cone of rays with its apex at the entrance pupil and its sides grazing the entrance window. In other words, the entrance window is the stop image in the object space which appears to subtend the smallest angle when viewed from the center of the entrance pupil. The *exit window* is similarly defined.

Problems

1. A thin lens of 3 cm. diameter and 6 cm. focal length is used as a magnifying glass. If the lens is held 5 cm. from a plane object, how far from the lens must the eye be placed if an area of the object 8 cm. in diameter is to be seen?

2. A telescope has for its objective a thin positive lens of 20 cm. focal length and 5 cm. aperture, and for its ocular a thin positive lens of 4 cm. focal length and 2 cm. aperture. Use a diagram and locate the position and size of the exit pupil, and the size of the field of view.

3. A lens system whose entrance pupil is 25 mm. and exit pupil is 20 mm. in diameter has a principal focal length of $+12.5$ cm. If an object whose height is 15 mm. is placed on the axis 30 cm. in front of the entrance pupil, where is the image, and what is its size?

4. A camera has a thin lens whose aperture is 8 mm. and whose focal length is 10 cm. What is the f/number of the system if a stop 7 mm. in diameter is mounted 5 mm. in front of the lens? If it is mounted 5 mm. behind the lens? (The f/number, or relative aperture, is the ratio of the focal length to the entrance pupil of the system.)

5. Two thin lenses are placed 3.5 cm. apart. The first, nearer the object, has a focal length of $+25$ cm. and an aperture of 3.5 cm. diameter; the second has a focal length of 30 cm. and an aperture of 4 cm. diameter. Which is the aperture stop for an object position 15 cm. from the first lens? If a stop with a diameter of 2.5 cm. is placed between them 2 cm. from the first lens, find the location of the aperture stop, the locations and apertures of the extrance and exit pupils for the object position given. What is the f/number of the system?

6. Using a diagram, describe a system which is telecentric on the side of the object.

CHAPTER V

PHOTOMETRY—THE MEASUREMENT OF LIGHT

1. Photometric Standards.—The unit of *luminous intensity* of a source of light is the *candle*. If the *candle power* of a source is said to be 10, its luminous intensity is 10 candles. The standard candle was originally of sperm wax, weighing $\frac{1}{6}$ lb., $\frac{7}{8}$ in. diameter, and burning 120 grains per hr. The primary standards used in Great Britain, France, and the United States are specially made carbon filament lamps, operated at 4 watts per candle. In Germany and some other European countries the legal standard is the Hefner lamp, which burns amyl acetate and has an intensity of 0.9 U. S. standard candles when the flame is at a height of 40 mm. The unit of measurement of the *light flux* or flow of radiant energy from a source is the *lumen*. This an arbitrary unit by which the flux is evaluated by its visual effect, and has the dimensions of power. The quantity of light radiated in any given direction from a point source of unit candle power into unit solid angle is 1 lumen. Hence the total luminous flux from a point source having unit candle power in all directions is 4π lumens.

A source rarely radiates with the same flux in all directions. If the actual candle power is I, then the total luminous flux is given by

$$F \text{ (in lumens)} = \int^{4\pi} I \, d\omega. \tag{5-1}$$

Hence we can define the *luminous intensity*, measured in candles, by

$$I = \frac{dF}{d\omega}. \tag{5-2}$$

If the mean candle power is I, $F = 4\pi I$.

At a distance r from the source let the light fall on a surface of area da, which subtends the solid angle $d\omega$ at the source, and whose normal makes an angle with the direction of the light as shown in Fig. 5-1; then, since the area da is given by

$$da = \frac{r^2 d\omega}{\cos\theta}, \qquad (5\text{-}3)$$

it follows by comparison with eq. 5-2 that

$$dF = I d\omega = \frac{I da \cos\theta}{r^2}. \qquad (5\text{-}4)$$

The illumination E on a surface is defined as the flux per unit area; *i.e.*,

$$E = \frac{dF}{da} = \frac{I \cos\theta}{r^2}. \qquad (5\text{-}5)$$

In the metric system the unit of illumination is the lumen per square meter.

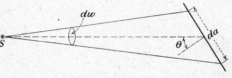

FIG. 5-1.

A simple method for comparing the luminous intensities (candle powers) of two point sources is at once evident. If two sources I_1 and I_2, at distances r_1 and r_2 respectively from a screen on which the light is incident at the same angle θ, produce on the screen equal illumination, then

$$\frac{I_1}{I_2} = \frac{r_1{}^2}{r_2{}^2}. \qquad (5\text{-}6)$$

The experimental determination of equality of illumination either by the eye or by some auxiliary device is a matter of considerable difficulty. This is especially true when the illumination is either very faint or very strong, or when the sources do not have the same color. The measurement of relative illumination is called *photometry*. If the measurement takes into account the wave-length of the light it is called *spectrophotometry*.

2. Brightness of Extended Sources.—If the source is not a point, but is of appreciable size, it is customary to speak of its *brightness* instead of its intensity. Brightness is defined as the intensity per unit area of the source, measured in candles per square centimeter in metric units. If B is the brightness, the intensity in a direction making an angle α with the normal to the radiating surface is given by

$$I = B \, ds \cos \alpha. \qquad (5\text{-}7)$$

Substituting in eq. 5-7 the value of I given by eq. 5-4, it follows that the flux through the solid angle subtended by the area da in Fig. 5-2 receiving the light is

$$dF = \frac{B \, ds \, da \cos \alpha \cos \theta}{r^2}, \qquad (5\text{-}8)$$

where θ is the angle between the normal to da and the direction of the light. Some luminous surfaces do not radiate uniformly in all directions, so that rigorously the variation of B with α should be taken into account. In what follows it is assumed that B is independent of α.

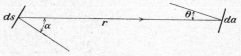

Fig. 5-2.

The term "brightness" is also used to mean the intensity of reflection of a *diffusely reflecting surface*. Such a surface has the same brightness at every angle of observation. Similarly, a radiating surface which has the same brightness in every direction is called a *diffusely radiating surface*.

Brightness may be measured in *lamberts* as well as in candles per square centimeter. The brightness of a perfectly diffusing surface which radiates or reflects 1 lumen per sq. cm. is 1 lambert.

3. Lambert's Cosine Law.—Consider a radiating sphere for which every element of surface has the same brightness. As seen from a point P, Fig. 5-3, whose distance r away from the sphere is large compared to the diameter of the sphere, it will appear as a flat disk. The flux from an element of area ds_1 at the center of this disk, falling normally upon an area da at P, will, by eq. 5-8, be

$$dF_1 = \frac{B \, ds_1 \, da}{r^2}. \qquad (5\text{-}9)$$

Also, the flux which appears to come from another element ds_1' of the same size on the apparent disk will in reality be that from an element ds_2 of the sphere, and will be

$$dF_2 = \frac{B \, ds_2 \, da \, \cos \alpha}{r^2}. \tag{5-10}$$

But since $ds_2 = ds_1/\cos \alpha$, $dF_2 = dF_1$. If da is the pupil of the eye, it follows that a sphere radiating with the same intensity over its entire surface will appear as a disk of uniform brightness.

It also follows that an element of surface ds on the sphere will have the same apparent brightness when observed from any direction, provided the point of observation is the same distance away. A luminous surface with these properties radiates according to *Lambert's cosine law*, which states that the intensity from a surface element of a diffuse radiator is proportional to the cosine of the angle between the direction of emission and the normal to the surface. This law may also be applied to diffusely reflecting surfaces.

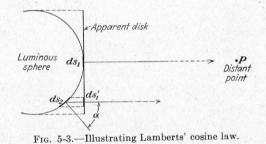

Fig. 5-3.—Illustrating Lamberts' cosine law.

4. Photometric Principles Applied to Optical Systems.—In

optics it is sometimes necessary to know the illumination of an image formed by an optical system. A knowledge of the entrance and exit pupils is important. Suppose we wish to find the total light from a surface ds of brightness B through a system whose entrance pupil radius subtends an angle U, as in Fig. 5-4. Consider at the entrance pupil a ring cut by two cones whose apices are at ds and whose generating lines make angles α and $\alpha + d\alpha$ with the normal to ds. If the distance r is unity, the area of this ring is $2\pi \sin \alpha \, d\alpha$.[1] The solid angle subtended by this ring is $d\omega$, which, by section 5-1 is $(da \cos \alpha)/r^2$. Substituting in eq. 5-8 for this quantity its equivalent, $2\pi \sin \alpha \, d\alpha$, it follows that the radiation through the ring is

---

[1] The area of a ring of width w whose mean radius is a is $2\pi a w$. In the case illustrated in the text, $a = \sin \alpha$ and $w = d\alpha$. This result neglects a second order term proportional to $(d\alpha)^2$.

$$dF = 2\pi B \ ds \ d\alpha \cos \alpha \sin \alpha \qquad (5\text{-}11)$$

and the total luminous flux through the pupil is

$$F_U = 2\pi B \ ds \int_0^U \sin \alpha \cos \alpha \ d\alpha = \pi B \ ds \sin^2 U. \qquad (5\text{-}12)$$

Similarly, if we consider the image ds' of ds to be formed by a system whose exit pupil has a radius subtending an angle U', corresponding to an entrance pupil of radius U, the luminous flux through the exit pupil is

$$F_{U'} = \pi B' \ ds' \sin^2 U', \qquad (5\text{-}13)$$

where B' is the brightness of the image ds'. Assuming the

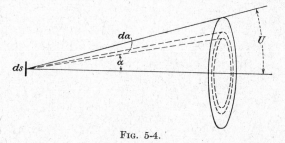

Fig. 5-4.

transmitting media to be transparent,

$$B \ ds \sin^2 U = B' \ ds' \sin^2 U'. \qquad (5\text{-}14)$$

Because of light absorption and reflection from the lens surfaces, in actual practice the right-hand member of the equation will be the smaller of the two.

It can be proved that in a so-called aplanatic system, for a single position on the axis

$$ny \sin u = n'y' \sin u' = \text{constant} \qquad (5\text{-}15)$$

for any number of media in an optical system. The angles u and u' are those made with the axis by a pair of conjugate rays; hence they can be identified with U and U', the rim rays to the boundaries of the entrance and exit pupils. In eq. 5-14, since ds and ds' are elements of area, we may write

$$\frac{ds}{ds'} = \left(\frac{y}{y'}\right)^2$$

and consequently,

$$\frac{B'}{B} = \frac{n'^2}{n^2}. \tag{5-16}$$

Equation 5-16 says that if it were possible to construct a lens system in which there are no losses by absorption and reflection, the brightness of the image is at best equal to that of the object, provided also that $n' = n$.

This may be further exemplified as follows: Suppose an area A in Fig. 5-5 to be illuminated by a source S. Its brightness will be given by eq. 5-4 or 5-8. The interposition of a condensing system at B will increase the intensity of illumination at A by concentrating the light intercepted by B on a smaller area, provided the losses by absorption and reflection at B are not too great. But the same increase could be obtained by bringing the source nearer to A. We can draw the important conclusion that *no device for concentrating the light from a source can produce an*

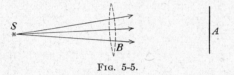

Fig. 5-5.

intensity of illumination in the image which is as great as that which would result from putting the same source at the image position.

5. Numerical Aperture.—From eq. 5-15 it follows that the quantity of light entering the instrument depends on $n^2 \sin^2 U$. Abbe called the quantity $n \sin U$ the *numerical aperture* (N.A.) of a system. In telescopes and cameras, another quantity called the *relative aperture*[1] is given by the ratio of the focal length of the system to the diameter of the entrance pupil. The choice of this designation depends upon the fact that in such instruments the object is either at a great distance or at infinity.

6. Natural Brightness.—It is important that we distinguish between the amount of light which falls on a screen from a luminous source and the brightness of the source as seen by the eye. The former, which has been discussed in Sec. **5-4,** is the brightness of the surface on which the light falls. If the source is observed with or without the aid of other optical systems, the image is formed on the retina of the eye. In case the unaided eye is used, it follows from eqs. 5-13 and 5-16 that the quantity of light falling on unit surface of the retina is

[1] Or $f/$ number.

$$E = \pi Bn^2 \sin^2 V, \qquad (5\text{-}17)$$

where n is the index of refraction of the vitreous humor and V is the angle subtended by the radius of the exit pupil at the retina, which is in this case the pupil of the eye. The quantity Bn^2 in eq. 5-17 is substituted for B' in eq. 5-13.

By eq. 5-17 we see that the brightness E of the object as seen by the eye is independent of the distance of the object, but depends on B and V. It is called the *natural brightness*. If the pupil of the eye enlarges, the natural brightness is increased.

7. Normal Magnification.—If the light is received by the eye with the aid of an external optical system, we can regard the whole as a single system for which the foregoing will be true. There will, however, be two cases, depending on the relative sizes of the exit pupils of the external system and of the eye: (*a*) When the exit pupil of the external system, whose radius subtends an angle which may be called V', is larger than the exit pupil of the eye, then the limitation on the natural brightness is imposed by the pupil of the eye and equation 5-17 holds. (*b*) When the exit pupil of the external system is smaller than the exit pupil of the eye, V' will limit the brightness on the retina, which will be given by

$$E' = \pi Bn^2 \sin^2 V'. \qquad (5\text{-}18)$$

Hence, from eqs. 5-17 and 5-18, for small angles

$$\frac{E'}{E} = \frac{V'^2}{V^2}. \qquad (5\text{-}19)$$

If the object has an extended area, so that the angle it subtends at the unaided eye is greater than V', the brightness will be no greater than that of an object with exit pupil whose radius subtends an angle V. Hence for sources of large area the external optical instrument does not increase the brightness of the image but merely increases the visual angle.

In the case of a microscope, where the radius of the exit pupil is smaller than the radius of the pupil of the eye, the numerical aperture is of great importance. For small angles, the radius of the exit pupil may be represented by $d \sin U'$, where U' is the angle subtended by the radius of the exit pupil of the optical instrument and d is the distance from the object to the pupil of the eye, the latter being placed at the exit pupil of the instrument. If h is used for the radius of the pupil of the eye, then

$$\frac{E'}{E} = \frac{d^2 \sin^2 U'}{h^2}. \tag{5-20}$$

Here E is the brightness without, and E' is that with, an external instrument. By eq. 5-15, it follows that

$$\sin^2 U' = \frac{n^2 y^2}{n'^2 y'^2} \cdot \sin^2 U.$$

Since $y'^2/y^2 = \beta^2$, where β is the lateral magnification, eq. 5-20 may be written

$$\frac{E'}{E} = \frac{d^2 n^2 \sin^2 U}{h^2 n'^2 \beta^2}, \tag{5-21}$$

whence, since $n^2 \sin^2 U = $ [N.A.]^2, it follows that E'/E is proportional to the square of the numerical aperature. Hence for the greatest brightness E' it is necessary to have as large a numerical aperture as possible. Also, for a numerical aperture of a certain size it is possible to have a magnification β such that E' equals the natural brightness E. A magnification of this amount is called the *normal magnification*.

8. Effects of Background.—For point sources and those of very small area, the foregoing rules do not hold, principally because of departures from the laws of rectilinear propagation. When small angular apertures such as that of the eye are used, diffraction plays an important part. Roughly speaking, the size of the image of a point source on the retina depends inversely on the size of the pupil of the eye. When a star is seen with the unaided eye, the light enters an area πh^2; if with a telescope, the light enters an area πa^2, where a is the radius of the telescope objective. If the exit pupil of the telescope is less than or equal to the pupil of the eye, all the light passing through the objective enters the eye. Hence the effect on the retina will be an increase on the brightness of the star in the ratio a^2/A^2, where A is the radius of the exit pupil of the telescope. If the exit pupil of the telescope is greater than h, not all of the light enters the eye, and in this case the increased brightness will be a^2/h^2 times that with the unaided eye. In either case, there will be an increase in the brightness of the starlight. On the other hand, as shown in Sec. **5-7,** the brightness of the background of the sky is not increased. If the magnification is greater than the normal magnification, it may even be diminished. Thus, with a telescope we can see stars of smaller luminosity than with the naked eye, even when a considerable amount of skylight is present. If nearby objects are viewed, the length of the telescope must be small in comparison to the distance of the object for an increase of brightness to be obtained.

In dealing with vision, the physiological aspects should not be neglected. Especially in the case of persons who are color-blind or partly so, objects of different sizes differ in their visibility. The effects of irradiation must also be taken into account. From the bottom of a deep shaft stars can be seen even in broad daylight. Here the starlight has not been reduced, neither has the brightness of the sky, but merely the total light sent into the eye from the whole sky. Objects not distinguishable in a dim light may be seen more easily by restricting the vision to those objects by masking off the light of nearby brighter areas. Irradiation of the eye by ultraviolet light from an otherwise invisible source will also serve to obscure the vision of surrounding objects.

The aperture of an optical instrument also serves to limit the ability to see separately objects which are close together, *i.e.,* it determines the resolving power of the instrument. The subject of resolving power will be discussed in the chapter on diffraction.

Problems

1. Find two points on the straight line joining two sources at which the illumination is the same. The sources are 20 candle power and 30 candle power, respectively, and are 300 cm. apart.

2. A simple lens having a diameter of 8 cm. and a focal length of 25 cm. is used to focus the light of the sun on a white screen. What is the ratio of the brightness of the image to the brightness when the screen is illuminated by the sunlight without the use of a lens?

3. A lamp whose intensity is 75 candles is placed 300 cm. from a screen whose reflecting power is 70 per cent. If the screen is a diffuse reflector, what is its brightness in candles per cm.²? In lamberts?

4. Why does a celestial telescope enable us to see stars brighter by contrast with the background of the sky?

CHAPTER VI

ABERRATIONS IN OPTICAL SYSTEMS

There are five aberrations, or faults, in ordinary lens or mirror systems, which are due to the shapes of the surfaces employed, the relative positions of the stops, or the position of the object: spherical aberration, astigmatism, coma, curvature of the image field, and distortion of the image. To these may be added, for lenses but not mirrors, the fault called chromatic aberration, which is due to the variation of index of refraction of transparent substances with color. Spherical and chromatic aberration occur even in the case of point objects on the axis of a lens system, while the other four—astigmatism, coma, curvature of the field, and distortion—occur in the case of point objects off the axis.

If the angle made by any ray with the axis is u, the assumption has been made in the theory of ideal optical systems that $\sin u = u$. This assumption leads to the so-called first-order theory. The expansion of $\sin u$ into a series results in

$$\sin u = u - \frac{u^3}{3!} + \frac{u^5}{5!} - \frac{u^7}{7!} + \cdots \qquad (6\text{-}1)$$

The extent of the departure from ideal theory depends upon the extent to which terms in odd orders of u must be added; this in turn depends either upon the size of the aperture of the lens, or the distance of the object point from the axis, or both. The rigorous mathematical analysis of these aberrations to the third and higher orders has been made the subject of a great deal of study. Indeed, the subject is one still engaging the attention of specialists in the field of optics, and a great deal of progress is being made in the development of new methods for reducing these aberrations to a minimum in optical systems. Although the subject is one which is too extensive to be mastered by any but highly trained specialists, the fundamental ideas involved are relatively simple.

The most comprehensive analysis of the five aberrations was made by von Seidel, who developed a group of five terms for their correction.[1] These terms are to be applied to first-order theory for ideal optical systems to take into account the third-order corrections for rays making appreciable angles with the axis. When the oblique rays fulfill the same conditions as the paraxial rays, the terms become zero. However, the equations thus obtained cannot be solved explicitly for the radii of curvature of the refracting surfaces, so that in practice it is more expedient to trace the path of each ray through the optical system and in this manner find the appropriate surface curvatures for the reduction of the aberrations to the required degree.

1. Spherical Aberration.—The equations for refraction in ideal optical systems given in Chap. II were derived on the assumption

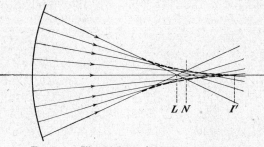

Fig. 6-1.—Illustrating spherical aberration.

that the aperture of the refracting surface was sufficiently small so that distances from the object to points on the surface could be considered equal. This was also assumed with regard to distances from the image to the refracting surface. For any optical system, the departure from this equality will depend on the size of the aperture used. On refraction at a spherical surface, as the ratio of aperture to focal length is increased, the *rim rays,* i.e., those which are refracted at the boundary of the surface, will converge to an image point considerably closer to the surface than will the paraxial rays, which are those lying extremely close to the axis throughout their lengths. The point *I'* in Fig. 6-1, to which the paraxial rays converge, is called the *Gaussian image point.* Each rim ray extended beyond the

[1] A simple treatment of the von Seidel equations is given in Whittaker's "Theory of Optical Instruments."

axis cuts the caustic (the envelope of all rays of different slopes) at N, where the diameter of the circular cross section of the entire bundle of rays has its minimum value in the range from L to I'. This area is called the *least circle of aberration.* It can be reduced in size by diminishing the aperture, at the expense of illumination, by changing the shape of the surface, or by combining several refracting surfaces which mutually compensate for the aberration. The last two methods may introduce other defects in the image, so that in most cases a compromise must be effected which will yield the result most satisfactory for the purpose of the particular optical system.

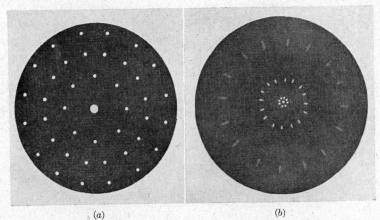

(a)   (b)

FIG. 6-2.—Demonstration of the effect of spherical aberration in a single lens. (a) is a photograph of a screen, (b) is a photograph taken of a point source of monochromatic light with the lens covered by the screen. The photographic plate was placed at the Gaussian image point. Only the rays through the large central hole in (a) are in focus in (b).

An excellent illustration of spherical aberration can be made with an ordinary plano-convex lens. Figure 6-2a is a photograph of an opaque screen having a hole in the middle and smaller holes in zones at different distances from the axial position. With this screen placed over the lens and a point of light about 1 mm. in diameter as a source, the photograph in Fig. 6-2b was made. A filter was used to render the light nearly monochromatic. The image at the center corresponds to the Gaussian image point and is formed by the rays through the central hole. The rings of images about this point show the rapid increase of spherical aberration for zones of larger radius. If the screen were not over the lens, the resulting image would be a bright image point at the center, with a circular area of smaller illumination about it, fading rapidly to its periphery.

2. Third-order Corrections to Spherical Aberration.—The third-order correction may be found algebraically without an undue amount of labor, but the calculation of terms of higher order is an extremely laborious process. Since the method used in getting the third-order term involves little of interest beyond the final result and the approximations involved, it is given in Appendix II, and the result alone is given here. The approximations depend upon the appropriate simplification of intermediate equations.[1]

The introduction of the third-order correction for a thin lens results in the equation

$$\frac{1}{a} + \frac{1}{a_k'} = (n-1)\left(\frac{1}{r_1} - \frac{1}{r_2}\right) + \tag{6-2}$$

$$\frac{n-1}{n^2} \cdot \frac{h^2}{2}\left[\left(\frac{1}{r_1} + \frac{1}{a}\right)^2\left(\frac{n+1}{a} + \frac{1}{r_1}\right) + \left(\frac{1}{r_2} - \frac{1}{a'}\right)^2\left(\frac{n+1}{a'} - \frac{1}{r_2}\right)\right],$$

in which a' is the distance of the image from the center of the lens, and a_k' is the image distance for an oblique ray cutting the refracting surface at a distance h from the axis. From a comparison of eq. 6-2 with the first-order equation

$$\frac{1}{a} + \frac{1}{a'} = (n-1)\left(\frac{1}{r_1} - \frac{1}{r_2}\right) \tag{6-2a}$$

it is evident that the term for the *lateral spherical aberration* is

$$\frac{n-1}{n^2} \cdot \frac{h^2}{2}\left\{\left(\frac{1}{r_1} + \frac{1}{a}\right)^2\left(\frac{n+1}{a} + \frac{1}{r_1}\right) + \left(\frac{1}{r_2} - \frac{1}{a'}\right)^2\left(\frac{n+1}{a'} - \frac{1}{r_2}\right)\right\} \tag{6-3}$$

for rays incident upon the lens at a distance h from the axis. Since the quantity given in 6-3 varies as h^2, it increases rapidly with an increase in the aperture of the lens.

The *longitudinal spherical aberration* in a thin lens, the radius of whose aperture is h, is given by $a_k' - a'$. This may be obtained by subtracting eq. 6-2 from eq. 6-2a, which gives

---

[1] A very complete discussion of the algebraic corrections to the third and higher orders is found in H. Dennis Taylor, "A System of Applied Optics."

$$\frac{1}{a'} - \frac{1}{a_k'} = -[\text{S.A.}],$$

where [S.A.] is written for the lateral spherical aberration, or,

$$a_k' - a' = -a'a_k'[\text{S.A.}].$$

If the difference between a' and a_k' is not too great, the last equation may be written

$$a_k' - a' = -a'^2[\text{S.A.}].$$

This is the difference between the focal lengths of the rim rays and paraxial rays. In using these equations, it should be remembered that by convention the radius r_2 of the second surface of a double-convex lens is negative.

3. Coddington's Shape and Position Factors.—Coddington has obtained an expression for the spherical aberration of a thin lens in terms of two quantities which we may denote by s and p, factors representing respectively the "shape" of the lens and the position of the object. The values of these factors in terms of known constants are stated as follows: In the first-order equation for a simple lens, eq. 6-2a, let

$$\frac{1}{a} = \frac{(1 + p)}{2f}, \qquad \frac{1}{a'} = \frac{(1 - p)}{2f},$$

$$\frac{1}{r_1} = \frac{(1 + s)}{2f(n - 1)}, \qquad \frac{1}{r_2} = -\frac{(1 - s)}{2f(n - 1)}.$$

Substituting these in 6-3, the lateral aberration becomes

$$\text{S.A.} = \frac{h^2}{8f^3} \cdot \frac{1}{n(n-1)}\left[\frac{n+2}{n-1}s^2 + 4(n+1)ps + (3n+2)(n-1)p^2 \right. $$
$$\left. + \frac{n^3}{n-1}\right]. \quad (6\text{-}4)$$

Differentiating with respect to s, we obtain

$$\frac{d[\text{S.A.}]}{ds} = \frac{h^2}{8f^3} \cdot \left[\frac{2(n+2)s + 4(n-1)(n+1)p}{n(n-1)^2}\right], \quad (6\text{-}5)$$

which becomes zero when

$$s = -\frac{2(n^2 - 1)p}{n + 2}. \quad (6\text{-}6)$$

Thus, for a lens to have a minimum lateral aberration for *distant objects* ($p = -1$), eq. 6-6 imposes on the surface curvatures the condition

$$\frac{r_1}{r_2} = \frac{s - 1}{s + 1} = \frac{2n^2 - n - 4}{n + 2n^2}. \tag{6-7}$$

If the index of the glass is 1.52, $s = 0.744$, and $r_1/r_2 = -0.148$; *i.e.*, for the most favorable form of convex lens the radius of curvature of the surface toward the object is about one-seventh of that toward the image. For a plano-convex lens with the curved surface toward the object the spherical aberration is almost as small as for a lens whose radii of curvature have the ratio given in eq. 6-7, but when the plane side of the lens is toward the object, the aberration is very large.

In the foregoing, it is assumed that the lens is so thin that its thickness has no appreciable effect. For thick lenses, special allowance must be made in correcting for the spherical aberration. It can never be eliminated entirely for a single lens, but a combination of a convergent and a divergent lens can be made for which the aberration is zero.

Since the index of refraction varies slightly with the wavelength, it is evident that there is some dependence of spherical aberration on the latter. It is not usual to take this into account, however, since in most cases the effect is small compared to the ordinary aberration.

4. Astigmatism.—When light spreads out from a point source, the wave front is spherical in form if the medium is isotropic and homogeneous. The wave front retains its symmetry if interrupted by a refracting or reflecting surface, and, if the point object is on the optic axis, the rays will converge to a point image provided spherical aberration is absent. If we consider only the rays refracted or reflected by a narrow ring-shaped zone, with its center at the vertex, the cross sections of the beam at various axial positions will be as shown in Fig. 6-3.

If, instead, the point source is not on the axis, the alteration of the curvature of the wave front upon refraction or reflection will not be symmetrical even in the absence of spherical aberration, and the rays will not converge to a single point image. This lack of symmetry will also exist for a point object on the axis if the surface is not symmetrical with respect to the axis, *i.e.*, if it is not a surface of revolution about the axis.   In either case, the resulting image will be *astigmatic*, and the cross sections of the wave front at positions near the focus will be as shown in Fig. 6-4.   When astigmatism is present, there are two line foci at right angles to each other, while the closest approach to a point image is a circular patch or confusion of light between them. Sometimes a distinction is made between the astigmatism produced by oblique rays, as described above, and that produced by

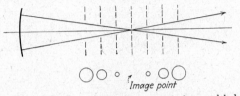

Fig. 6-3.—Showing the shapes of *stigmatic* bundles before and behind the image point.

the refraction or reflection by cylindrical surfaces.   In the latter case, there is merely one focal position, so that the image of a point source is drawn out into a line parallel to the axis of the cylinder.   For simplicity, only the first case will be discussed, as it is more definitely classified as an aberration.

5. Primary and Secondary Foci.—The two line foci shown in Fig. 6-4 are known as the *primary* and *secondary* foci, the former

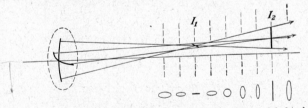

Fig. 6-4.—Showing the shapes of *astigmatic* bundles before and behind the two astigmatic line images of a point object.

being nearer to the system in the illustration.   The primary focus is sometimes called the *meridional* and sometimes the *tangential* focus, while the secondary is sometimes called the *sagittal* focus.

The equations giving the distances from a single refracting surface to the two astigmatic image positions are derived in Appendix III.   They are, for the primary and secondary foci, respectively,

$$\left.\begin{array}{c} \dfrac{n\cos^2\varphi}{s} + \dfrac{n'\cos^2\varphi'}{s_1'} = \dfrac{n'\cos\varphi' - n\cos\varphi}{r}, \\[3mm] \dfrac{n}{s} + \dfrac{n'}{s_2'} = \dfrac{n'\cos\varphi' - n\cos\varphi}{r}, \end{array}\right\} \quad (6\text{-}8)$$

in which φ and φ' are the angles of incidence and refraction, respectively, n and n' are the indices of refraction of the first and second media, r is the radius of curvature of the surface, s is the distance from the point source to the surface, and s_1' and s_2' are the distances, *measured along the chief ray*, from the surface to the primary and secondary astigmatic images, respectively. For a spherical mirror, these equations reduce to

$$\left.\begin{array}{c} \dfrac{1}{s} + \dfrac{1}{s_1'} = \dfrac{2}{r\cos\varphi} = \dfrac{1}{f\cos\varphi}, \\[3mm] \dfrac{1}{s} + \dfrac{1}{s_2'} = \dfrac{2\cos\varphi}{r} = \dfrac{\cos\varphi}{f}. \end{array}\right\} \quad (6\text{-}9)$$

Coddington has shown that for a thin lens in air with a small aperture stop the following equations give the positions of the astigmatic foci. The conventions regarding the signs of r_1 and r_2 are the same as those previously used.

$$\left.\begin{array}{c} \dfrac{1}{s} + \dfrac{1}{s_1} = \dfrac{1}{\cos}\left(\dfrac{1}{r_1} - \dfrac{1}{r_2}\right)\left(\dfrac{n\cos\varphi'}{\cos\varphi} - 1\right), \\[3mm] \dfrac{1}{s} + \dfrac{1}{s_2} = \cos\left(\dfrac{1}{r_1} - \dfrac{1}{r_2}\right)\left(\dfrac{n\cos\varphi'}{\cos\varphi} - 1\right). \end{array}\right\} \quad (6\text{-}10)$$

These equations reduce at once to the ordinary formula for a thin lens in air if φ and φ' become zero whereupon the astigmatism disappears.

6. Astigmatic Difference.—The difference between the distances from the lens of I_1 and I_2 is called the *astigmatic difference;* it is found by subtracting the value of s_1' from that of s_2'. For the mirror the astigmatic difference is

$$s_2' - s_1' = \frac{2s_1's_2'}{f} \cdot \sin\varphi\tan\varphi, \quad (6\text{-}11)$$

from which it can be seen that the difference increases rapidly with the angle of incidence. This is also true for lenses. Since this defect is due to the angle of incidence of oblique rays upon the surface, it is evident that its form will be different for divergent systems. In Fig. 6-5 are shown characteristic positions of the loci of primary and secondary foci for convergent and divergent systems.[1]   From this figure it is evident that combinations of systems may be made in which the astigmatic differences compensate for one another to some extent.   In the photographic *anastigmat* combination, not only is the astigmatism but also the curvature of the field largely eliminated over a considerable

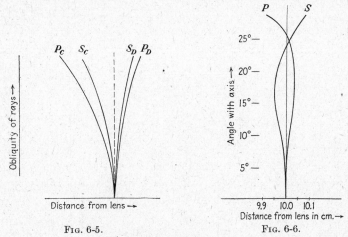

Fig. 6-5.   Fig. 6-6.

Fig. 6-5.—Loci of astigmatic focal positions for convergent and divergent lenses.

Fig. 6-6.—Showing the loci of positions of astigmatic images at different angles with axis for a corrected photographic lens of 10 cm. focal length.

area in the image plane.   A diagram of the focal positions for this combination is shown in Fig. 6-6.

7. Coma.—A system is corrected for spherical aberration when rays from an object point all intersect at the same point. This may be effected for axial points, while for objects having appreciable area there may still be a variation of lateral magnification with zonal height h as illustrated in Fig. 6-7.   Moreover the rays contributing to the image which pass through the lens at a distance h from the axis may pass through the focal plane, not at a common point, but in a circle of points, the size of the circle depending on the radius of the zone and several factors in the construction of the system.   Figure 6-8 illustrates the formation of the so-called *comatic circles*.   The numbers on the largest circle correspond to numbered pairs of points on a zone of the lens, indicating the origin of the pair of rays which intersect at each point on the comatic circle.   The heavy line *PI* represents

---

[1] The shapes of the focal curves vary also with stop positions, and not necessarily with focal length.

the chief ray of the bundle. Each zone of the lens produces a comatic circle, the radius increasing as h increases. The centers of the comatic circles will also be displaced, either toward or

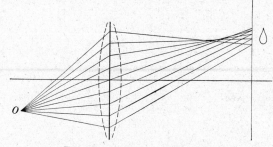

Fig. 6-7.—Illustrating pure coma.

away from the axis. In the case illustrated, the resulting flare of the pear-shaped image is away from the axis, and the coma is said to be positive. If the flare is nearer the axis than the image point of the chief ray, the coma is negative.

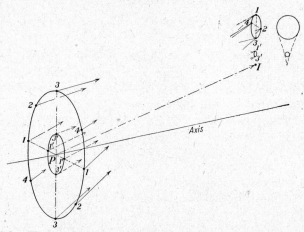

Fig. 6-8.—The formation of comatic images. Pairs of rays from a given zone, such as 1 and 1, 2 and 2, etc., meet at points not common to all rays, but lying on a *comatic circle* whose distance from the axis varies with the radius of the zone.

Since the condition which results in coma is a difference of lateral magnification for rays passing through different zones of a lens, the constancy of y'/y for all zones will result in its elimination. It can be shown that provided y' and y are small distances in the object and image planes,

$$n'y' \sin u' = ny \sin u, \tag{6-12}$$

where u and u' are the angles between conjugate rays and the axis.[1]   Hence the magnification will be constant and coma will be absent, provided $\sin u'/\sin u$ is constant.   This is known as Abbe's sine condition.   For small angles u and u', it is the same as LaGrange's law.

Figure 6-9 is a photograph of a region of the sky taken with a 24-in. reflecting telescope.   The effect of coma shows in stellar images which are some distance from the center of the field.

For a very distant object near the axis coma will be absent if

$$\frac{h}{\sin u'} = \text{constant.} \tag{6-13}$$

This equation is easily derived from eq. 6-12.

8. Elimination of Coma.—It can be shown that the condition for no coma, *i.e.*, the sine condition, can also be stated in the terminology of Coddington as

$$s(2n + 1)(n - 1) + (n + 1)p = 0, \tag{6-14}$$

in which s and p are, respectively, the *shape factor* and the *position factor* as before.   Since this equation is linear in s, it is possible to eliminate coma entirely from a lens system for a single object position.   A lens system which is corrected for both spherical aberration and coma for a single object position is called *aplanatic*.

It can be shown[2] that the condition for no spherical aberration for two positions P_1 and P_2 of the object, when they are near each other on the axis, is

$$\frac{\sin^2 \frac{1}{2}u'}{\sin^2 \frac{1}{2}u} = \frac{nP_2P_1}{n'P_2'P_1'},$$

where P_2' and P_1' are the images of P_2 and P_1.   Since this condition and the sine law cannot be true at the same time, an optical system cannot be made aplanatic for more than one position of the object.

9. Aplanatic Points.—Two points on the axis which have the property that rays proceeding from one of them shall all converge to, or appear to diverge from, the other are called *aplanatic*

---

[1] For a simple proof of the sine law, see Drude, "Theory of Optics," pp. 58 and 505, in the English translation.

[2] See Drude, "Theory of Optics," p. 62 of the English translation.

Edge of field

Center of field

FIG. 6-9.—Effect of coma in a paraboloidal reflecting telescope. *(Courtesy of Professor G. A. Van Biesbroeck.)*

points. A useful device for describing their properties, originally discovered by Thomas Young, although later independently discussed by Weierstrass, is illustrated in Fig. 6-10. Light from a medium of index n is refracted at a spherical surface into a medium of index n'. The surface is given by a circle drawn

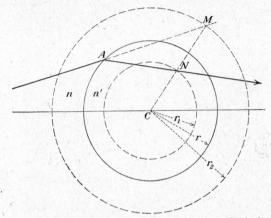

Fig. 6-10.—Young's construction for refraction at a spherical surface.

concentrically with two circles whose radii are equal to rn/n' and rn'/n, where r is the radius of curvature of the surface. The projection of an incident ray cuts the larger circle at point M, and a line drawn from M to the center C cuts the smaller circle at N.

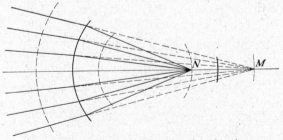

Fig. 6-11.—Axial aplanatic points in refraction.

A straight line from the point of incidence A through N is the refracted ray. The construction of a few such rays, incident on the surface at different distances from the axis, will readily illustrate that they cannot intersect in a single given point. If however, the points M and N are on the axis, as illustrated in

Fig. 6-11, the refracted rays will all meet at N.   Conversely, if rays originate at N, after refraction they will appear to come from a virtual source M.   In this case the points M and N are called *aplanatic points* of the refracting surface.   They have the property that rays originating at one of them will be refracted so as to pass through or be projected back through the other.   These points have an important practical application in the construction of microscope objectives.   As illustrated in Fig. 6-12, the lens closest to the object is made hemispherical, with the flat surface near the object.   Light from P, the object position, will be refracted so that there will be a virtual image at P'.   The

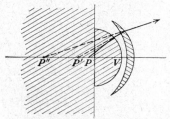

medium between P and the spherical surface is made practically continuous by immersing the object in an oil of index of refraction about the same as that of the glass.

The lateral magnification of the image at P' will be $P'V/PV$.   If a second lens L_2 is added in the form of a meniscus with its concave spherical surface having a center of curvature at P', there will be a

Fig. 6-12.—The principle of aplanatic points applied to a microscope objective.

second refraction at the rear, convex, surface, giving rise to a virtual image at P'' with a second lateral magnification.   There is a limit to which the magnification can be repeated in this manner, because of the introduction of chromatic aberration.

An aplanatic refracting surface has the equation

$$na - n'a' = \text{constant},$$

in which a and a' are the distances from the object and image, respectively, to the surface.   This is the equation of a Cartesian oval.   For an aplanatic reflecting surface, the equation is $a - a' = $ constant.   This is the equation of an ellipsoid of revolution about the line joining the object and image points.

10. Curvature of Field.—It has been shown that for an object point not on the axis there are two line or astigmatic foci.   If the object is an extended plane, the astigmatic images will not be planes, but curved surfaces.   For object points on or near the axis, there will be sharp point-to-point representation in the image plane, but as the distance from the axis is increased, the sharpness of the image will decrease. Instead, each point of the object will be represented by a blurred patch, the size of which will be greater for greater distances from the axis. Even if the defects of spherical aberration, astigmatism, and coma are corrected, this patch will be a circle of confusion and will be the closest approach possible to a sharp-point focus. The surface containing this best possible focus for all parts of the image will not be a plane, but a surface of revolution of a curved line about the axis. This defect is known as *curvature of the field*. The condition for its removal was first stated by Petzval. While this condition may be applied to systems composed of a number of lenses, for a pair of thin lenses in air it reduces to

$$\frac{1}{f_1 n_1} + \frac{1}{f_2 n_2} = 0. \tag{6-15}$$

For a convergent combination in which f_1 is the focal length of the positive, and f_2 is the focal length of the negative component, f_2 must be greater than f_1. Therefore, in order that eq. 6-15 may be satisfied, it is necessary that n_2 be less than n_1. In the earlier days of the past half century it was not possible to fulfill this condition for an ordinary achromatic doublet. Such a doublet is made of a convergent lens of crown glass in contact with a divergent lens of flint glass, the reason for this combination being that the flint glass, having a higher index of refraction, also has higher dispersive power necessary for the correction of chromatic aberration. About 50 years ago, however, under the leadership of Abbe, there were developed at the Jena glass works certain kinds of glasses for which, in a given pair, the one having a higher index had the lower dispersive power. With these glasses achromatic doublets can be made which also have a flat field free from astigmatism.

Astigmatism may be corrected to a considerable extent by the use of an aperture stop which will limit each bundle of rays to those in the neighborhood of the chief ray from any object point. Similarly, curvature of the field may also be corrected. The proper use of a front stop is made in certain kinds of inexpensive cameras to reduce curvature of the field, at the expense of aperture. Usually a meniscus lens is employed, as illustrated in Fig. 6-13. While for objects off the axis there is some astigmatism, by the proper location of the aperture stop it is possible to obtain fairly good images on a flat field. This is due to the fact that at all parts of the field the circles of least confusion, midway between the astigmatic image surfaces, lie very nearly in a plane.

To eliminate both curvature of the field and astigmatism or, rather, to correct them to a suitable degree simultaneously, it is necessary to use at least two thin lenses. In photographic

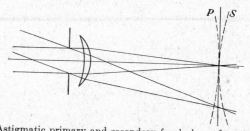

FIG. 6-13.—Astigmatic primary and secondary focal planes for a meniscus lens.

objectives, where the elimination of these defects is desirable, the lens combination is sometimes a triplet of two convergent lenses and one divergent lens.

11. Distortion.—One of the requirements of an ideal optical system is that the magnification is to be constant, no matter at what angle the rays cross the axis. The failure of actual systems to conform to this condition is called *distortion*. The introduction

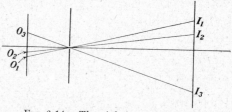

FIG. 6-14.—The pinhole optical system.

of a stop, useful in reducing astigmatism and curvature, will also aid in correcting distortion. If an image is formed by means of a pinhole in a screen, the magnification will be constant, as shown in Fig. 6-14, since each pair of conjugate points in the object and image planes will be joined by a straight line. This constancy of magnification can be expressed by the equation

$$\frac{\tan u'}{\tan u} = \text{constant}$$

for all values of u.   If a lens is used in place of the pinhole, there will still be constant magnification, or, as it is called, rectilinear projection, provided the lens is sufficiently thin.   For an ordinary lens, the presence and location of a stop will make a considerable difference in the amount and character of the distortion.

If the lens system is made of two symmetrically placed elements with the aperture stop midway beween them, the entrance and exit pupils will be at the principal planes of the combination. This system is free from distortion for unit magnification.   For other magnifications, on account of the large angles of incidence for points far from the axis, spherical aberration will be present. The emergent ray, traced backward, will seem to come from a point P_1' not coincident with the emergent principal plane. Similarly, for large angles, the incident ray will intersect the axis

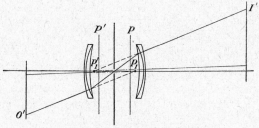

FIG. 6-15.—A symmetrical doublet.

at P_1, near P.   Only for paraxial rays will the chief ray of any bundle intersect the axis at the principal planes, as shown in Fig. 6-15.   The result is that the system of rays from an extended object will suffer a change of magnification with increasing distance from the axis.   To be free from the resulting distortion, the system must be corrected for spherical aberration with respect to the pupils and must fulfill the condition that $\tan u'/\tan u =$ constant.   Any system thus corrected for both distortion and spherical aberration is called an *orthoscopic* or *rectilinear* system.

Since the change of magnification present in distortion may be either an increase or a decrease, there are two kinds of distortion, illustrated by diagrams in Fig. 6-16, and by photographs in Fig. 6-17.

12. Chromatic Aberration.—In the development of simple lens theory, the variation of index of refraction with wavelength was ignored.   While this variation can be turned to useful account in prismatic dispersion, in lens systems it is responsible for the serious defect of *chromatic aberration.*

In a simple lens, short waves are refracted more than long and

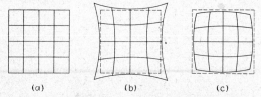

(a)   (b)   (c)

FIG. 6-16.—Illustrating distortion. (a) The undistorted image of a square lattice; (b) the same image with "pin-cushion" distortion present; (c) the same image with "barrel-shaped" distortion.

FIG. 6-17.—Photographs to correspond to Fig. 6-16.

will therefore be brought to a focus nearer the lens as shown in Fig. 6-18. This variation of focal position with wave-length is chromatic aberration.

An ordinary uncorrected lens possesses this fault to a marked degree, shown in Fig. 6-19. This illustration was made in the same manner as that shown in Fig. 6-2b, except that the light

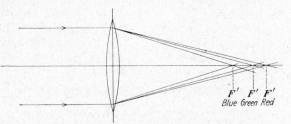

F' F' F'
Blue Green Red

FIG. 6-18.—Illustrating chromatic aberration.

of a mercury arc was used as a source instead of light of a single wave-length. The separate rings of images of the source owe their positions to spherical aberration, but for each hole in the screen, except the center one, a small spectrum is formed. There is a small amount of dispersion in the central image, since the hole at the center of the screen is not vanishingly small. Likewise, for each other hole, there is a small amount of spherical aberration, which results in a blurring of the spectrum so that the separate images of the mercury spectrum have a tendency to overlap. For each hole in the ring nearest the center, however, the spectrum is distinct.

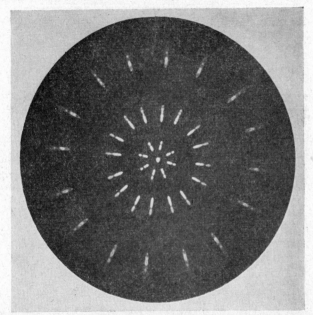

FIG. 6-19.—Showing both spherical and chromatic aberration of a single lens. The screen shown in Fig. 6-2a was placed over the lens and the photographic plate placed at the Gaussian image point. Since the unfiltered mercury arc was used, each out-of-focus image is a spectrum.

13. Cauchy's Dispersion Formula.—The index of refraction of a transparent substance may be represented with sufficient accuracy for many purposes by Cauchy's formula

$$n = n_0 + \frac{B}{\lambda^2} + \frac{C}{\lambda^4} + \cdots, \qquad (6\text{-}16)$$

in which n_0, B, C, etc., are constants depending on the substance. For practical purposes it is sufficient to use only the first two terms of the right-hand side of eq. 6-16.

14. The Fraunhofer Lines.—Accurate knowledge of indices of refraction of glass dates from the time of Fraunhofer, who was the first to measure the indices in terms of definite spectral positions instead of colors. He utilized the positions of the strong absorption lines in the solar spectrum, whose wave-lengths he found to be constant. His designations of these lines by letters are still used in optics. Since the development of strong laboratory sources of light, other reference lines have come into use, to most of which small letters have been assigned. In the following table a number of wave-lengths are given, including all the principal Fraunhofer lines. The unit used is the angstrom, equal to 10^{-8} cm.

Wave-length, angstroms	Due to element	Approximate color	Designation
7685	K	Deep red	A'
7630	O	Deep red	A
6870	O	Deep red	B
6563	H	Red	C
5893	Na	Orange	D
5876	He	Yellow	d
5461	Hg	Green	e
5270	Fe	Green	E
4861	H	Blue	F
4359	Hg	Blue	g
4340	H	Violet	G
4047	Hg	Violet	h
3968	Ca	Deep violet	H
3934	Ca	Deep violet	K

The variation of index of refraction with wave-length is small compared to the index itself. For ordinary glass it is never more than 2 per cent for the visible spectrum, *i.e.*, for the range of wave-length represented in the table above, and it is frequently less. In designating a particular kind of glass it is customary among manufacturers to give as the principal means of identification the index of refraction for the D-line of Fraunhofer, and to add for working purposes the indices for several other lines, and the dispersive power, defined in Sec. 6–16.

15. Two Kinds of Chromatism.—By the term *chromatic aberration* is usually meant the difference with color of image-position distance from the lens. Even if a system is corrected for this defect, there might still be chromatism present, for, especially if the lens is thick, the principal planes for different colors will not necessarily coincide. The result will be a difference of focal length for different wave-lengths, giving rise to a difference of magnification. This defect is known as *chromatic difference of magnification*, and sometimes as *lateral chromatism*. Difference of image position for different wave-lengths is known as *axial*, or *longitudinal*, *chromatic aberration*.

16. Achromatizing of a Thin Lens.—The focal length of a thin lens is given by

$$\frac{1}{f} = (n-1)\left(\frac{1}{r_1} - \frac{1}{r_2}\right) = (n-1)k, \qquad (6\text{-}17)$$

in which k is a constant for a given lens. By differentiation,

$$-\frac{df}{f^2} = k \cdot dn = \frac{dn}{f(n-1)} = \frac{\omega}{f}, \qquad (6\text{-}18)$$

where the quantity $\omega = dn/(n-1)$ is called the *dispersive power*.[1] For a range of wave-length from the C- to the G-lines, for instance, it may be written

$$\omega = \frac{n_G - n_C}{n-1}. \qquad (6\text{-}19)$$

It should be pointed out that the numerator in eq 6-19 is not strictly an infinitesimal dn but a finite Δn. In other words, ω is not the dispersive power for a particular wave-length, but the average dispersive power over a range of wave-length. The use of the symbol, dn, is justified by the fact that the difference of index over the visible spectrum is rarely more than about 2 per cent of the index itself.

For a lens made of two thin lenses in contact,

$$\frac{1}{f} = \frac{1}{f_1} + \frac{1}{f_2}, \qquad (6\text{-}20)$$

from which, by differentiation, is obtained

$$-\frac{df}{f^2} = -\frac{df_1}{f_1{}^2} - \frac{df_2}{f_2{}^2}$$

$$= \frac{\omega_1}{f_1} + \frac{\omega_2}{f_2},$$

[1] It is customary for glass makers to give the value of $1/\omega$, sometimes called the *Abbe number* ν.

since eq. 6-18 applies to each component separately. If the system is to be corrected for chromatic aberration, df/f^2 must be zero, and therefore

$$\frac{\omega_1}{f_1} + \frac{\omega_2}{f_2} = 0. \tag{6-21}$$

Hence f_1 and f_2 must be of opposite sign, since for all transparent substances ω_1 and ω_2 have the same sign.[1] Equation 6-21 says that achromatism is obtained by combining two thin lenses, one convergent and one divergent, of different dispersive powers. Their focal lengths may now be calculated.

From eqs. 6-20 and 6-21,

$$f_1 = \frac{f(\omega_2 - \omega_1)}{\omega_2} \quad \text{and} \quad f_2 = -\frac{f(\omega_2 - \omega_1)}{\omega_1}. \tag{6-22}$$

Using eqs. 6-19 to 6-22, it is possible to calculate the correction over any desired range. First must be decided for what wavelengths equality of focal length is desired. It is also important to notice that if the first lens is to be convergent and the combination also convergent, by eq. 6-22, $f_1 < -f_2$. Hence, by eq. 6-21, $\omega_1 < \omega_2$.

A common combination is a convergent lens of crown glass, and a divergent lens of flint glass, corrected for equality of focus for the F- and C-lines. Representative glasses of this type have the following indices:

	1. Crown	2. Flint
n_C	1.52293	1.61549
n_D	1.52541	1.62036
n_F	1.53162	1.63265
n_G	1.53652	1.64307

To calculate the focal lengths of the two lenses so that the focal length f_D of the combination is 50 cm., we may proceed as follows: From eq. 6-19,

$$\omega_1(\text{crown}) = \frac{n_{1F} - n_{1C}}{n_{1D} - 1} \equiv \frac{1.53162 - 1.52293}{0.52541} = 0.0165395.$$

$$\omega_2 \,(\text{flint}) = \frac{n_{2F} - n_{2C}}{n_{2D} - 1} = \frac{1.63265 - 1.61549}{0.62036} = 0.0276614.$$

[1] That is, in the Cauchy formula, the constant B is always positive.

By eq. 6-22,

$$f_{1D} = \frac{f_D(\omega_2 - \omega_1)}{\omega_2} = 20.1037,$$

and

$$f_{2D} = -\frac{f_D(\omega_2 - \omega_1)}{\omega_1} = -33.6223.$$

To check,

$$\frac{1}{f_D} = \frac{1}{f_{1D}} + \frac{1}{f_{2D}} = \frac{1}{20.1037} - \frac{1}{33.6223} = \frac{1}{50.0000}.$$

By eq. 6-17

$$\frac{f_C}{f_D} = \frac{n_D - 1}{n_C - 1},$$

so that

$$f_{1C} = \frac{f_{1D}(n_{1D} - 1)}{n_{1C} - 1} = 20.1990,$$

$$f_{2C} = \frac{f_{2D}(n_{2D} - 1)}{n_{2C} - 1} = -33.8883;$$

and

$$f_C = \frac{f_{1C} \times f_{2C}}{f_{1C} + f_{2C}} = 50.0033.$$

By a similar procedure it is found that

$$f_F = 50.0030 \qquad \text{and} \qquad f_G = 50.0925.$$

The differences between f_C, f_D, and f_F are negligible, but f_G is almost 1 mm. larger than either. This departure for wavelengths outside of the range $C - F$ results in a diffuse circular area of color about an image point, which is known as a *secondary spectrum*.

The radii of curvature of the lens surfaces may be found if the shape of one lens is decided upon. The choice of radii is ordinarily such as to reduce other aberrations to a minimum. A common form of achromat is an equiconvex lens of crown with a divergent lens of flint glass cemented to it. Let $r_1 = -r_2$ for the convergent lens. Then the first surface of the divergent lens will have the same radius as r_2.   Using the index for the D-line and applying eq. 6-17 in turn for each of the lenses, we obtain

$$r_1 = \quad 22.1061, \quad r_2 = \quad -22.1061,$$
$$r_3 = -22.1061, \quad r_4 = -369.402.$$

It is important to point out that the achromatism thus obtained is an equality of focal length only, unless the lenses are very thin; also that combining two lenses of different indices does not accurately achromatize the combination for more than two wavelengths.   In order to make a system achromatic or nearly so for any appreciable region of the spectrum it is necessary to use more than two elements.   For the lens to be achromatic with respect to image position, each element must be separately achromatized. This is because the focal planes are not the same for different

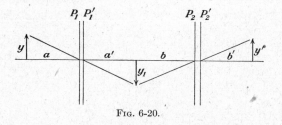

FIG. 6-20.

wave-lengths.   In Fig. 6-20 the lateral magnification of the first lens is $y_1/y = a'/a$, that of the second is $y'/y_1 = b'/b$, and that of the whole system is $y'/y = b'a'/ba$.   In order that the system may be achromatized with respect to image position, there must be no difference of the distance b' for different wave-lengths, or

$$\Delta b' = 0, \tag{6-23a}$$

and for constancy of lateral magnification for different wave-lengths,

$$\Delta\left(\frac{y'}{y}\right) = 0. \tag{6-23b}$$

Since a is constant, the condition in eq. 6-23b may be written $\Delta(b'a'/b) = 0$.   But $b + a'$ is constant for all wave-lengths, hence

$$\Delta a' = -\Delta b. \tag{6-24}$$

By eqs. 6-23a and 6-23b, $\Delta(b/a') = 0$ and $\Delta b' = 0$. This means that each of the lenses must be achromatized separately in order that the combination may be achromatic both with respect to focal length and to focal plane. The condition $a = $ constant means that the system will be achromatic for only one position of the object. Usually a combination is corrected for the object at infinity. For objects nearer to the lens the achromatism will be sufficient for most purposes.

17. The Huygens Ocular.—It is possible to arrange a combination of two thin lenses in such a manner that a high degree of achromatism is attained, even though the two are of the same kind of glass. For thin lenses separated by a distance t,

$$\frac{1}{f} = \frac{1}{f_1} + \frac{1}{f_2} - \frac{t}{f_1 f_2}.$$

Differentiating,

$$-\frac{df}{f^2} = -\frac{df_1}{f_1^2} - \frac{df_2}{f_2^2} - t\left(-\frac{df_2}{f_1 f_2^2} - \frac{df_1}{f_1^2 f_2}\right).$$

But $\omega = -\dfrac{df}{f}$, so

$$-\frac{df}{f^2} = \frac{\omega_1}{f_1} + \frac{\omega_2}{f_2} - \frac{(\omega_1 + \omega_2)t}{f_1 f_2}.$$

If the combination is achromatic with respect to focal length, this must be zero, *i.e.*,

$$t = \frac{\omega_2 f_1 + \omega_1 f_2}{\omega_1 + \omega_2}.$$

If $\omega_2 = \omega_1$, *i.e.*, if the elements are of the same kind of glass,

$$t = \frac{f_1 + f_2}{2}. \tag{6-25}$$

Thus, if two thin lenses are placed a distance apart equal to half the sum of their focal lengths, the combination is achromatic with respect to focal length for all colors, but it possesses bad axial chromatic aberration.

18. The secondary spectrum can be reduced with two lens elements of different indices of refraction, provided the lens having the higher index has the smaller dispersive power. This is true of glasses developed at the Jena Glass Works. With these glasses it is also possible to correct for chromatic aberration and curvature of the field at the same time. The Petzval condition for no curvature of the field may be written

$$f_1 n_1 + f_2 n_2 = 0,$$

while eq. 6-21 may be written

$$f_1 \omega_2 + f_2 \omega_1 = 0;$$

eliminating f_1 and f_2, the result is

$$\omega_1 n_1 = \omega_2 n_2.$$

This result holds, it must be remembered, only for lens systems which are so thin that no variation of the position of the principal planes with color exists. Actually, very good achromats which are not ideally thin can be made. A system which is aplanatic and achromatic for two or more colors, and is free from secondary spectrum is called *apochromatic*.

It is clear that there can be no such thing as perfect image formation such as is postulated by the theory of ideal optical systems. Some of the aberrations cannot be entirely eliminated, and it is possible only to reduce them to a degree consistent with the purpose for which the system is intended. The practical lens maker accomplishes this by tracing representative rays through the system.[1]

Problems

1. The radii of curvature of both faces of a thin convergent lens are the same length. Show that for an object placed a distance from the lens equal to twice its focal length the longitudinal spherical aberration is given by

$$-\frac{h^2 n^2}{2f(n-1)^2}.$$

2. A spherical wave from a near-by source is refracted at a plane surface of glass. What will be the character of the wave front after refraction? Will it be free from aberrations?

3. Find the lengths and positions of the astigmatic line images formed by a concave mirror whose diameter is 10 cm. and whose radius of

---

[1] For an exposition of these methods the student is referred to Hardy and Perrin, "The Principles of Optics," McGraw-Hill.

curvature is 50 cm. if the source is a point 75 cm. from the axis on a plane 125 cm. from the vertex of the mirror. Find also the astigmatic difference.

4. Using Young's construction, show the path of a ray refracted at a convex lens surface of radius $+r$, $(n' < n)$.

5. Locate the conjugate aplanatic points of a spherical glass refracting surface of radius $+5$, if the index is 1.57.

6. Calculate the constants of the doublet described in Sec. **6-16,** if it is achromatized for the C- and G-lines, instead of for the C- and F-lines.

CHAPTER VII

OPTICAL INSTRUMENTS

1. The Simple Microscope. The Magnifier.—If an object is held somewhat closer to a thin positive lens than its principal focal point and viewed through the lens, an enlarged, erect, virtual image will be seen. Used in this way, the lens is a simple magnifier. Its magnification is the ratio of the size of the image formed on the retina with the aid of the lens to its size when viewed by the unaided eye at normal reading distance. If this distance is called N, and the virtual image formed by the magnifier is considered to be N cm. away from the eye, then by eq. 2-7 the lateral magnification is

$$\beta = \frac{x'}{f'} = \frac{N + E}{f'}.$$

But E, the distance between the emergent focal point F' of the magnifier and the eye, is usually very small compared to N and may be neglected. Also, it is customary to consider N to be about 25 cm., so that the magnification of a simple magnifier may be written

$$\beta = \frac{25}{f} \qquad (f \text{ in centimeters}). \qquad (7-1)$$

Here f is used instead of f', since for a lens in air they are the same. It is best to avoid eyestrain by placing the object at the principal focus F of the lens (see Fig. 7-1) so that the virtual image is at infinity. This does not invalidate eq. 7-1, as a good working rule, since the angle subtended by the virtual image at infinity is not much different from that at normal reading distance, and the virtual image is about the same size. This may be quickly verified by experiment. To obtain the largest field, the eye should be close to the lens. A simple magnifier may be corrected in the usual manner for chromatic aberration.

2. Compound Magnifiers.—Because large magnification causes great increase of the aberrations, simple magnifiers are usually limited to magnifications smaller than about 15. Compound magnifiers usually consist of two lenses. One type of compound magnifier is the *Ramsden eyepiece*, ordinarily used as an *ocular* in a telescope or microscope. As shown in Fig. 7-12, page 83, it is made of two plano-convex lenses with their convex surfaces toward each other. Two thin lenses thus used, it was shown in Chap. VI, form a combination which is achromatic with respect to focal length, provided the distance between the lenses is one-

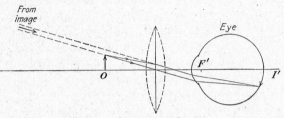

FIG. 7-1.—The simple microscope.

half the sum of their focal lengths, and provided they are made of the same kind of glass. There is, however, always some axial chromatic aberration present, and on this account the focal lengths are calculated for the yellow green (about 5500 angstroms), to which the eye has maximum sensitivity. An eyepiece thus constructed will, however, have its incident focal plane at the first surface of the field lens,[1] and dirt or surface imperfections of that lens will be in sharp focus. Consequently, at some sacrifice of achromatism the distance between the lenses is made two-thirds the focal length of either, instead of one-half the sum of the focal lengths.

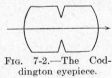

FIG. 7-2.—The Coddington eyepiece.

The *Coddington* eyepiece (Fig. 7-2) is made of a single piece of glass cut from a sphere, with a groove cut in its sides to form a stop. Loss of light by reflection between surfaces is reduced by this eyepiece, but it is expensive to make.

The *triple aplanat* (Fig. 7-3) is made of two negative lenses of flint glass, between which is cemented a double-convex lens of crown glass. In this magnifier a high degree of achromatism is attained.

[1] The *field lens* is the one closer to the focal plane of the objective of the telescope or microscope.

There are several other types of magnifiers, most of which are constructed for special purposes. One of these is a single block of glass with a spherical top and with a flat or slightly concave base to be placed in contact with the object.

3. The Gauss Eyepiece.—For laboratory telescopes, especially those used with spectrometers, the *Gauss eyepiece* is

Fig. 7-3.—The triple aplanat.

very convenient. Its construction is shown in Fig. 7-4. It is the same as the Ramsden eyepiece, except that between the two elements a thin plane plate of glass is placed at an angle of 45 deg. with the axis. Light admitted through an opening in the side of the tube is reflected down the axis of the telescope, illuminating the cross hairs in its path. When the telescope is focused for parallel light and has its axis perpendicular to a plane reflecting surface placed before the objective, images of the cross hair will be at the principal focus of the objective. When these images coincide exactly with the cross hairs themselves, the axis of the telescope is exactly perpendicu-

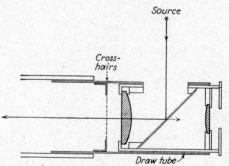

Fig. 7-4.—The Gauss eyepiece and draw tube.

lar to the reflecting surface. The focusing of the telescope for parallel light may also be made more exact by eliminating all difference of sharpness between the cross hairs and their images.[1]

4. The Micrometer Eyepiece.—When small distances are to be measured, a convenient instrument is the *micrometer eyepiece*. This can be constructed in several forms, one of which is illustrated in Fig. 7-5. At the focal plane of the eyepiece are a fixed

---

[1] For instructions concerning the use of the Gauss eyepiece, see Appendix IV.

cross hair F, and a movable cross hair M.   The latter may be moved perpendicularly to the axis of the eyepiece by means of a fine-pitched screw.   The head H may be divided into appropriate divisions, usually small fractions of a millimeter, although for

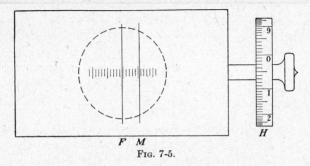

Fig. 7-5.

some purposes angular measure is more convenient.   With a head of sufficient diameter the divisions may represent very small distances or fractions of a degree, and in addition a vernier may be used.   It is not practical, however, to make divisions smaller than are justified by the accuracy of the micrometer screw. Sometimes a small-toothed edge is provided in the focal plane so that whole turns of the micrometer head may be easily counted. If the ocular is of the Huygens type (see Sec. 7-12), the cross hairs are placed at the focal plane of the eye lens, and for the toothed edge may be substituted a scale finely ruled on glass.

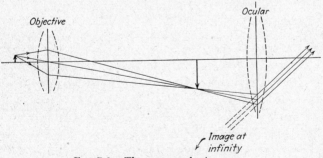

Fig. 7-6.—The compound microscope.

5. The Compound Microscope.—The optical parts of a compound microscope consist of an *objective* and an *eyepiece* or *ocular*. The former serves to produce a much enlarged real image of the object; the latter, to view this image with still further magnification, in comparison with a scale if measurements of the object are to be made. A schematic diagram is shown in Fig. 7-6. The magnification is the product of the magnifying powers of the two elements. Frequently a microscope is equipped with a variety of objectives and oculars for different magnifications.

6. Numerical Aperture.—In the chapter on diffraction it will be shown that the radius of the image of a point object, *i.e.*, the distance from the center of the image to the first minimum of the diffraction pattern, is given by

$$r = \frac{0.61\lambda}{\sin \theta}, \qquad (7\text{-}2)$$

where θ is the angle of diffraction, *i.e.*, the angle subtended at the lens by r. By convention, the limit of resolution of an optical instrument is said to be reached when the center of the image of one object just coincides with the first dark minimum of the diffraction pattern of a second object. Hence images of two point objects can just be resolved when their distance apart is r.

In the microscope, on account of the greater magnification, the angle θ is large. Moreover, the object points seen with a microscope are not self-luminous, and hence in themselves produce diffraction images of the source. Abbe has shown that in consequence the smallest distance between two points in the object which can be resolved is given by $\lambda/2n \sin \alpha$, where n is the index of refraction of the medium between the object and the objective, and α is the angle between the axis and the limiting rays which pass through the entrance pupil of the microscope. The quantity $n \sin \alpha$ was called by Abbe the numerical aperture (N.A.) of a microscope. It is obvious that the limitation thus set on the magnifying power is not due to aberrations but to the effects of diffraction. From eq. 7-2 it follows that the size of the central bright maximum of the diffraction pattern of a point object is proportional to the wave-length of the light used. For this reason, sometimes ultraviolet light is used to obtain higher resolving power.

The *oil-immersion* microscope[1] is one in which the numerical aperture and hence the resolving power is increased by the use of an oil, usually oil of cedarwood, between the object and the objective. Loss of light by reflection is thereby also eliminated.

[1] See Sec. 6-9.

7. Condensers.—If the object is viewed with transmitted light, it is frequently desirable to obtain greater illumination by means of a condenser. Sometimes this is merely a concave mirror, which can be adjusted to reflect a convergent beam of light from a nearby source into the objective. For short-focus objectives more powerful condensers are used. They become in fact integral parts of the optical system, and are often corrected for aberrations so as to improve their light-gathering power.

The larger the numerical aperture, the more important does the efficiency of the condenser become.

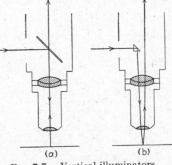

(a)   (b)

FIG. 7-7.—Vertical illuminators.

8. Vertical and Dark-field Illuminators.—When very short-focus objectives are used to view opaque objects which must be illuminated from above, it is difficult to illuminate the object by ordinary means. To overcome this difficulty, a *vertical illuminator* may be used. This may consist of a prism or mirror which reflects to the object a beam of light admitted into the tube from the side, as shown in Fig. 7-7.

For observing small particles in colloidal suspensions, or fine rulings on surfaces, it is desirable to use a *dark-field illuminator*. In this type the light is incident upon the object at angles such that it does not pass by transmission or ordinary specular[1] reflection directly into the objective. Small particles or lines, however, serve to diffract the light, and it is by means of the pencil of diffracted light from each particle that the presence of the particle is observed. One means of effecting this is by means of condensers such as are illustrated in Fig. 7-8. The condenser contains an opaque centered disk which allows only a ring of light to pass obliquely through a point in the object just below the center of the objective. With dark-field illumination, particles as small as 5×10^{-7} cm. in diameter, or about $\frac{1}{100}$ of the wave-length of light, may be observed.

---

[1] Specular reflection is ordinary reflection from a polished surface, diffuse reflection from a matt surface.

9. Telescopes.—In Chap. III it was shown that the lateral magnification β of a telescope is given by $-\dfrac{f_2}{f_1}$, the negative sign indicating that the image is inverted. The angular magnification is given by f_1/f_2. The latter is commonly spoken of as the *magnifying power* of the telescope. Rigorously, a telescopic system is one which forms at infinity an image of an infinitely distant object. In practice the term telescope is also applied to any instrument used for forming images of nearby objects, or for

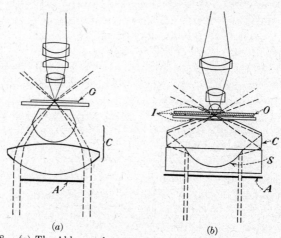

(a)   (b)

Fig. 7-8.—(a) The Abbe condenser. *A* is an opaque screen; *C*, the condenser system; *O*, the object. (b) The Cardioid condenser. *A* is the opaque screen; *S*, a spherical reflector; *C*, the cardioid surface; *O*, the object. At points *I* are layers of oil.

forming images at finite distances. An example of the first-mentioned use is the ordinary laboratory telescope, used for observing objects a few feet away. If it is used to observe objects closer than the normal reading distance of 25 cm., such an instrument is called, instead, a microscope. Optically, for such ranges of distance, there is little difference between a short-range telescope and a long-focus microscope.

The modern astronomical telescope is used principally for photographic purposes; it consists of a single lens or mirror for focusing images of celestial objects on the photographic plate. The modern telescope is thus principally an instrument of great light-gathering power. From the laws of diffraction it can be shown that the resolving power of a telescope is determined by the size of the objective.   To take full advantage of this, however, in visual use, it is necessary that the objective be the aperture stop of the system.   It is then the entrance pupil.   In a visual astronomical telescope in which both objective and ocular are positive systems, a measure of the magnifying power may be made by comparing the diameter of the objective with that of the exit pupil, since the ratio of these two dimensions is equal to f_1/f_2.   To find the size of the exit pupil, the telescope may be pointed to the sky and a ground glass or paper screen used to locate the position where the beam emerging from the eyepiece is smallest.   The well-defined disk of light at this point is the exit pupil.

In order that the maximum field may be viewed, the entrance pupil of the eye should be made to coincide with the exit pupil of the telescope.   In the Galilean telescope, the exit pupil is virtual, and the field of view is in consequence restricted.   This form has, however, the advantage of shorter overall length, since the eyepiece is a negative lens placed closer to the objective than its principal focal point.

10. The Reflecting Telescope.—Large modern astronomical telescopes which are used principally for photographic observations are of the reflecting type.   The mirror is a parabolized surface, usually of glass coated with metal of high reflecting power.   Silver, chemically deposited, was until recently the metal used.   The disadvantage of silver is that it tarnishes readily and loses its reflecting power.   With recent improvement in technique it is now possible to deposit aluminum by evaporation in a high vacuum on even the largest mirrors.   The oxide formed on the aluminum on exposure to the air is an extremely thin coat of transparent substance preserving the metal from tarnish.   Sometimes combinations of two metals prove more satisfactory than aluminum alone, as, for instance, a base coat of chromium with a top coat of aluminum.   Indeed, the technique of evaporation of metals for the production of reflecting surfaces is so new that probably great improvements will be made in the future.   In addition to its value in the visible spectrum because of superior reflecting power and durability, aluminum has proved of great service in extending astronomical spectroscopic observations into the ultraviolet.   Silver is almost transparent in the region of 3300 angstroms, a fact which previously limited the ultraviolet spectroscopy of stellar objects.

The image formed with a paraboloidal mirror is free from spherical aberration on the axis and from chromatic aberration over the entire field. For this reason, it is possible to make the focal length shorter with relation to the aperture than in a refracting telescope. The new telescope of the McDonald observatory has a diameter of 82 in. and a focal length of 26 ft., or a relative aperture of $f/3.8$, resulting in a reduction of photographic exposure time. In this way, the range of the instrument for faint celestial objects is effectively increased.

In the neighborhood of the axis, the field of a paraboloidal reflecting telescope suffers from coma, a defect in which each image is elongated as shown in Fig. 6-9. The length of the comatic image, *i.e.*, its dimension measured along a radius from the center of the field, is given approximately by $L = 3D^2\theta/16F^2$, where D/F is the relative aperture and θ is the angular distance of the star image in seconds of arc from the center of the field. The breadth of the comatic image is approximately two-thirds of the length. While the defect of coma thus increases in proportion to θ, the astigmatism is proportional to θ^2, so that for the region close to the axis the elimination of coma is more important. In actual practice, differences of temperature in a turbulent atmosphere cause a blurring or "boiling," so that even stellar images at the axis are enlarged and irregular. For this reason the distance from the axis at which coma becomes noticeable depends upon the definition, or "seeing," as it is called. For correcting this defect of coma the telescopes which have been developed may be classified in three groups.

a. In the first group may be placed those which achieve their purpose to some extent by the addition of other mirror surfaces, which may or may not be modified from a spherical shape. While the original two-surface reflecting telescope proposed by Gregory (Fig. 7-9a) and the Cassegrain form (Fig. 7-9b) fall in this group, the greatest advance was made by Schwarzschild who, in 1905, designed a two-mirror telescope of the Gregorian type in which each surface was modified in shape so that coma and spherical aberration were reduced to a minimum in the neighborhood of the axis. It had a relative aperture of 1/3.5. Since in this instrument the field is flat and the residual astigmatism is balanced so that the primary and secondary foci coincide at short distances from the axis, it fulfills the conditions for the *anastigmat* described in Sec. 6-6, and can be called the *Schwarzschild anastigmat*.

b. In a second group may be placed those telescopes in which the coma of a paraboloidal mirror is corrected by the use of a specially designed lens placed between the mirror and its principal focus. The disadvantage of correcting lenses of this type is that in many cases they reduce the relative aperture by increasing the focal length.

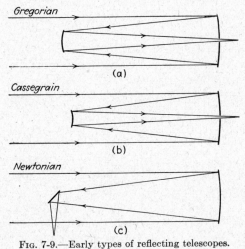

Gregorian

(a)

Cassegrain

(b)

Newtonian

(c)

Fig. 7-9.—Early types of reflecting telescopes.

Professor Frank E. Ross of the Yerkes Observatory has designed a "zero-power" lens combination[1] placed between the mirror and its focal point, which makes no essential change in the position of the principal focal plane of the telescope mirror, but corrects for coma over a considerable area. It makes no reduction in relative aperture, and actually increases the photographic speed of the telescope since the comatic images are decreased in size.

c. A third type of correcting device is a single plate which has surfaces so shaped that it modifies the character of the bundle of rays from a point source *before* it reaches the reflecting mirror. A most successful corrector of this type designed by B. Schmidt

[1] *Astrophysical Journal*, **81**, 156, 1935.

is illustrated in Fig. 7-10.   The reflector is made spherical instead of paraboloidal, so that coma is absent.   At its center of curvature is placed a disk of glass, one of whose surfaces is plane and the other shaped so that the light refracted by it is made slightly divergent by an amount necessary to eliminate spherical aberration.   With a telescope of this type in which the mirror has a diameter of 71 cm. and a focal length of 1 m. good star images have been obtained over a field 12 degrees in diameter.

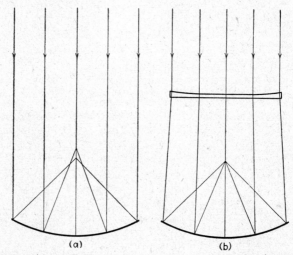

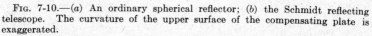

(a)   (b)

Fig. 7-10.—(*a*) An ordinary spherical reflector; (*b*) the Schmidt reflecting telescope.   The curvature of the upper surface of the compensating plate is exaggerated.

11. Oculars (Eyepieces).—In the section on magnifiers it was pointed out that a Ramsden eyepiece makes an excellent reading glass or magnifier.   In fact the only difference between magnifiers and oculars is that while the former are used to view real objects, the latter are used to view images formed by another part of an optical system.   Any magnifier will serve as an eyepiece for a telescope or microscope, but most of them not so well as an eyepiece specially constructed for the purpose.   The triple aplanat in particular makes an excellent eyepiece.

12. The Huygens Eyepiece.—The two principal types of oculars are the Huygens and the Ramsden.   The Huygens, sometimes called a *negative* ocular, is illustrated in Fig. 7-11.   It is made of two elements of the same kind of glass separated by a distance equal to one-half the sum of their focal lengths. The *field lens A* is placed just inside the focus *F* of the objective, this focus serving for the field lens as a virtual object of which an erect image *I* is formed closer to *A*. The *eye lens B* is so placed that *I* is at its focal point, thus forming an image at infinity. The ratio of the focal length of the field lens to that of the eye lens is about 2:1 if the eyepiece is to be used for a microscope and somewhat larger for a telescope. Sometimes a scale or cross

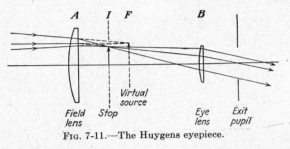

Fig. 7-11.—The Huygens eyepiece.

hairs, or both, are placed at *I*, but if the eye lens is uncorrected for aberrations, the scale cannot be very long. Because the distance between the elements is $(f_1 + f_2)/2$, the Huygens ocular is free from chromatic aberration with respect to focal length, although the longitudinal aberration and curvature of the field are considerable. These may be corrected by special means, such as changing the curvature of the surfaces of the field lens

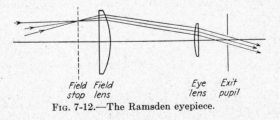

Fig. 7-12.—The Ramsden eyepiece.

while retaining its converging power, or achromatizing the eye lens.

13. The Ramsden Eyepiece.—The essentials of construction of the Ramsden eyepiece, shown in Fig. 7-12, have been described in the section on magnifiers. This ocular has a flatter field than the Huygens and possesses the added advantage that the focal plane of the objective precedes the field lens, so that a scale or traveling cross hair can be used more successfully.   The Ramsden also has the added advantage that it may be focused very sharply on the cross hairs or scale.   This is important if eyestrain is to be avoided.   The observer should first relax the accommodation by resting the eye on a distant view; then, while looking in the eyepiece, he should draw it away from the cross hairs until they just begin to appear diffuse.   Two or three trials will quickly determine the correct focal position for the eyepiece.

14. Erecting the Image.—Sometimes it is desirable to have an erect image instead of the inverted image seen in the ordinary

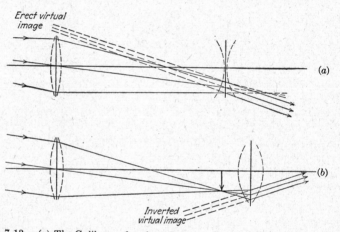

Fig. 7-13.—(*a*) The Galilean refracting telescope; (*b*) the astronomical refracting telescope.

eyepiece.   In the *prism binocular* this is done by means of prismatic reflections.   The simple negative lens of the Galilean telescope (Fig. 7-13*a*) also serves to erect the image.   In terrestrial telescopes, where it is desirable that a distant scene be erected, a four-element eyepiece, illustrated in Fig. 7-14 is used.

15. The Spectrometer.—Perhaps the most important optical instrument for the study of light is the *spectrometer*.   It may be used to determine indices of refraction, to study the effects of diffraction, interference, and polarization, and to make observations on spectra.   For the last-named purpose it has reached its greatest development in the *spectrograph* which is essentially a spectrometer equipped with a camera in place of the eyepiece.

The essential parts of a spectrometer are shown in Fig. 7-15. At S is a slit, with accurately parallel jaws, which may be altered in width from about 0.001 mm. to a few millimeters. The variation in width may be accomplished by a motion of one jaw (unilateral), if only narrow slits are to be used, or of both jaws equally (bilateral) in case wide apertures are desired, or sym-

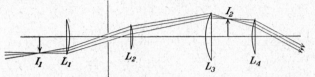

FIG. 7-14.—The erecting eyepiece.

metry of widening is to be maintained. The slit is mounted at one end of a tube, at the other end of which is the *collimator lens* L_1 which for ordinary visual purposes must be a good crown-flint achromat. The collimator tube is equipped with one or more devices for altering its length. Usually this is accomplished by a rack and pinion which can be turned to change the slit distance from the lens. At L_2 is a second lens, preferably an

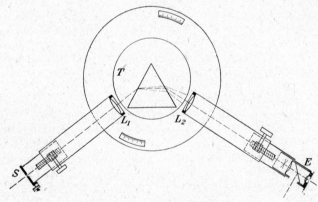

FIG. 7-15.—The spectrometer.

achromat identical with L_1. This lens, the tube on which it is mounted, and the eyepiece E constitute a telescope. At the focal plane of the objective are mounted the cross hairs. The distance of the cross hairs and eyepiece from the objective may be changed by means of a rack and pinion. In some cases, the lenses L_1 and L_2 are also independently mounted on drawtubes

which may be clamped to the main tubes at different distances.
The collimator and telescope tubes are mounted on arms which
have as an axis of rotation the central vertical axis of the spectrometer. With this axis as a center of rotation also are the
spectrometer *table T* on which prisms or other optical parts may
be mounted between the collimator and telescope, and a graduated circular scale. The circular scale should be as large as the
dimensions of the instrument will permit. It is divided into
units of angle, and may be graduated from 0 to 180 deg. in two
equal sections or from 0 to 90 deg. in each quadrant. It should
be read at opposite sides, either by means of verniers or by
microscopes. In addition to being adjustable about the central
axis, the collimator and telescope are also adjustable about
vertical axes and horizontal axes perpendicular to their lengths.
When the instrument is in adjustment, the longitudinal axes of
the collimator and telescope should meet at the central vertical
axis of the spectrometer.

Directions for the adjustment of a spectrometer will be found
in Appendix IV.

Problems

1. What is the magnifying power of a glass ball 1.5 cm. in diameter?
($n = 1.5$)

2. A piece of capillary glass tubing has an outside diameter of 7 mm.
The capillary appears to be about 1 mm. wide when looked at through
the glass wall. What is its real diameter? ($n = 1.5$)

3. A magnifying glass whose focal length is 6 cm. is used to view an
object by a person whose smallest distance of distinct vision is 25 cm.
If he holds the glass close to the eye, what is the best position of the
object?

4. The objective of a telescope has a diameter of 30 mm. and a focal
length of 20 cm. When focused on a distant object, it is found that the
diameter of the exit pupil is 2.5 mm. What is the magnifying power
of the system? If the eyepiece is a single thin lens what is its focal
length?

5. A celestial telescope has a focal length of 25 ft. What must be the
focal length of an eyepiece which will give a magnification of 300
diameters?

6. The objective of a telescope has a focal length of 40 cm. and the
ocular has a focal length of 5 cm. Plot the magnification as a function
of object distance, if the latter varies from 5 m. to infinity.

7. The objective of a field glass has a focal length of 24 cm. When it is used to view an object 2 m. away the magnification is 3.5. What is the focal length of the ocular? What will be the magnification for an object a great distance away?

8. A large astronomical telescope usually has a "finder" attached to it, which consists of a short-focus telescope fastened to the cylinder of the larger one. Explain the use of the finder.

CHAPTER VIII

THE PRISM AND PRISM INSTRUMENTS

1. The Prism Spectrometer.—Probably the most important
use of the prism is for the spectroscopic analysis of light. Because
of the variation with wave-length of the index of glass and other
transparent substances, light passed through a prism is spread
out into a spectrum by means of which the analysis may be made.

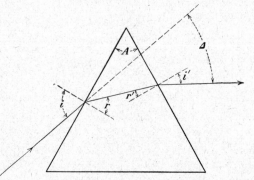

Fig. 8-1.—A section through a prism perpendicular to the refracting edge.

In Fig. 8-1 is shown a section made by passing a plane through a
prism perpendicular to the two refracting surfaces and the
refracting edge of the prism, *i.e.*, the edge in which the refracting
surfaces intersect. The plane of the paper is the plane of
incidence. A beam of light incident on the first surface is bent
by refraction through an angle $i - r$, and at the second surface
through an angle $i' - r'$, where i and i' are the angles made
between the directions of the beam in air and the normals to the
surfaces. The total deviation is thus $\Delta = i + i' - r - r'$.
From the geometry of the figure it is easily proved that A, the
refracting angle of the prism, is equal to $r + r'$, so that

$$\Delta = i + i' - A. \tag{8-1}$$

If the incident beam is fixed in direction, and the prism rotated clockwise, i and r will increase, and r' and i' will decrease, while a counterclockwise rotation will cause i and r to decrease and i' and r' to increase. It can easily be shown by a simple experiment that the value of Δ for any wave-length will pass through a minimum as this rotation takes place. A necessary condition for this minimum is that the derivative of Δ with respect to i shall be zero, *i.e.*,

$$\frac{d\Delta}{di} = 1 + \frac{di'}{di} = 0,$$

or

$$\frac{di'}{di} = -1. \tag{8-2}$$

To evaluate this, the equations for Snell's law applied to the refractions at each surface may be differentiated, resulting in

$$\cos i \; di = n \cos r \; dr,$$
$$\cos i' \; di' = n \cos r' \; dr'. \tag{8-3}$$

Then since $A = r + r'$,

$$dr = -dr'. \tag{8-4}$$

It follows from eqs. 8-2, 8-3, and 8-4 that Δ is a minimum if

$$\frac{\cos i}{\cos i'} = \frac{\cos r}{\cos r'},$$

i.e., if $i = i'$. Therefore at *minimum deviation*, $i = i'$ and $r = r' = A/2$; and by eq. 8-1, $i = (A + \Delta)/2$. Substituting these values in Snell's law, we have for the index of refraction.

$$n = \frac{\sin\left(\dfrac{A + \Delta}{2}\right)}{\sin\left(A/2\right)}. \tag{8-5}$$

Thus the index of refraction of a transparent substance may be found if it is cut into a prism for which the angle A and the minimum deviation Δ are measured. It should be noted that there will be a different angle of minimum deviation for every wave-length.

2. Dispersion of a Prism.—If the source is made a very narrow illuminated slit perpendicular to the plane of incidence, then the *dispersion* resulting from the dependence of n upon λ will result in a spectrum in which each wave-length of the incident light will be a line, *i.e.*, an image of the slit,[1] whose magnification depends upon the focal lengths and the adjustment of the telescope and collimator.

Dispersion can be defined as the rate of change of deviation with wave-length. For a given prism angle A and a constant angle i the deviation changes with index of refraction and with i'. Thus the definition of dispersion just given becomes, from eq. 8-1,

$$D = \frac{d\Delta}{d\lambda} = \frac{di'}{d\lambda}.$$ (8-6)

This expression is for the *angular dispersion*, and not for the actual separation of the spectral lines at the focal plane of the telescope objective. Its value cannot be obtained in a single step since there is no simple expression connecting i' and λ. It is possible to find di'/dn from Snell's law and $dn/d\lambda$ by differentiation of the Cauchy dispersion function of eq. 6-16; these multiplied together give the desired expression for $di'/d\lambda$. This derivation will now be made.

The Cauchy dispersion formula

$$n = n_0 + \frac{B}{\lambda^2} + \ \cdots$$

is an empirical relation in which the values of n_0 and B are experimentally determined. It is not valid when the region of the spectrum to be considered contains absorption bands, but it is satisfactory for ordinary transparent substances such as glass, quartz, fluorite, etc. By differentiation,

$$\frac{dn}{d\lambda} = -\frac{2B}{\lambda^3}.$$ (8-7)

In order to obtain di'/dn we may proceed as follows: From Snell's law, for the second surface,

$$\cos i' \ di' = dn \sin r' + n \cos r' \ dr',$$ (8-8)

---

[1] If only a slit and prism are used, and the spectrum lines viewed with the unaided eye, the optical system of the eye produces the images of the slit.

while for the first surface, since i is constant,

$$n \cos r \, dr + dn \sin r = 0. \qquad (8\text{-}9)$$

Since $dr = -dr'$, eq. 8-9 may be written

$$dr' = \frac{dn \sin r}{n \cos r},$$

which, substituted in eq. 8-8, gives

$$\frac{di'}{dn} = \frac{\sin (r + r')}{\cos i' \cos r} = \frac{\sin A}{\cos i' \cos r}. \qquad (8\text{-}10)$$

Multiplying eqs. 8-7 and 8-10 gives for the dispersion

$$D = \frac{di'}{d\lambda} = \frac{-2B}{\lambda^3} \cdot \frac{\sin A}{\cos i' \cos r}. \qquad (8\text{-}11)$$

Thus the dispersion of a prism depends on four factors: (1) the

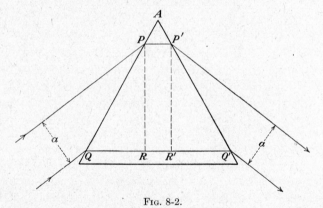

Fig. 8-2.

character of the glass, given by the constant B, (2) the wavelength λ, (3) the refracting angle A of the prism, and (4) the direction of the light through the prism as given by the angle r. The value of i' will, of course, depend on r, A, and B, and also on i. For the case of minimum deviation, eq. 8-11 may be simplified. Consider a beam of light of width a, composed of parallel rays, emerging from the prism. At minimum deviation (Fig. 8-2), $a = P'Q' \cos i'$, $R'Q' = P'Q' \sin (A/2)$, whence

$$P'Q' = \frac{(QQ' - PP')}{2 \sin (A/2)}.$$

If we call $QQ' - PP'$ the effective thickness t, then

$$a = \frac{t \cos i'}{2 \sin (A/2)}.$$

Putting the value of $\cos i'$ from this equation in eq. 8-11, modified for the condition of minimum deviation, we obtain

$$D = \frac{di'}{d\lambda} = \frac{2Bt}{a\lambda^3}. \tag{8-12}$$

The negative sign has been dropped since it merely indicates, as shown by eq. 8-7, that as λ increases, n decreases.

Each image of the slit, or *spectrum line*, is observed to be curved. Rays from the upper and lower ends of the slit undergo greater dispersion than those from the center, having a longer path through the prism because they pass through at an angle with the optical axis of the system, *i.e.*, with the plane of Fig. 8-1. The greater the distance above or below the axis is the part of the slit from which a ray comes, the greater is the dispersion, thus accounting for the fact that all lines are curved, with their ends pointing toward shorter wave-lengths.

It should be emphasized that the dispersion D given by eqs. 8-11 and 8-12 is the change of angle with wave-length. Sometimes the term dispersion is used to mean the separation in angstroms per millimeter in the field of the telescope or on the photograph of the spectrum. Thus a spectrum is said to have a dispersion of 10 angstroms per millimeter when two spectrum lines whose difference of wave-length is 10 angstroms are just 1 mm. apart. Obviously this quantity will depend not only on the angular dispersion D, but also on the focal length, *i.e.*, on the magnification of the telescope or camera objective.

3. Resolving Power of a Prism.—It is customary to define the resolving power of a dispersive instrument as

$$R = \frac{\lambda}{d\lambda}, \tag{8-13}$$

where $d\lambda$ is the smallest wave-length difference which can be detected at the wave-length λ. It will be shown in the chapter on diffraction that limitation of the wave front from a narrow-slit source by an aperture of width a results in an intensity distribution in the image, shown in Fig. 12-17. Moreover, two such images are said to be just resolved when the middle of one coincides with the first minimum of intensity of the other.[1]   The angular separation between the two images is then $\theta = \lambda/a$. In case the angular separation is that between two spectral lines, $\theta = di'$.   Hence for λ in eq. 8-13 may be substituted $a \cdot di'$, so that the resolving power is

$$R = \frac{a \cdot di'}{d\lambda}.$$

But by eq. 8-12 this is equal to $a \cdot D$, so that

$$R = \frac{2Bt}{\lambda^3}, \qquad (8\text{-}14)$$

provided the prism is set for minimum deviation.

Thus the resolving power of a prism at minimum deviation depends on the character of the glass, the wave-length, and the effective thickness of the prism.   Since the effective thickness depends on the refracting angle A and the aperture a, any increase in either will result in an increase in the resolving power.   The limit to the value of A for a single prism is imposed by the necessity for keeping r' less than the critical angle of refraction. Sometimes the light is passed through two or more prisms in succession in order to obtain greater dispersion, but this involves other optical problems which limit the usefulness of the method.

Further consideration of eqs. 8-12 and 8-14, both of which, it must be remembered, apply only in the case of minimum deviation, is desirable to point out that while the width a of the beam of light intercepted by the prism appears explicitly in the expression for D, it does not appear in that for R.   Nevertheless, while the resolving power depends on the aperture in the case of the prism, the dispersion does not.   This apparent paradox is because, in eq. 8-12, t is always proportional to a; if a is decreased in a certain ratio, the effective thickness t is reduced in the same ratio, and the dispersion will be unchanged.   On the other hand, if a is reduced, R will be reduced in proportion, since R is equal to $a \cdot D$.

The resolving power of a prism is not necessarily that of the spectrometer on which it is mounted.   If the aperture of the system is limited by the sizes of the collimator and telescope,

[1] See Fig. 12-19a.

or camera objective, the value of the resolving power will be smaller than that of the prism alone. In visual observations the quality of the vision, the accuracy of focal adjustments, and the judgment of the observer also enter to increase or decrease the numerical value of R. Also, the definition of limit of resolution given in the preceding paragraph, originally due to Rayleigh, is an arbitrary one, and does not agree with experiment in case the two lines under observation are unsymmetrical or quite different in intensity. The numerical value obtained by eq. 8-14 should be taken as indicating only the *order of magnitude* of the resolving power of a prism. In particular cases the value obtained by actual observation of two lines which are just distinguishable as separate may be larger than that calculated from Rayleigh's criterion.

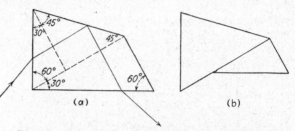

Fig. 8-3.—Two forms of the constant-deviation prism.

4. The Constant-deviation Prism.

In the measurement of spectra with an ordinary prism spectrometer used visually it is necessary to calibrate the instrument for a given setting of the prism, in order to obtain any degree of accuracy. Not only is this calibration time consuming, but the translation of the settings of the telescope into wave-lengths is a tedious process. To avoid these calculations, a *constant-deviation* spectrometer may be used. In this instrument the prism is constructed as shown in Fig. 8-3. For any angle of incidence i the light of the wavelength which is at minimum deviation emerges at right angles to the direction of the incident beam, after one total reflection in the prism. The prism may be made of two 30- and one 45-deg. prisms cemented together as shown by the dotted lines, or it can be cut from a single block of glass. A convenient construction is to make it of two prisms as shown in Fig. 8-3b. The advantage here is that the glass path is diminished and loss of light by absorption reduced.   This is particularly desirable when the prism is of quartz for use in the ultraviolet region of the spectrum.   This type of spectrometer is often made with exceedingly precise adjustments for focusing and setting on particular wave-lengths; it is illustrated in Fig. 8-4.   This is really a spectrograph, made for photographic purposes, but it is equipped with special eyepieces which can be substituted for the plate-holder.   The prism is rotatable about a vertical axis so that any given wave-length region may be brought into coincidence with the cross hairs, or set at a particular point on the photographic

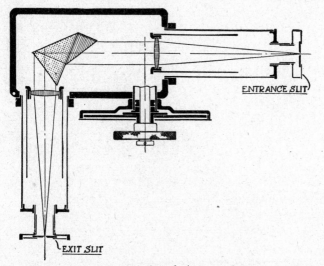

ENTRANCE SLIT

EXIT SLIT

Fig. 8-4.—Diagram showing optical path in monochromator.   (*Courtesy of Gaertner Scientific Co.*)

plate.   This rotation is controlled by a micrometer and screw, accurately calibrated in angstrom units.   Since particular wave-lengths may be brought precisely to a given point in the field, this instrument is also called a *monochromator*, since a suitable aperture may be placed in the focal plane of the spectrum which isolates in turn those wave-lengths which fall upon it as the prism is rotated.

5. The Direct-vision Spectroscope.—Because of the primary importance of accuracy of measurement, ordinary spectroscopes, being massive and rigid, are heavy in construction and unwieldy in shape.   For work which does not require a high degree of precision, a lighter and less cumbersome instrument, the *direct-*

vision spectroscope, is used. If two prisms, one of flint glass and the other of crown are placed together as shown in Fig. 8-5, the difference of dispersion will result in a difference of deviation and the production of a spectrum, for if the deviations of the two prisms are equal for one wave-length, they will not be so for any other wave-length. To obtain sufficient dispersion it is customary to cement together three or five prisms, as illustrated in Fig. 8-6. It is evident that the entire optical system is nearly in a straight line. The composite prism is usually cemented, or otherwise firmly fixed, in a tube provided with a slit at one end, an appropriate collimator and telescope, and cross hairs or scale for calibration. Since the whole instrument can be pointed easily at a source and used in a manner similar to a monocular, is extremely useful for rapid visual inspection of spectra. Some of the more elaborate direct-vision spectroscopes may even be used for measurement of spectral-line positions with an accuracy of about 1 angstrom.

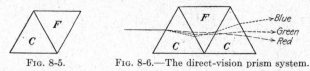

Fig. 8-5.   Fig. 8-6.—The direct-vision prism system.

6. Critical Angle of Refraction.—If the angle of incidence of a beam of light on a glass surface is increased until it approaches 90 deg., the angle of refraction will approach a limiting value which depends on the indices of refraction of the glass and of the air traversed by the incident beam. In the case of a glass plate in air, the index of the air may be taken as unity, so that for $i = 90°$, the index of refraction of the glass is given by

$$n = \frac{1}{\sin r_c},$$ (8-15)

where r_c is called the critical angle of refraction. For glass whose index is 1.5, r_c is approximately 41.8 deg. Consequently any light incident from the glass side on the air-glass interface at an angle greater than r_c will be totally reflected, since there can be none refracted. *Total-reflection prisms* so constructed as to take advantage of this principle are often better than mirrors for turning beams of light through right angles. The reflecting power of most metal mirrors is far from unity and varies with the wave-length. The total-reflection prism is free from dispersion, since the angle of reflection is independent of the wavelength. On the other hand, a glass prism absorbs some light, and for regions of the spectrum not transmitted by ordinary glass the prism must be made of quartz or fluorite. In some cases rock salt or lithium fluoride prisms are used.

It is necessary that the reflecting surface of the prism be free from dirt, oxidation, or other contamination, since the presence of a film other than air will change the critical angle, and more often than not cause light to be refracted out of the prism. By means of prisms of special design, the light can be turned through angles other than a right angle.[1]

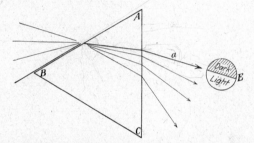

FIG. 8-7.—Critical angle of refraction. If the direction of the light is reversed, all rays incident on *AB* at angles greater than that for ray *a* will be totally reflected.

7. Index of Refraction by Means of Total Reflection.—The

phenomenon of total reflection of light provides a useful means of determining the index of refraction of transparent substances. If a prism is illuminated by a broad beam of convergent light as shown in Fig. 8-7, the field at *E* will be divided into a dark portion on one side of the ray *a* and a bright portion on the other. If the refracting angle *A* of the prism is measured, and the angle i' between the normal to the surface *AC* and the emergent ray *a*, and these two values substituted in eq. 8-20, the index of the prism may be calculated. It will then be possible to measure the index of refraction of a liquid placed in contact with the side *AB*.

Let the index of refraction of this medium be n, and that of the glass prism, n_g. Then Snell's law,

[1] A fairly complete discussion of total-reflection prisms of a variety of designs is found in *Bureau of Standards Scientific Paper* No. 550, 1927, by I. C. Gardner.

$$n \sin i = n_g \sin r,$$

at grazing incidence becomes

$$\frac{n_g}{n} = \frac{1}{\sin r}. \tag{8-16}$$

At the surface AC the prism is in contact with air, and Snell's law for this case is

$$\sin i' = n_g \sin r'. \tag{8-17}$$

Also

$$A = r + r'. \tag{8-18}$$

Eliminating r and r' from these three equations, we have

$$n = \sin A \sqrt{n_g^2 - \sin^2 i'} - \sin i' \cos A. \tag{8-19}$$

The measured values of A, i', and n_g substituted in eq. 8-19 will

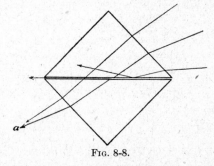

Fig. 8-8.

give the value of n, the desired index of refraction of the liquid. The value of n_g, the index of refraction of the glass prism, may be found with great precision for any wave-length by measuring the angle A and the minimum deviation Δ, and substituting their values in eq. 8-5. This method is to be preferred to the measurement of n_g by a measurement of i' for grazing incidence as suggested above. If, however, the latter method is to be used, eq. 8-19 may be put into a suitable form by putting $n = 1$, whereupon

$$n_g^2 = 1 + \left[\frac{\sin i' + \cos A}{\sin A} \right]^2. \tag{8-20}$$

8. The Abbe Refractometer.—This is an instrument designed to make use of the principles outlined in the two preceding sections for measuring the indices of refraction of liquids.   While many refinements are built into the best instruments, the essential optical part is a pair of right-angle prisms illustrated in Fig. 8-8.   When placed with their diagonal sides face to face with a thin film of liquid between, the index of refraction of the liquid may be found by measuring the angle i' corresponding to the light which enters the prism A and is refracted at the critical angle.   Substituting of this value, and the measured values of A and n_g in eq. 8-19, yields the value of the index of refraction of the liquid.

Problems

1. Show that the constants of the Cauchy dispersion formula are given by

$$n_0 = \frac{n_1\lambda_1{}^2 - n_2\lambda_2{}^2}{\lambda_1{}^2 - \lambda_2{}^2},$$

$$B = \frac{\lambda_1{}^2\lambda_2{}^2(n_2 - n_1)}{\lambda_1{}^2 - \lambda_2{}^2},$$

in which n_1 and n_2 are the indices of refraction at two wave-lengths λ_1 and λ_2.

2. What will be the dispersion of a 60-deg. prism made of glass No. 3 in Table 2 at the end of this volume, at 7000 angstroms?   At 4000 angstroms?   Give the units in each case.   If the prism face is completely filled with light, how wide must it be if the sodium doublet 5890 and 5896 angstroms is to be just resolved?

3. What factors actually enter into an experimental determination of resolving power other than those considered in the preceding problem?

4. A prism for a spectrograph is to be made out of glass whose index n_D is 1.72.   What is the maximum prism angle which can be used?

5. The critical angle of refraction of a substance is 58 deg.   What is its index of refraction?

6. Show that if the angle of a glass prism is larger than twice the critical angle of refraction, no light can be passed through it by refraction.

CHAPTER IX

THE NATURE OF LIGHT

1. Light as a Wave Motion.—Speculations, theories, and investigations concerning the nature of light have had a prominent place in man's intellectual endeavors since the beginning of history. There have been short periods of time when groups, sometimes including practically all students of natural philosophy, have been convinced that the nature of light was understood. On the whole, however, during most of the time, diverse opinions have been held, based on conflicting theories and speculations or on apparently conflicting experimental evidence. It is not within the province of an intermediate course in optics to present the history, or the arguments concerning different theories, of the nature of light, or, more generally, of radiation. But just as in the introduction to geometrical optics the concept of the *ray* was adopted because it enabled us to continue expeditiously our development of the subject of image formation, so in physical optics we can adopt the concept of light as a *wave motion* propagated from a source in all directions through space. Moreover, we can make use of the wave theory only as long as it is not in conflict with observations, whether these be in the limited field of the topic under discussion or in some other part of the larger field of physical phenomena.

The quantum theory introduces a concept of light which is more complex than a mere wave motion. According to this view, when light is emitted or absorbed, the energy of the light appears in the form of concentrated units, called *photons*.[1] These photons are supposed to move in straight lines, when in free space, with the speed of light, and to have an energy which is related in a simple manner to the frequency of the associated

[1] It is perhaps worthwhile to warn the student against the indiscriminate use of the words "photon" and "quantum." A *photon* consists of a certain amount or *quantum* of energy, but not all quanta are photons.

ight wave. In problems of the *transmission* of light, where no
interchange of energy between radiation and matter is involved,
the quantum theory, like the classical wave theory, describes the
propagation of the light in terms of a wave motion. It is problems of this kind, including mainly *refraction, diffraction, interference,* and *polarization,* with which we shall be concerned in the
next few chapters. For these purposes, therefore, the assumption of light waves is entirely adequate, and it is not necessary
that we concern ourselves with the complementary assumption
of the existence of photons. On the other hand, the origin of
spectra, the interaction of light with material media through
which it passes, and certain phenomena classified under the
headings of magneto- and electro-optics cannot be satisfactorily
explained by the classical wave theory of radiation. For these,
the quantum theory signalized by the names of Planck, Einstein, Bohr, and others offers a satisfactory explanation. This
early quantum theory, however, in turn fails to encompass *all*
the intricacy of detail in modern observations in the field of light.
To take its place has arisen what is known as *quantum mechanics.*
While this later quantum theory goes far in unifying the classical
and earlier quantum concepts, we have not lived long enough
with it to reduce it to simple terms. Accordingly, for an elementary presentation, it is necessary to rely upon classical or
quantum theories in turn to "explain" those phenomena to
which they are individually best fitted. This process is, however,
not entirely without a satisfactory basis, for, it will be noted, in
order to deal with either the *origin* of the radiant energy (as
photons) in atoms or molecules, as in spectra, or its *interaction*
with material media, as in the photoelectric effect, the quantum
theory is more suitable, while the classical wave theory is quite
sufficient to explain those light phenomena which deal only with
the passage of the light through space. In *diffraction,* where we are
accustomed to thinking of a material obstacle as taking part in
what happens, it is entirely immaterial of what elements the
obstacle is made; the important detail is that a part of the
"front" of the light propagated through space is obstructed and
cannot pass on to the place where the image is formed. Even in
polarization, where the nature of the medium assuredly enters
into the entire problem, we can describe the characteristics of the
transmitted light adequately by means of the classical theory.

Experimental evidence supports the hypothesis that light is a wave motion, transverse in character, propagated through space with a finite velocity. The theory of light as a transverse wave motion has gone through several phases. In the earliest of these, it was felt absolutely necessary to suppose space to consist of an elastic-solid medium of great rarity, patterned in its characteristics after those substances which were known to be the medium of transfer of other disturbances such as sound and water waves. This elastic-solid medium could, therefore, be considered to consist of particles obeying the same laws as ordinary matter, but in such a way that suitable density and elasticity could be assigned to the medium. Later, this hypothetical medium was abandoned in favor of the more abstract idea of an all-pervading "luminiferous ether," different from the elastic-solid medium in that it possessed no such definite "particle" characteristics, but retaining the properties of elasticity and density so necessary for the representation of the wave motion which traverses it. With Maxwell's introduction of the electromagnetic theory of light, this elastic medium was replaced by one with the electrical characteristics of a dielectric constant and a magnetic permeability. On this view the wave has an electric field and a magnetic field, each transverse to the direction of propagation and perpendicular to the other. This electromagnetic theory of light waves has now completely superseded the idea of waves in an elastic ether. The ether, if we continue to use the term, is now thought of as a region with certain electrical characteristics rather than as an elastic solid. In this sense the idea of transverse waves in the ether is in accord with the latest developments of relativity and quantum theory.

2. Velocity, Frequency, and Wave-length.—The velocity of light in free space is the same for all wave-lengths. This conclusion is supported by a variety of observation. A wave disturbance propagated through space with a *velocity* c and a *frequency* n will have a wave-length λ. These three quantities are related by the equation

$$c = n\lambda. \tag{9-1}$$

The value of c is approximately 3×10^{10} cm. sec.$^{-1}$; hence for a wave-length $\lambda = 5 \times 10^{-5}$ cm., the frequency n will be 0.6×10^{15} sec.$^{-1}$. If the time it takes a point on the wave train to pass through a complete cycle of phases is called the *period T*, then $n = 1/T$, and

$$c = \frac{\lambda}{T}. \tag{9-2}$$

3. Simple Harmonic Motion.—It has been pointed out in Sec. **9-1** that our concept of the nature of a light disturbance has passed beyond the stage at which it was considered to be an oscillatory displacement of material particles. The form of analytical expression, however, need not be changed. At a point in space, the disturbance due to the passage of a train of light waves may be a simple or a complex wave motion. Also, it can be shown that a complex oscillatory motion may be represented

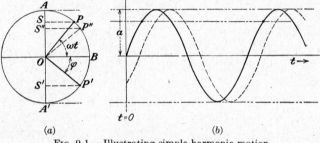

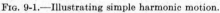

(a)   (b)

Fig. 9-1.—Illustrating simple harmonic motion.

as a summation of a number of simple harmonic motions. We may therefore arrive at equations describing wave motions by the development of the summation of a number of simple harmonic disturbances of a material particle.

The equation for a simple harmonic motion may be obtained by considering the motion executed by a point P moving with uniform angular speed in a fixed circle. The projection of this motion upon a diameter of the circle is a simple harmonic motion. We may thus consider the motion of a particle S in a straight line (Fig. 9-1*a*) to be a simple harmonic motion, provided the displacement of S is always given by

$$s = a \sin \omega t,$$

in which a is the maximum displacement, *i.e.*, the radius of the circle, ω is the angular velocity of the point P, and t is the time which has elapsed since the particle left the point O in its upward journey. If T is the time taken for one complete cycle, then

$\omega = 2\pi/T$, and the displacement will be

$$s = a \sin 2\pi\frac{t}{T}. \tag{9-3}$$

In Fig. 9-1b the displacement is plotted as a function of the time, the solid curve being the graph of eq. 9-3.   In general, however, it is desirable to express the displacement in terms of the time which has elapsed since the beginning of the motion, *i.e.*, since the particle was at some other point such as S'.   In eq. 9-3, however, it is assumed that the particle is at the position of zero displacement at the beginning of the time t.   In general this will not be true.   To represent the most general case, therefore, we must consider that the particle is at some position S' when $t = 0$; the displacement s is, as before, the distance from O to S, and instead of eq. 9-3, we have

$$s = a \sin (POP' - BOP') = a \sin \left(2\pi\frac{t}{T} - \varphi\right). \tag{9-4}$$

If the point S' should be above the middle point O, as S'', the sign of φ is positive.   The dotted curve in Fig. 9-1b is the graph of eq. 9-4.

4. Phase and Phase Angle.—The phase of a simple harmonic motion refers to the particular stage of the cycle of motion being executed.   Two particles executing simple harmonic motions parallel to AA' in Fig. 9-1a are in the same phase if they are at the positions of zero displacement at the same time and are also moving in the same direction; if moving in opposite directions they are in opposite phase.   It is not necessary, however, that the simple harmonic motions be executed in parallel lines nor that they be of the same amplitude.   They must be going through the same part of their cyclical motion at the same time, so that the equations for the displacements are the same functions (sines or cosines) of the same angles.   The motions represented by eqs. 9-3 and 9-4 are not in the same phase, the difference of *phase angle* between them being φ.   On the other hand, the motions given by

$$x = a \sin \left(2\pi\frac{t}{T} - \varphi\right),$$

$$y = b \sin \left(2\pi\frac{t}{T} - \varphi\right),$$

are in the same phase, even though they are along x- and y-directions perpendicular to each other, and have different maximum amplitudes.

Obviously the phase angle corresponding to the displacement passes through all values from 0 to 2π in succession, repeating this change as long as the motion continues. It follows that the phase angle in eq. 9-4 is given by

$$2\pi\frac{t}{T} - \varphi.$$

5. Composition of Simple Harmonic Motions.—There are two cases to be considered: The composition of (1) simple harmonic

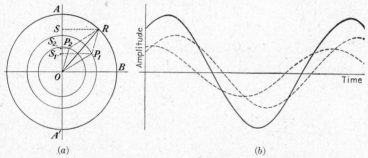

(a) (b)

Fig. 9-2.—(a) Graphical method of composition of two simple harmonic motions. (b) The solid line gives the resultant of two simple harmonic motions which are shown by the dotted lines.

motions in the same direction, and (2) simple harmonic motions at right angles. All cases come under these two heads, since two or more motions at an angle not 0 nor 90 deg. can be separately resolved into components at right angles, which may thereupon be composed. There are two general methods, the graphical and the analytical, for effecting this composition. The graphical method will be discussed first.

Graphical Methods.—The composition of two simple harmonic motions of the same period T, executed in the same direction, but not necessarily of the same amplitude, may be represented as in Fig. 9-2a. The displacements s_1 and s_2 differ in phase angle by $P_2\widehat{O}P_1$. The total displacement OS along AA' is given by the projection of the resultant radius OR, which is the diagonal of the parallelogram formed by the radii OP_1 and OP_2. Also, $OS = OS_1 + OS_2$. The individual simple harmonic motions and their resultant are plotted in Fig. 9-2b.

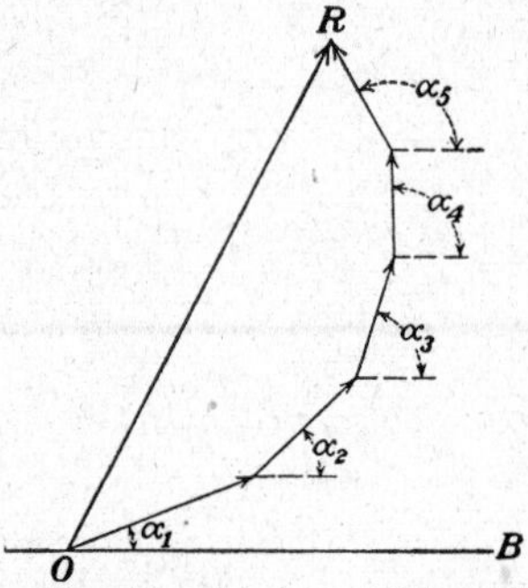

While this method may be applied successively to as many components as desired, a much easier method is to make use of the vector polygon, illustrated in Fig. 9-3. The lengths of the vectors are the amplitudes of the separate components; the angles α_1, α_2, etc., are the phase angles; OR is the amplitude of the resultant, and its phase angle is $\widehat{ROB}$. This method, which may be extended to give the summation of any number of components, is extremely useful in the solution of problems in diffraction and will be made use of in Chap. XII.

Fig. 9-3.—Vector addition of simple harmonic motions in same line.

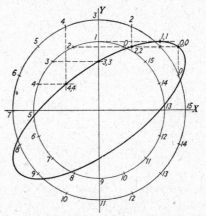

Fig. 9-4.—Composition of two simple harmonic motions at right angles.

If the two component vibrations are at right angles, they may be compounded graphically as illustrated in Fig. 9-4. The basis of the method is to make use of a series of equidistant points on circles drawn concentrically, with their radii equal to the maximum amplitudes of the two disturbances. These points are numbered so that the zero point in each case corresponds to the displacement for which $t = 0$. The values of the simultaneous displacements corresponding to the number k may be called x_k and y_k, respectively. In order to get the displacement due to the composition of the two disturbances at any instant i, it is necessary to find on this coordinate diagram the position of the point (x_i, y_i). The resultant disturbance will be the curve plotted through a series of points thus found.

Analytical Methods.—As in the case of graphical methods there are two general cases to be considered: (*a*) when the vibrations take place in the same direction, (*b*) when at right angles. The first of these is important in diffraction and interference, which are dealt with in the chapters immediately following this. Since the only problem of vibrations at right angles with which we have to deal is in the case of double refraction in crystals, case (*b*) will not be discussed here. The special case referred to will be found in the treatment of elliptically polarized light, Sec. **13-11**.

For case (*a*) consider two simple harmonic motions executed in the same direction with the same period T. They may be represented by

$$\left. \begin{aligned} s_1 &= a_1 \sin\left(2\pi\frac{t}{T} - \varphi_1\right), \\ s_2 &= a_2 \sin\left(2\pi\frac{t}{T} - \varphi_2\right). \end{aligned} \right\} \tag{9-5}$$

The difference in phase between them is given by $\varphi_1 - \varphi_2$. Expanding each sine term in eq. 9-5, and adding,

$$s = s_1 + s_2 = a_1(\sin\theta\cos\varphi_1 - \cos\theta\sin\varphi_1) \\ + a_2(\sin\theta\cos\varphi_2 - \cos\theta\sin\varphi_2), \quad (9\text{-}6)$$

in which for convenience the symbol θ has been substituted for $2\pi t/T$. At this point it is convenient to choose an angle δ such that

$$\left. \begin{aligned} A\cos\delta &= a_1\cos\varphi_1 + a_2\cos\varphi_2, \\ A\sin\delta &= a_1\sin\varphi_1 + a_2\sin\varphi_2. \end{aligned} \right\} \tag{9-7}$$

If the first of eqs. 9-7 is multiplied by $\sin\theta$ and the second by $\cos\theta$, and the second subtracted from the first,

$$A(\cos\delta\sin\theta - \sin\delta\cos\theta) = a_1\sin\theta\cos\varphi_1 + a_2\sin\theta\cos\varphi_2 \\ - a_1\cos\theta\sin\varphi_1 - a_2\cos\theta\sin\varphi_2,$$

in which the right-hand side is the same as the right-hand side of eq. 9-6. Hence,

$$s = s_1 + s_2 = A\left(\sin 2\pi \frac{t}{T} \cos \delta - \cos 2\pi \frac{t}{T} \sin \delta \right)$$
$$= A \sin \left(2\pi \frac{t}{T} - \delta \right). \quad (9\text{-}8)$$

Also, if eqs. 9-7 are squared and added, the result is

$$A^2 = a_1{}^2 + a_2{}^2 + 2a_1a_2 \cos (\varphi_2 - \varphi_1). \quad (9\text{-}9)$$

It is evident that A is the resultant amplitude of the composition of the two simple harmonic motions, for if $\varphi_2 - \varphi_1$ is zero or any integral multiple of 2π, the disturbances are in the same phase and $A^2 = (a_1 + a_2)^2$; while if $\varphi_2 - \varphi_1$ is equal to $(2n - 1)/2$ times 2π, where n is a whole number, the disturbances are in the opposite phase, and $A^2 = (a_1 - a_2)^2$. In this case, the amplitude will be zero provided $a_1 = a_2$.

6. Characteristics of a Wave Motion.—Although, as has been pointed out in Sec. **9-1,** light waves are no longer thought of as disturbances in an elastic-solid medium, in order to develop the equation of a wave motion adequate for present purposes, we may consider the form of the wave to depend upon the motion transmitted to the particles of such a medium. A particle moving with a harmonic motion of the kind described in the previous sections will act as the source of a wave train. Let O (Fig. 9-5) be a source communicating its harmonic motion to a medium having an elasticity E and a density d. The velocity of propagation of the wave is $c = \sqrt{E/d}$. The displacement at a given instant along the line OS is given by $s = a \sin 2\pi t/T$, and the displacement at the same instant of a particle from a point X a distance x from O is given by $s = a \sin 2\pi\left(\dfrac{t}{T} - \dfrac{t'}{T} \right)$, where t' is the time it takes the wave to travel from O to X. In other words, the difference of phase between the motions at O and X is given by t'/T. But since the time taken by the wave to travel from O to X is $t' = x/c$, and since $c = \lambda/T$, $t'/T = x/\lambda$. Hence the displacement at X is given by

$$s = a \sin 2\pi\left(\frac{t}{T} - \frac{x}{\lambda} \right). \quad (9\text{-}10)$$

Although eq. 9-4 bears a superficial resemblance to eq. 9-10, it is not the same. The former gives the displacement at any time t of a single vibrating particle; the latter gives at any one

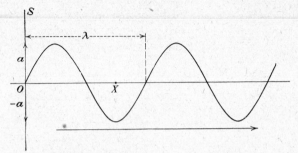

Fig. 9-5.—Illustrating the characteristics of a simple wave motion.

instant an instantaneous "snapshot" of the displacements of all the particles along the path of the wave.

The difference of phase between the motions at O and X is $2\pi x/\lambda$; if x/λ is a whole number, the motions at the two points are in the same phase. Two particles at points X_1 and X_2 will execute motions whose difference of phase is given by the difference of their phase angles

$$\Delta = \frac{2\pi(x_2 - x_1)}{\lambda}. \qquad (9\text{-}11)$$

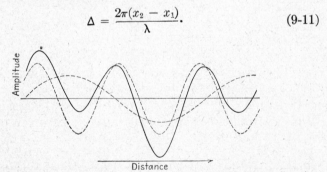

Fig. 9-6.—Superposition of two wave trains traveling in the same direction.

7. The Principle of Superposition.—If light from two sources passes through a small opening at the same time, two separate images will be formed, each of which will in no way be affected by the presence or absence of the other. This will be true, unless the sources are so close together that their images overlap, even though at the opening the wave trains pass through the

same space at the same time.   Hence we may say that if two
or more wave trains travel through the same space at the same
time, each will thereafter be the same as if the others were not
present.   At a point where they act simultaneously, however,
the resulting disturbance will be that due to the *superposition*
of the wave trains.   This is illustrated graphically in Fig. 9-6,
where the dotted curves represent the separate disturbances and
the solid curve the result of their superposition at any one
instant.

8. The Wave Front.—A simple concept of a wave front is
that of a surface A (Fig. 9-7), traveling from a source S.   From

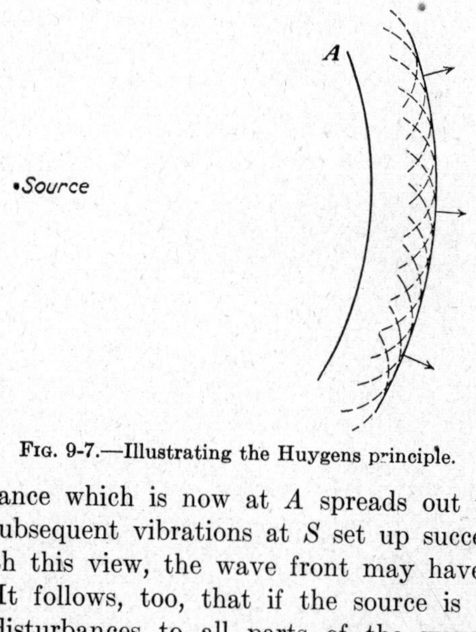

Fig. 9-7.—Illustrating the Huygens principle.

S a disturbance which is now at A spreads out through the
medium.   Subsequent vibrations at S set up succeeding wave
fronts.   With this view, the wave front may have any shape
whatever.   It follows, too, that if the source is sending out
oscillatory disturbances to all parts of the wave front, the
motions at all points in it will be in the same phase.   It is not
necessary that the medium be homogeneous; the wave front may
lie part in one medium and part in another.   Rigorously, however, the definition breaks down if different wave-lengths are
propagated in any of the media with different speeds.   In such
a case we may continue to use the term wave front only with
regard to homogeneous waves.

9. The Huygens Principle.   Secondary Waves.—In order to
account for the manner in which light waves are propagated,

Huygens supposed that each point on a wave front may be considered as the source of a new disturbance. The envelope of these secondary waves—Huygens wavelets—constitutes the new wave front, as illustrated in Fig. 9-7. These secondary-wave sources are not of the same character as original sources, since they act only upon the communication of the disturbance from points behind them, and hence propagate the light only in a forward direction. Huygens assumed that the only effective part of a wavelet is the point which is tangent to the common enveloping surface which constitutes the new wave front. This is not only a violent assumption, but it is contrary to experiment, for it can be shown that light actually bends around the corner of an obstacle. Fresnel showed that destructive interference

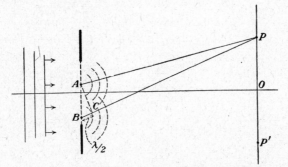

FIG. 9-8.—Superposition of two Huygens wavelets.

reconciled the facts of experiment with Huygens' concept of secondary waves. Although a fuller discussion of Fresnel's treatment will be given in the chapter on diffraction, a brief application of the Huygens principle and the principle of super-position will be given here.

If the extent of the primary wave front is limited by one or more obstacles, the formation of the new wave front is modified in a manner which may be simply described by considering the light to pass through a narrow slit. In Fig. 9-8 a plane wave, advancing to the right from a distant point source S, is inter-cepted by a slit of width a. According to the Huygens principle, the wave front at the slit plane may be considered as consisting of a number of elements. Two of these, A and B, are chosen with a separation of $a/2$. If on a screen OP a point P is chosen such that the difference of path $BC = BP - AP = \lambda/2$, the phase difference at P between the light waves from A and B will be π, and no disturbance will result from A and B combined. This is also true for all other pairs of points, such as A and B, which are separated by the same distance at the plane of the slit. At points above P and below P' for which the difference of path $BP - AP = 3\lambda/2$, $5\lambda/2$, etc., there will also be no light, but at points in between these some light will be seen. The same arguments hold for the region below O. At O, and at all other points where the difference of path is $n\lambda$, if $n = 1, 2, 3$, etc., the light will be a maximum. It may easily be proved that for small angles θ, where θ is the angle subtended at the slit by PO, $\lambda/2AB = \theta$, or, if the width of the slit is a,

$$\theta = \frac{\lambda}{a} \qquad (9\text{-}12)$$

10. Amplitude and Intensity.—Thus far we have considered only the amplitude of a single wave disturbance and the resultant disturbance due to the superposition of waves. In actual practice, however, it is not the amplitude of the disturbance which is measured, but the intensity of illumination due to the light waves. The intensity of illumination may be defined as the total energy transmitted per second across a unit plane normal to the direction of propagation. According to eq. 5-5, this total energy through unit plane is inversely proportional to the square of the distance of the plane from the source, so that by the foregoing definition the intensity also is inversely proportional to the distance squared from the source, provided the light is spreading out uniformly in all directions, and suffers no absorption by the medium.

The relation between the amplitude and the energy, and hence between the amplitude and the intensity, in a wave train, may be arrived at by different methods, depending upon the particular dynamical concept of waves employed. For radiation in an elastic-solid medium the energy may be shown to be proportional to the square of the amplitude by finding the sum of the kinetic and potential energies of the vibrating particles in the unit plane as the wave train sweeps across it.[1] The same relation may also be derived for an electromagnetic wave train.[2] If then, the

[1] See, for instance, Preston, "Theory of Light," 4th ed., p. 44, Macmillan.
[2] See, for instance, Houstoun, "A Treatise on Light," Chap. XXII, Longmans.

energy upon a plane normal to the direction of propagation is proportional to the *square of the amplitude* of the disturbance, and is also defined as the *intensity* of the light in that plane, it follows that the intensity is proportional to the square of the amplitude. Figure 9-9 shows graphically the relation between the two. The dotted curve is the graph of $S = \cos x$, the maximum amplitude being unity. The solid curve is the graph of the intensity $I = S^2 = \cos^2 x$.

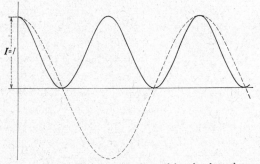

Fig. 9-9.—Amplitude in a wave train is indicated by the dotted curve, intensity by the solid curve.

11. The Velocity of Light.—The first determination of a finite velocity of light was made by Römer, who in 1676 noted that inequalities in the time intervals between eclipses of Jupiter's satellites depended upon whether the earth was on the same side of the sun as Jupiter, or on the opposite side. In the former case the eclipses occurred earlier, and in the latter case, later than the predicted times. Römer inferred that the difference was because the time taken by the light from Jupiter to reach the earth is finite, and greater when the two planets are farther apart. His calculated velocity was a little over 300,000 km. per sec. His conclusion was ignored by many until in 1728 Bradley discovered the so-called *aberration of light*. This is really an aberration in the positions of fixed stars, which were found to have slight displacements in position, depending on the motion of the earth in its orbit. The effect is illustrated in Fig. 9-10. When the earth is moving to the left, in order to bring the star image on the center of the field, the telescope must be pointed a little forward in the direction of the earth's motion, that is it must be pointed a little to the left in the figure, while at position B, it must be

pointed a little to the right. The *angle of aberration* α is about
20.5 sec. of arc. Bradley concluded that this alteration of the
apparent direction of the light was due to the relative velocities,
c of the light and v of the earth. The relation between these
velocities and $α$ is given by $\tan α = v/c$. This gives a value of a
little less than 300,000 km. per sec. for c.

In 1849, Fizeau made a preliminary experimental determination of the velocity of light, using the *toothed-wheel* method,
illustrated schematically in Fig. 9-11. A simple illustration will

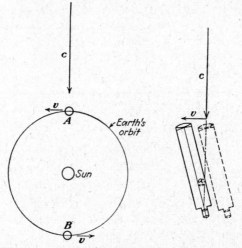

Fig. 9-10.—Illustrating how the angle of aberration arises. During the time
the light traverses the length of the telescope, the latter moves from the position
indicated by the dotted outline to that given by the solid outline.

suffice to show the manner in which this device may be used to
measure c. Suppose the light beam passes through a slot on
the rim, is reflected from the distant mirror, and returns on the
same path just as the next slot is exactly in position to receive it.
Then the ratio of the velocity of the wheel's rim to the velocity
of light is the same as the ratio of the distance between the two
slots to the distance traveled by the light, which is $2TM$ in the
figure.

In the year following Fizeau's experiment, the *rotating-mirror*
method was used by Foucault. This method is shown schematically in Fig. 9-12. Light from the source S is reflected from the
rotating mirror R to a distant mirror M. The center of curvature

of M is at R so that with a stationary mirror R the light will be reflected directly back on its path, to S. Actually it returns to S_1, having been reflected by mirror M_2. If R is turning at high speed, in the time during which the light passes from R to M and back, the mirror has turned through a small angle, so that

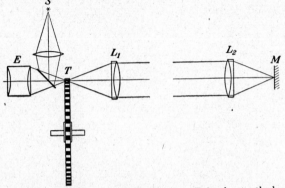

FIG. 9-11.—Fizeau's *toothed-wheel* apparatus. T is the toothed wheel; L_1 collimates the beam of light; L_2 at the distant station focuses the light upon the mirror M; the source is at S; and the eyepiece or telescope at E.

the return beam, instead of arriving at S_1', is observed at S_1', a small distance from S_1. From a measurement of S_1S_1', the angle through which R has turned may be calculated. If also the angular velocity of R and the distance $2RM$ are known, the velocity of light may be found.

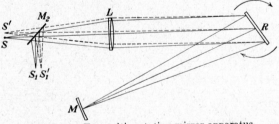

FIG. 9-12.—Foucault's rotating-mirror apparatus.

The actual experimental technique and calculations involved in both Fizeau's and Foucault's experiments are far more than the bare details just given, and the reader is referred to more extended treatises for their complete description.[1]

[1] See, for instance, Preston, "Theory of Light," 4th ed., Macmillan.

The experiments of Fizeau and Foucault were preliminary trials of their respective methods. In the years following, both methods were used extensively to find the velocity of light.[1] The method of Foucault has proved to have experimentally fewer inherent objections. Of these, two are worthy of mention. When the lens L is placed as shown in Fig. 9-12, the amount of light returned to S' is inversely proportional to RM, since in any given revolution of R the light sweeps around on a circumference $4\pi RM$. In order to avoid this difficulty, Michelson moved the lens to a position between R and M and close to R. Another difficulty of the Foucault method is the possibility of error in measuring the very small displacement SS'. This and other optical difficulties were eliminated by Michelson in his final

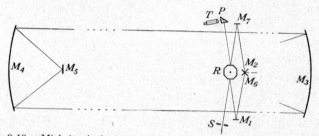

Fig. 9-13.—Michelson's final apparatus for measuring the velocity of light. The path of the light beam is S, R, M_1, M_2, M_3, M_4, M_5, M_4, M_3 M_6, M_7, R, P, T.

series of experiments, carried out at Mt. Wilson during the past decade. The final form of his apparatus is shown in Fig. 9-13. In order to avoid excessively high speeds of rotation, mirrors of 8, 12, and 16 faces were used. These were rotated at such speeds that while the light reflected from R was traveling over its journey to the distant station and back to R, the latter turned through an angle equal to that between two faces. Thus by a sort of "null-point" method the measurement of the image displacement SS' (Fig. 9-12) was eliminated.

With this apparatus, and a light path between mountain peaks of about 35 km., Michelson obtained a value for c of 299,796 km. per sec.[2] This value is the velocity of light *in vacuo* and is

[1] There is a complete table of experimental values obtained by different workers, and references to original sources, in an article by Gheury de Bray, *Nature*, **120**, 602, 1927.

[2] *Astrophysical Journal*, **65**, 1, 1927.

obtained by adding to the observed velocity a correction for the index of refraction of the atmosphere. In a later experiment, carried to conclusion after his death in 1931, the light path was enclosed in an evacuated tube 1 mile long. By means of multiple reflections, the actual path was made eight to ten times as great. A rotating mirror with 32 faces was used. The mean value of many determinations was 299,774 km. per sec.[1]

These later determinations of *c* by Michelson and his associates were made with such a degree of precision that there was remarkable consistency between the individual observations of which the published values are the mean. Conservatively estimated, this consistency was between 50 and 500 times as great as in previous experimental determinations.

The velocity of light has also been obtained by using the *Kerr cell* (effect of electrical birefringence) as a shutter to cut off the light beam. By this method, which is discussed in Sec. **16-11,** the value of *c* is found to be 299,778 km. per sec.

12. Wave Velocity and Group Velocity.—Rayleigh was the first to point out that the velocity of light measured in a refracting medium is not the velocity of the individual waves. Instead, because of the difference of velocity with wave-length, the measured value will be that of a periodicity impressed upon the wave train. The velocity of this periodicity is called the *group velocity*. Consider a wave train having two wave-lengths, as illustrated in Fig. 9-14a, in which the dotted line represents the longer wave-length, traveling faster than the shorter. While at the instant represented the two are in phase at point *A*, giving rise to a group amplitude shown in Fig. 9-14b, somewhat later the amplitude will build up a little to the left of the point *A*. In other words, the group will have a slightly smaller velocity than that of the individual waves. The energy belongs to the group rather than to the waves, and the observed velocity will be that of the group.

The effect may be illustrated by the manner in which waves travel over the surface of water. It will be noticed that the

---

[1] MICHELSON, PEASE, and PEARSON, *Astrophysical Journal*, **82,** 935, 1935. This series of experiments indicated also a monthly variation over a range of about 20 km. per sec., but the spread of the observations was sufficiently great to render its reality questionable. Whether this is real or is due to some instrumental effect is not at present known.

group as a whole does not move as fast as the waves, which run forward and die out in the advancing front.

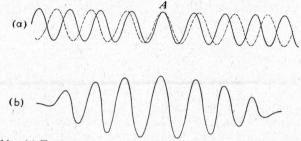

Fig. 9-14.—(a) Two wave trains of different wave-length traveling toward the right; (b) the sum of their amplitudes.

In order to obtain an analytical relationship between the wave velocity V and the group velocity U, consider two infinitely long trains of waves to be represented by $\sin \frac{2\pi}{T_1}\left(t - \frac{x}{V_1}\right)$ and $\sin \frac{2\pi}{T_2}\left(t - \frac{x}{V_2}\right)$. Their resultant will be

$$S = \sin \frac{2\pi}{T_1}\left(t - \frac{x}{V_1}\right) + \sin \frac{2\pi}{T_2}\left(t - \frac{x}{V_2}\right),$$

which can be put in the form

$$S = 2\cos 2\pi\left[\frac{t}{2}\left(\frac{1}{T_1} - \frac{1}{T_2}\right) - \frac{x}{2}\left(\frac{1}{T_1 V_1} - \frac{1}{T_2 V_2}\right)\right] \times$$
$$\sin 2\pi\left[\frac{t}{2}\left(\frac{1}{T_1} + \frac{1}{T_2}\right) - \frac{x}{2}\left(\frac{1}{T_1 V_1} + \frac{1}{T_2 V_2}\right)\right]. \quad (9\text{-}13)$$

If T_1 is almost equal to T_2, and V_1 almost equal to V_2, the following approximations may be made:

$$\frac{1}{2}\left(\frac{1}{T_1} + \frac{1}{T_2}\right) = \frac{1}{T}; \quad \frac{1}{2}\left(\frac{1}{T_1 V_1} + \frac{1}{T_2 V_2}\right) = \frac{1}{TV};$$
$$\frac{1}{T_1} - \frac{1}{T_2} = \frac{dT}{T^2}; \quad \frac{1}{T_1 V_1} - \frac{1}{T_2 V_2} = \frac{d(TV)}{T^2 V^2},$$

so that eq. 9-13 becomes

$$S = \cos \pi\left[\frac{t \cdot dT}{T^2} - \frac{x \cdot d(TV)}{T^2 V^2}\right] \sin \frac{2\pi}{T}\left(t - \frac{x}{V}\right).$$

This is an equation in which the cosine part is a periodically varying amplitude factor, representing a wave group which moves with a velocity U equal to the ratio of dT/T^2 to $d(TV)/T^2V^2$, so that, using the relationship $V = \lambda/T$, we obtain

$$U = \frac{V^2 dT}{d(TV)} = \frac{V d\lambda - \lambda dV}{d\lambda} = V - \frac{\lambda dV}{d\lambda}. \qquad (9\text{-}14)$$

In an experimental determination of the velocity of light in carbon bisulphide, Michelson found that the ratio of the velocity in air to that in carbon bisulphide was 1.76. The ratio of the indices of refraction, however, gave a value of 1.64. The difference is because the index of refraction is expressed as the ratio of the wave velocities, while, as pointed out above, the measured velocity is that of the group. By applying the correction term in eq. 9-14 the figures were found to agree.

Problems

1. Plot the graph of the simple harmonic motion given by

$$s = 5 \cos \frac{2\pi t}{6}.$$

2. Using the parallelogram method, draw the graph of

$$s_1 = a_1 \sin 2\pi \frac{t}{T_1} \qquad \text{and} \qquad s_2 = a_2 \sin \left(2\pi \frac{t}{T_2} + \varphi \right),$$

representing two displacements along the same axis, for $a_1 = 5$, $a_2 = 6$, $T_1 = 2T_2$, $\varphi = \pi/4$.

3. Draw a graph of the resultant motion of displacements

$$x = a \sin \left(2\pi \frac{t}{T} - \theta_1 \right),$$

$$y = b \sin \left(2\pi \frac{t}{T} - \theta_2 \right),$$

where $a = 7$, $b = 10$, $\theta_1 = \pi/6$, $\theta_2 = \pi/2$.

CHAPTER X

INTERFERENCE OF LIGHT

1. Interference and Diffraction Compared.—In Sec. **9-9** it was shown that two Huygens wavelets will unite to produce light, provided the difference of path from their starting points to the point where they combine is equal to an even number of half wave-lengths; and that they will unite to produce darkness if the difference of path is an odd number of half wave-lengths. Similarly it was shown that the effect of restricting the light to a portion of the wave front by a narrow slit will produce an intensity pattern in which the distribution of energy depends on the wave-length of the light and the width of the slit. All such patterns which similarly depend on the *limitation of the wave front* are called *diffraction patterns.* They may be shown to owe their appearance to the fact that in directions other than that of the incident wave there is not complete mutual cancellation of the light. A phenomenon bearing a superficial resemblance to that of diffraction is obtained if the beams of light from *two separate parts of the wave front* are made to reunite under conditions which will be described. The result is called *interference of light.* It is similar to diffraction in the sense that there exist alternate light and dark regions, depending on whether the two wave trains cancel each other, wholly or in part, or whether they reinforce each other. It is different from diffraction, however, since it does not necessarily depend upon any restriction of the wave front. Instead, the best interference patterns are produced with wave-fronts so extended that no diffraction phenomena of ordinary magnitudes exist.

2. Conditions for Interference.—There are certain experimental conditions which must be fulfilled for the production of observable interference. These are:

a. The light in the two wave fronts which combine to give interference must originally come from the same source.

b. The difference of optical path between the beams must be very small, unless the light is monochromatic or nearly so.

c. The wave fronts, on recombining to form interference patterns, must be at a small angle to each other.

There is a fourth condition concerning the state of *polarization* of the light, which may be left to the chapter dealing with that subject.

The first condition is made necessary by the nature of light itself. According to spectral theory, radiation of a particular frequency occurs when an atom or molecule undergoes a transition from a given energy state to one of smaller energy. Such

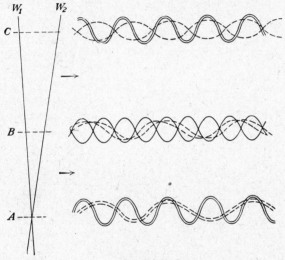

Fig. 10-1.

transitions occupy a time of the order of 10^{-8} sec., during which a photon, or quantum, of radiant energy, passes out into space. The chance is believed to be extremely small that the same or another atom or molecule in another part of the source will emit a train of waves of any duration capable of producing interference with that from the first.

The second condition may be illustrated by the diagrammatic representation in Fig. 10-1 of two interfering trains of white light. These are originally from the same source, but by some sort of apparatus the original wave train has been divided into two at a very small angle, advancing toward the right. The difference of optical path from the source to the position *A* is zero, and there the two waves, indicated by solid curves, will be in the same phase and will also reinforce each other throughout their paths. Since the difference of path from the source is zero, the reinforcement will take place for all wave-lengths. At a position B, where the difference of path is $\lambda/2$, the two wave trains indicated by solid curves are opposite in phase and will cancel each other, provided they are of the same amplitude, while some other pair of wave trains of different wave-length λ', indicated by the dotted curves, will not be opposite in phase and will to some degree reinforce each other. At a position C, as at A, there is again reinforcement for wave trains of wave-length λ, and cancellation for those of wave-length λ'. Thus, for white light, only a few fringes are seen on either side of the middle position A. Outside of the region where fringes are seen, although at each point destructive interference exists for some wave-length, partial or complete reinforcement exists for all others. This results in a complete masking of all interference except for the few fringes already mentioned. Except for the middle one, these will be colored, with the dispersion increasing with increasing distance from the middle.

If the source is one which contains only a few strong monochromatic radiations, interference fringes will appear with fair visibility over a considerable range on either side of the middle position. The mercury arc and the neon discharge tube are examples of this type of source.

If there are only two wave-lengths, the fringes will have maximum visibility at the point of zero difference of path, and also at the points where the path difference is an integral number of times one wave-length and also an integral number of times the other. At points in between, reinforcement will take place for one wave-length and partial or complete cancellation for the other, with the result that the visibility of the fringes will be low or zero.[1] There will be a more extended treatment of this

---

[1] The appearance or nonappearance of the fringes depends also upon the difference of color, *i.e.*, upon the sensitivity of the eye for the two colors. If one wave-length is in the yellow, to which the eye is most sensitive, and the other in the deep blue, the fringes due to the yellow will be seen even if the intrinsic intensity of the blue is equal to that of the yellow. But by a proper adjustment of the intensity of each one, they may be made to cancel each other.

topic in Chap. XI, in the discussion of the Michelson interferometer.

The third condition for interference, which applies rather to the observation than the production of the fringes, is illustrated in Fig. 10-2a and b.   In a are represented two plane wave trains from the same source which have been made to cross each other at a small angle.   At all positions indicated by solid lines, the phase is the same.   It is different from this phase by a half period at all positions indicated by the dotted lines.   Hence the crossing of two solid or two dotted lines marks a position of

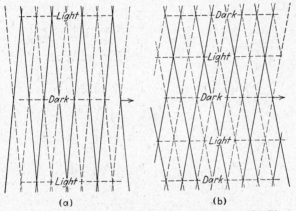

Fig. 10-2.—Superposition of two plane waves (a) at a small angle, (b) at a larger angle.

reinforcement, while the crossing of a solid and a dotted line marks a position of cancellation.   In Fig. 10-2b the angle between the wave fronts is greater than in Fig. 10-2a, and the positions of reinforcement, or interference maxima of intensity, are closer together.   As the angle between the two wave fronts is increased, the spacing of the fringes becomes smaller, until finally they are indistinguishable even with large magnification.

3. No Destruction of Energy.—The use of the term "destructive interference" does not imply that where two wave trains from the same source cross each other some of the radiant energy is destroyed.   At a position of minimum intensity, because of partial or complete cancellation of the amplitude, the intensity is very small, while at a maximum, since the amplitudes are added, the intensity, which is the square of the amplitude, is correspondingly large.   Consider a region of maxima and minima due to two wave fronts of equal amplitude a, in which the intensity pattern is that shown graphically in Fig. 10-3.   It is required to find the total illumination over a range from $x = 0$ to $x = k$, as shown by the shaded area.   According to eq. 9-9 this will be given by

$$I = \int_{x=0}^{x=k} (2a^2 + 2a^2 \cos \varphi)dx, \qquad (10\text{-}1)$$

where φ is the amount by which the difference of phase between the interfering wave fronts varies along the wave front between

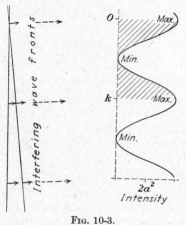

$x = 0$ and $x = k$.   Since φ is a linear function of x, we may write $\varphi = mx$ (see eq. 9-10).   By integrating, we have

$$I = 2a^2k + \frac{2a^2 \sin mk}{m}. \qquad (10\text{-}2)$$

Since the interference pattern is at a maximum at both 0 and k, $km = 2\pi$, the second term on the right is zero, and the total illumination in any such area of the field of view is $I = 2a^2k$. This is exactly the illumination

Fig. 10-3.

in the area if the two waves had combined without interference. Hence in the phenomenon of interference there is no destruction of energy, but only a redistribution.

4. Methods for Producing Interference.—Instruments for producing interference phenomena may be divided into two general classes: (A) Those which by reflection, refraction, or diffraction change the directions of two parts of the wave front so that afterward they reunite at a small angle; (B) those which, usually by a combination of reflection and refraction, divide the amplitude of a section of the wave front into two parts to be later reunited to produce interference.   In both cases the usual conditions for interference must always be observed.   In all instruments of class A it is necessary to use either a point source or a very narrow elongated source such as an illuminated slit parallel to the intersection of the two wave fronts.   With instruments of class *A*, which may be characterized as effecting a *division of wave front*, diffraction will also usually be observed, although often the spacing between the maxima and minima of the diffraction pattern is so large in comparison with the spacing between the interference fringes that it is easy to distinguish between the two effects.   In the instruments of class *B*, which may be characterized as effecting a *division of amplitude* in a more extended portion of the wave front, it is not necessary to use a point or narrow line source.   Since the wave front is divided in amplitude, if upon reunion corresponding points in the separate parts are superposed, the first condition for interference will hold.

While the classification just given is probably the most important, all instruments for producing interference patterns may also be grouped in two other categories, depending upon the existence or nonexistence of a *complementary pattern*.   In general, those of class *A* (division of wave front) do not possess complementary patterns, while those of class *B* (division of amplitude), with a few exceptions, do possess them.   Since a more extended discussion of this distinction involves a description of the details of each instrument, it will not be carried out here.

5. Young's Experiment.—Historically the first true interference effect to be recognized as such was due to Thomas Young.   It belongs to class *A*, since the device he used recombined two different parts of the wave front so as to produce alternate light and dark fringes.   His apparatus consisted of a pinhole to admit the light of the sun, and, in another screen a short distance away, two pinholes sufficiently close together so that the light diffracted at the first hole entered both of them. The arrangement is illustrated in Fig. 10-4.

Diffraction also occurred at each of the two holes in the second screen, and in the overlapping portions of the diffracted wave fronts interference was observed.   For best results it is more convenient to use narrow slits instead of pinholes, care being taken to make all the slits perpendicular to a common plane. The maxima and minima will then be evenly spaced bright and dark lines of equal width.   The maxima will appear where the difference of path between the two wave fronts is an even number of half wave-lengths.   Figure 12-13*b*, page 177, in the chapter on diffraction is a photograph of the pattern obtained with Young's apparatus, using slits instead of pinholes. The large scale pattern of maxima and minima is due to diffraction, while interference is responsible for the finer pattern which is most pronounced in the middle but extends over practically the entire field.

The analysis of the conditions for the production of this interference pattern will not be undertaken here. While the results are strictly due to what has been called interference of light, it is customary to treat the effects due to two or more parallel slits as extensions of the diffraction due to one slit. Since it is somewhat easier to handle the analysis in this way, a more complete discussion will be given in Chap. XII.

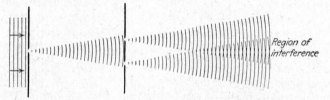

FIG. 10-4.—Illustrating Young's apparatus.

Among the devices for obtaining interference by a *division of the wave front* into two parts, three will be selected for discussion, since they illustrate most generally the variety of conditions which may exist. These are the Fresnel mirrors, the Fresnel biprism, and the Rayleigh refractometer.

6. The Fresnel Mirrors.—The first of these is in a sense an adaptation of Young's apparatus, designed to eliminate as far as possible the presence of the diffraction pattern due to the narrow slits in the second screen. It is illustrated in Fig. 10-5. Light from a source S, which is usually a narrow illuminated slit, passes to two mirrors which are inclined at a very small angle, with their line of intersection parallel to the slit S. The fringes may be seen by placing the eye near the mirrors so as to receive the reflected light, but ordinarily an eyepiece will be needed to magnify them. If monochromatic light is used, its wave length may be determined. Let α be the angle between the mirrors, D_1 the distance from the slit S to the intersection of the mirrors, D_2 the distance from the mirrors to the point of observation, and e the distance between two adjacent bright fringes F_1 and F_2.

The difference of path between the distances SF_1 and SF_2 is λ. The light appears to come from two virtual sources S_1 and S_2, whose distances from the point of observation are $D_1 + D_2$, and whose linear separation may be called d. Since the angle

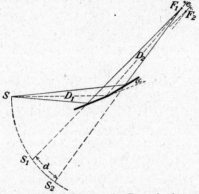

FIG. 10-5.—Illustrating the Fresnel mirrors.

between the reflected beams is twice that between the mirrors, to a sufficient degree of approximation,

$$2\alpha = \frac{d}{D_1}. \tag{10-3}$$

Also,

$$\frac{\lambda}{d} = \frac{e}{D_1 + D_2}. \tag{10-4}$$

Combining these,

$$\lambda = \frac{2\alpha e D_1}{D_1 + D_2}. \tag{10-5}$$

Since all the dimensions on the right-hand side of eq. 10-5 may be measured with considerable accuracy, a fairly precise value of the wave-length λ may be found. Usually the mirrors are set so that the angle of incidence is large. In this case the angular aperture subtended at the source slit by each mirror is small, and diffraction is present. An added drawback is that the diffraction pattern has approximately the same spacing as the interference pattern, so that the two are not always distinguishable. A photograph of the fringes obtained with the Fresnel mirrors is shown in Fig. 10-6.

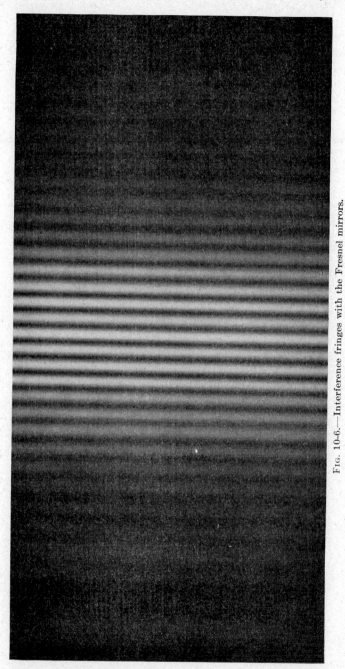

Fig. 10-6.—Interference fringes with the Fresnel mirrors.

7. The Fresnel Biprism.—A much better device for obtaining the interference between two sections of a wave front, with diffraction either largely eliminated or distinctly separated in appearance from the interference pattern, is the Fresnel biprism, illustrated in Fig. 10-7. The biprism is usually made of a single piece of glass so shaped that it is in reality two triangular prisms base to base, with equal and small refracting angles α. The biprism is set so that it is illuminated by light from a slit S. In order that the interference fringes may be distinct, the refracting edges of the two prisms should be parallel to each other, and the

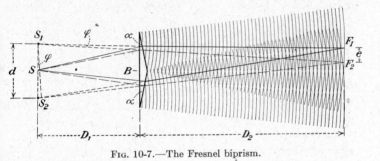

FIG. 10-7.—The Fresnel biprism.

intersection of the two inclined faces should be accurately parallel to the slit.

To find the wave-length λ of monochromatic light, it is necessary to know the distance d between the virtual images S_1 and S_2 from which the rays bent by refraction seem to come, the distances D_1 and D_2, and the separation e of two adjacent bright fringes in the field of view at the cross hairs. The value of d may be calculated if the index of refraction n of the biprism and its refracting angle α are known. Since the angles are small, we may consider the light to be passing through the prisms at minimum deviation, whence

$$n = \frac{\sin \frac{1}{2}(\alpha + \delta)}{\sin \frac{1}{2}\alpha}, \tag{10-6}$$

where δ is the angle of deviation. Equation 10-6 may be put in the form

$$n \sin \frac{\alpha}{2} = \sin \frac{\alpha}{2} \cos \frac{\delta}{2} + \cos \frac{\alpha}{2} \sin \frac{\delta}{2},$$

which, since the angles are small, may be reduced to

$$(n - 1)\frac{\alpha}{2} = \frac{\delta}{2}. \tag{10-7}$$

But from the figure, $\sin \frac{1}{2} \delta = d/4D_1 = \delta/2$, approximately, so that

$$d = 2D_1\alpha(n - 1). \tag{10-8}$$

The value of d may also be obtained experimentally, making it unnecessary to know the index of refraction of the biprism. If a lens whose focal length is less than one fourth of the distance $D_1 + D_2$ is placed between the biprism and the eyepiece, two positions may be found at which real images of the slit, one formed through each prism, may be focused at the plane of the crosshairs, where the fringe width e has been observed. From

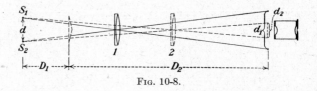

Fig. 10-8.

elementary geometrical optics it may be shown that if d_1 (Fig. 10-8) is the separation of the images for the first of these lens positions and d_2 that for the second, then $d = \sqrt{d_1 d_2}$. The distances D_1, D_2, and e may be measured directly.

Having found d, we may proceed to find λ. In Fig. 10-7 consider the paths S_1F_1 and S_2F_1 to be such that a bright fringe is formed at F_1. Then, if the adjacent bright fringe is at F_2, the paths S_1F_2 and S_2F_2 will differ by the wave-length λ. From the geometry of the figure,

$$\sin \varphi = \frac{\lambda}{d} = \frac{e}{D_1 + D_2},$$

or

$$\lambda = \frac{ed}{D_1 + D_2}. \tag{10-9}$$

This equation applies in the case where the light from the slit incident upon the prism is divergent. If the incident light is changed into a parallel beam by means of a collimating lens

FIG. 10-9.—Interference fringes with a Fresnel biprism. The two diffraction patterns which show at the sides are due to the common base of the two prisms, at position *B*, Fig. 10-7, and are thus illustrations of diffraction at a straight edge. Compare with Fig. 12-7 in the chapter on diffraction. The diffraction patterns due to the two refracting edges are not seen, since they are outside the range of the photograph.

after leaving the slit, D_1 is very large compared to D_2, so that the latter may be ignored, and eq. 10-9 becomes

$$\lambda = \frac{ed}{D_1}.$$

Substituting in this the value of d given in eq. **10-8,**

$$\lambda = \frac{2eD_1\alpha(n - 1)}{D_1},$$

or, finally,

$$\lambda = 2e\alpha(n - 1). \tag{10-10}$$

But for small prism angles $\alpha(n - 1) = \delta$, the angle of deviation, so that

$$\lambda = 2e\delta. \tag{10-11}$$

The fringes obtained with a biprism are shown in Fig. 10-9.

8. The Rayleigh Refractometer.—This instrument, illustrated in Fig. 10-10, has been used extensively for the determina-

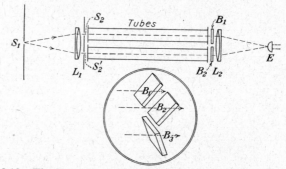

Fig. 10-10.—The Rayleigh refractometer.   The figure in the circle illustrates the arrangement of the compensating mirrors; B_1 and B_2 are in front of the tubes, while B_3 is below them.

tion of indices of refraction of liquids and gases.   While it possesses some of the general features of Young's apparatus, as do the Fresnel biprism and mirrors, there are important differences to be noted.   In the Rayleigh refractometer the two interfering beams are originally at a large angle when they leave the source S_1, while in Young's apparatus they travel over nearly adjacent paths in a diffracted beam.   In the second place, the two portions of the wave front passing through the slits S_2 and S_2'

are collimated by a lens L_1 so that they remain parallel for some distance. They then pass through a second lens L_2, placed some distance from the first, which focuses the two beams, forming an image of the slit S_1 at its principal focus. This image will, however, be a wide diffraction pattern similar to that shown in Fig. 12-14, page 179, with fine interference fringes superposed upon it. The greater the distance between S_2 and S_2', the finer will be the interference fringes. Since focusing in only one plane is required, the eyepiece E may be a cylinder with its axis parallel to the slits. Since this has a magnification in only one plane it gives a brighter image. The distance between L_1 and L_2 is made great enough, and the separation of S_2 and S_2' is made wide enough, so that two tubes containing liquids or gases whose indices are to be compared may be placed side by side in the paths of the beams. The glass windows at the ends of these tubes must be of good optical glass with accurately plane faces.

A change in the index of refraction of the substance in the tubes may be found as follows: Let us suppose that the two tubes contain a gas under the same conditions of pressure and temperature. Given equal lengths, the optical paths are equal. A slight change in the conditions in one tube will cause a change in the optical path there, and hence a displacement of the fringes. A measurement of the amount of this shift, which under actual conditions is very small, is difficult and subject to uncertainty because of the narrowness of the fringes. Instead, it is customary to make use of a so-called coincidence method. At B_1 and B_2 in the paths of the beams are placed two plane-parallel plates of optical glass, of the same thickness, each at an angle of about 45 deg. to the vertical. Under these conditions the optical paths through them are the same and will produce no displacement of the fringes. If, however, the index of refraction of the gas, and hence the optical path through B_1, is altered, the fringes, having been shifted on that account, may be brought back to their original position by a rotation of B_1 about a horizontal axis perpendicular to the length of the tubes. When this rotation is made, the optical path through B_1 will be changed by an amount which is a measure of the index change. In order to provide a fiducial position to which the fringes may be brought back each time, there is placed across the lower part of the field, below the level of the tubes, a plate of glass B_3, whose retardation is the same as that of B_2. Through this may be observed a set of fringes undisturbed by any changes in the tubes. The presence of this set of fringes as a fiducial system renders the use of a cylindrical eyepiece necessary, since one of the ordinary type will result in the superposition of all rays from a single source point, whether they pass through the tubes or below them. It is desirable to use white light, as the central bright fringe is easily identified, while over a considerable range all monochromatic fringes look alike. Moreover, because of selective absorption in the tubes, the fringes in the upper and lower parts of the field of view may not be the same in appearance. This makes it difficult to find accurately the fractional part of a fringe in white-light fringes, which are colored except for the central fringe. On

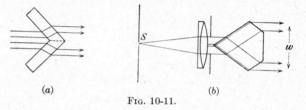

(a)   (b)

Fig. 10-11.

this account it is customary to locate the central fringe of the system in white light, and substitute monochromatic light to measure the fractional part of a fringe. The motion of plate B_1 must be controlled and calibrated with extreme accuracy by means of a micrometer screw.[1]

The Rayleigh refractometer has some serious drawbacks. It will be seen in the discussion of the Michelson interferometer that these are inherent in interference apparatus of class A, and are absent when those of class B are used. On the other hand, the Rayleigh refractometer in its most modern form is still used a great deal for measurements of refractive index, and at least one portable instrument is on the market. The principal drawback is that the slits S_2 and S_2' must be put as far apart as possible so that tubes of sufficient width may be used. It is also desirable that the tubes be sufficiently far from each other so that the physical conditions in them may be controlled separately. On the other hand, the farther apart the slits are, *i.e.*, the greater

---

[1] In some forms of this instrument B_1 and B_2 are fixed at right angles and turned together about a horizontal axis.

the angle their separation subtends at the primary slit S_1, the finer will be the fringes.   The resulting loss of intensity when these are magnified makes measurements difficult.   One of the most useful devices for increasing the separation of a pair of interfering beams without increasing the angle subtended at the primary slit is the biplate illustrated in Fig. 10-11a.   An ingenious application of the principle of the biplate has been made by W. E. Williams in a modification of the Rayleigh refractometer.[1]

9. The Williams Refractometer.—The essential feature of this instrument is illustrated in Fig. 10-11b.   Instead of passing through two narrow slits, each of width a, the light after collimation passes through a slit of width $2a$ and is then divided into equal parallel beams by refraction through a five-sided prism. Thus the beams are separated by a distance w which depends on the size of the prism.   Williams has shown that with this arrangement the primary slit S_1 may be opened to a width $0.715w/a$ times the maximum value used in the Rayleigh refractometer, resulting in a considerable increase in the intensity of the fringes, which permits greater accuracy of measurement.

Problems

1. The light from a straight incandescent filament falls on two parallel slits separated by 0.2 mm.   If the interference fringes on a screen 75 cm. away have a spacing of 2.2 mm., what is the wave-length of the light used?

2. One of the tubes of a Rayleigh refractometer is filled with air, the other being evacuated.   Then the second is filled with air under the same conditions of temperature and pressure and 98 fringes are seen to pass the field of view.   What is the index of refraction of the air if sodium light is used and the tubes are each 20 cm. long?

3. What will be the angle of tilt of the compensating plate required to restore the fringes to their original condition, in the preceding problem, if the plate has a thickness of 5.1 mm.?   (Use $n = 1.5$ and derive an equation similar to that used in Experiment 10.)

4. The interference pattern shown in Fig. 10-9 is twice the size of the original photograph.   If the biprism was 35 cm. from the slit, and the photographic plate 448 cm. from the biprism, what was the wave-length of the light used?   (NOTE: the diffraction patterns also shown in the photograph, on either side, are those due to the common base of the

[1] WILLIAMS, W. E., *Proceedings of the Physical Society of London,* **44,** 451, 1932.

prisms. By measurements of their separation, the distance d in eq. 10-9 may be obtained.)

5. A Fresnel biprism, in which the refracting angles are 2 deg. and the index of refraction is 1.5, receives from a narrow slit the light of the mercury green line, 5461 angstroms. A soap film is placed in the path of the light which has passed through one of the prisms, and the interference fringes shift 3.5 fringes. What is the thickness of the film in millimeters? (Assume $n = 1.33$ for the soap solution.)

CHAPTER XI

INTERFERENCE OF LIGHT—DIVISION OF AMPLITUDE

In Chap. X it was pointed out that in general there are two ways of producing interference of light: (A) By a *division of the wave front* into two or more sections restricted in width, which are later recombined, and (B) by a *division of amplitude* of a more or less extended portion of the wave front into beams which are afterward recombined to produce interference. The first of these methods has been illustrated in Chap. X by Young's apparatus, the Fresnel biprism and mirrors, and the Rayleigh refractometer.

1. Colors in Thin Films.—Perhaps the simplest example of the division of amplitude is the colors in thin films. A simple device showing this type of interference is a pair of plane glass plates pressed close together at one edge and separated by a very thin sheet of foil at the opposite edge, so that the enclosed air film is in the shape of a wedge. In Fig. 11-1*a* is a sketch of the arrangement, and in Fig. 11-1*b* is a photograph of fringes obtained with it. In the sketch the angle of the wedge is much exaggerated. Also, for simplicity the changes of wave-length and direction which take place in the glass because of refraction are ignored. In Fig. 11-1*b* the slight curvature of the fringes is due to unequal pressure on the ends of the plates, which were bent a little by clamping.

2. Newton's Rings.—The first accurate measurements of interference fringes were made by Newton, although he did not recognize in the phenomenon of Newton's rings the superposition of two wave fronts. Instead, he proposed an explanation based on a corpuscular theory of radiation, making certain assumptions as to the manner in which the reflection and refraction of the light took place.

The rings are obtained when two plates of glass having slightly different curvatures are pressed together so that they touch at one point. The thin wedge-shaped film of air enclosed between the plates provides a path difference between the two reflected beams (see Fig. 11-3) of at most a few wave-lengths, so that the fringes may be observed with white light. If one of the glass plates is accurately plane and the other slightly convex and spherical, the fringes are concentric rings of color.

It is perhaps less complicated to consider first the general case of interference in the case of films instead of proceeding at once to the particular case of Newton's rings. Although in

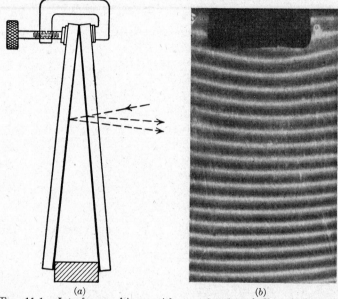

(a)   (b)

Fig. 11-1.—Interference fringes with a wedge-shaped film of air enclosed between two plane plates. The fine lines in the photograph are due to scratches on the glass plates, which were old interferometer plates.

the following derivations the phase difference, and hence the interference, between *beams* will be referred to, it must be kept in mind that the interference is actually between pairs of *wave fronts* which owe their presence to a division of amplitude of the primary wave front incident upon the apparatus.

Consider light to be incident in air upon a thin film of transparent medium having plane-parallel surfaces, an index of refraction μ, and a thickness e, as illustrated in Fig. 11-2. While the beam reflected at A is proceeding toward G, that refracted at A and reflected at B must traverse the path ABA'. Hence the difference of path at any front as indicated by the line $A'F$, drawn normal to AG and $A'H$, will be $\mu(AB + BA') - AF$. But this is equal to $2e\mu \cos i'$, where i' is the angle at which the ray strikes the surface BB'. If, then, the two reflected rays are brought to a focus on a screen by means of a lens, it appears that there would be a maximum of intensity when $2e\mu \cos i' = n\lambda$, and a minimum when $2e\mu \cos i' = (n + \tfrac{1}{2})\lambda$, where n is an integer representing the number of waves in the difference of path. Actually, however, the conditions of reflections are not the same at A and B. At A the reflection takes place in air from the bounding surface of a denser medium, while at B the reflection is in the denser medium from a bounding surface of air. It has been found by experiment that in the former case there is a change of phase of π, corresponding to a path difference of $\lambda/2$, while in the latter case there is no change of phase, so that the

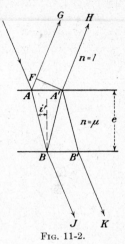

FIG. 11-2.

situation is exactly opposite to that stated above, and the beams AG and $A'H$ will reinforce each other to produce a maximum when

$$2e\mu \cos i' = (n + \tfrac{1}{2})\lambda, \tag{11-1a}$$

while they will produce a minimum when

$$2e\mu \cos i' = n\lambda. \tag{11-1b}$$

On the other hand, since the transmitted rays BJ and $B'K$ suffer no difference of phase, they will reinforce each other when

$$2e\mu \cos i' = n\lambda, \tag{11-2a}$$

and counteract each other when

$$2e\mu \cos i' = (n + \tfrac{1}{2})\lambda. \tag{11-2b}$$

In the case of Newton's rings, eqs. 11-1a and 11-1b will hold for reflected light, provided μ is put equal to unity, since the two interfering reflections take place with opposite phase exactly as in the case described above.

The radius of any ring may be found as follows: Let r (Fig. 11-3), be the radius of curvature of a curved glass surface AOM which rests upon a plane glass surface OB. Then, since LA is nearly the same as OB, and AB is nearly the same as e, the separation between the two surfaces at B, it follows that

$$\rho^2 = r^2 - (r - e)^2 = 2re - e^2,$$

where ρ is the radius of the fringe caused by the interference

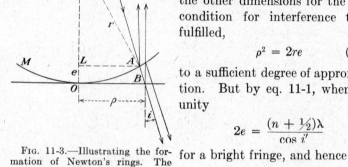

of the two beams, one reflected from the upper surface at A, the other from the lower surface at B. Since e must be small compared to the other dimensions for the third condition for interference to be fulfilled,

$$\rho^2 = 2re \qquad (11\text{-}3)$$

to a sufficient degree of approximation. But by eq. 11-1, when μ is unity

$$2e = \frac{(n + \frac{1}{2})\lambda}{\cos i'}$$

Fig. 11-3.—Illustrating the formation of Newton's rings. The curvature of AOM is exaggerated; actually i at A and B would be almost the same.

for a bright fringe, and hence

$$\rho^2 = \frac{r(n + \frac{1}{2})\lambda}{\cos i'}.$$

For small angles i', $\cos i'$ is approximately unity, and the radius of the fringe is given by

$$\rho = \sqrt{r(n + \frac{1}{2})\lambda}, \qquad (11\text{-}4)$$

where n has the values 0, 1, 2, 3, etc., for the first, second, third, etc., rings, respectively. The radius of a dark fringe will be given by

$$\rho = \sqrt{rn\lambda}. \qquad (11\text{-}5)$$

Since for $n = 0$, by eq. 11-5, $\rho = 0$, for reflected light there will be a dark spot at the center of the fringe system. Also, the radii of the dark fringes are proportional to the square roots of whole numbers. Similarly, for the transmitted light, there will be a bright spot at the center, and the radii of the bright rings are proportional to the square roots of whole numbers. Thus the interference patterns produced by reflection and transmission are complementary.

A photograph of Newton's rings obtained with monochromatic light is shown in Fig. 11-4.

If the upper plate is made of glass of a smaller index of refraction than the lower one and a liquid of intermediate index is placed between them, the pattern obtained by reflection will be complementary to that obtained with an air film between the plates, since at each interface the reflection will take place in a medium of a given index at the bounding surface of one of higher

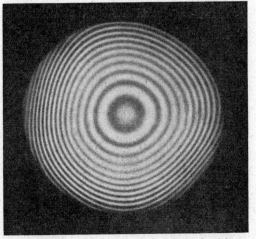

Fig. 11-4.—Photograph of Newton's rings obtained with an uncemented achromat. The white spot occurs at the center because the two surfaces were slightly separated there.

index of refraction, and in both cases a change of phase of π will occur.

The pattern obtained by transmission is not as easy to see as that obtained by reflection, since the light transmitted is much greater than that reflected, resulting in a background of light against which the interference pattern is dimly observed.

It is desirable that the surfaces for producing Newton's rings be clean and free from oxidation. In order that the best results may be obtained it is necessary that the glass surfaces be freshly ground and polished, since the films which develop with age are not removable by ordinary means.[1]

[1] See, for instance, a brief paper on this subject by W. W. Sleator and A. E. Martin in the *Journal of the Optical Society of America* **24**, 29, 1934.

The colors sometimes seen in films of oil on wet pavements, in soap bubbles, in fractures along cleavage planes of crystals, etc., are all analogous to Newton's rings, since they are due to interference between wave fronts reflected from the surfaces of thin films. For this reason they may be observed with white light, since the path difference is small. All such interference fringes belong to class *B*.

3. Double and Multiple Beams.—Any apparatus for producing interference by a division of amplitude has as one of its principal features a surface, illustrated in Fig. 11-5, which reflects part of the light and transmits as much of the remainder as is not

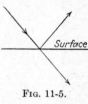

absorbed. The two parts of the amplitude thus divided must be recombined later in such a manner that the conditions for interference stated in Sec. **10-2** are fulfilled. The particular manner in which this recombination takes place depends on the type of instrument used. In some, the beams are recombined without further subdivision. The best known and most useful instrument of this type

Fig. 11-5.

is the *Michelson interferometer*. In others, a second reflecting surface is placed parallel to the first as illustrated in Fig. 11-6. If this surface is also partly transmitting, it is evident that there will be two sets of parallel beams, one on either side of the pair of surfaces. Moreover, between the successive beams in either set there will be a constant difference of path. When the beams in either or both sets are collected by image producing mirrors or lenses, an interference pattern will appear at the focal plane of the system. It will be seen in the discussion of

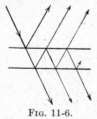

Fig. 11-6.

the *Fabry-Perot interferometer*, which best exemplifies this type of instrument, that this superposition of many beams results in a great increase in the resolving power of the instrument. It should be remarked, however, that the term "resolving power" in its broadest sense does not mean merely the ability to produce on a screen or on the retina of the eye two actual and distinct images of the object. It may mean the ability to produce phenomena from which may be deduced the existence of two objects whose relative intensities and separation may be found. Later we shall see that in this sense of the term the

Michelson interferometer possesses theoretically unlimited resolving power.

All instruments which make use of the principle of division of amplitude may be considered as modifications of the Michelson or Fabry-Perot interferometers, which are accordingly described in the following pages in some detail.[1]

4. The Michelson Interferometer.—The many forms of this instrument are alike in that the amplitude of a wide beam of light is divided into two parts by means of a semitransparent plate. The form which Michelson adopted as most useful for a variety of purposes is illustrated in Fig. 11-7. Here the division of amplitude is effected by the plate A, a plate of glass

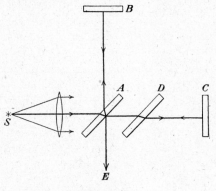

FIG. 11-7.

with parallel surfaces, one side of which is usually lightly coated with metal so as to divide the intensity of the beam into two equal parts. Half the light is thus transmitted to the plane mirror C, the other half reflected to the plane mirror B. The plane parallel plate D is cut from the same plate as A but is not metallically coated. It is placed between A and C, parallel to A, so that the optical paths ABA and ACA contain the same thickness of glass. This is important whenever observations are made of fringes due to light of many wave-lengths, as in white light, since the index of refraction of the glass varies with the wave-length.

The interference pattern is observed at E. Here the light from B and C appears to have originated in two virtual image

[1] For a description of many types of interferometers and a good bibliography see Williams, "Applications of Interferometry," Dutton.

planes situated in the neighborhood of B. We may consider one of the virtual image planes to be M_1 (Fig. 11-8). Let M_1 be the plane which replaces mirror B. If M_2 is, likewise, the plane which replaces mirror C in the field of view, then the virtual image due to the light from C must be in a plane M_1' which makes an angle with M_1 twice that between M_1 and M_2.[1] Thus for purposes of analysis the mirrors B and C are replaced by two virtual image planes M_1 and M_1', and the interferometer is considered as a pair of plane wave fronts with an air space between them. If the distances from A to B and A to C are not equal, and if B and C are not at right angles, these wave

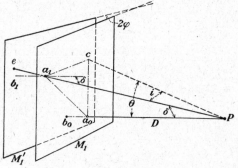

Fig. 11-9.

fronts will be as shown in Fig. 11-9. It is desired to find the character of the fringes formed at some point P. The first step is to find the path difference between the two virtual wave fronts.[2]

The following notation will be used:

D = the distance from a point P, where the fringes seen are formed, perpendicular to the planes M_1 and M_1', which must for the production of fringes be at such a small angle that they can be considered to have a common perpendicular.

2φ = the small angle between the surfaces, in a plane perpendicular to their line of intersection. The plane in which

---

[1] Since, when a reflector is turned through an angle, the reflected beam is turned through twice that angle.

[2] The derivation given here is essentially that presented by Michelson in *Philosophical Magazine*, (5), **13**, 236, 1882.

this angle lies will depend on the adjustment of the two mirrors A and B.

δ = the angle between the perpendicular D and the line joining P and a_1.

i = the projection of the angle δ on a plane containing 2φ.

θ = the projection of the angle δ on a plane perpendicular to that containing 2φ.

Δ = the difference of path between e and a_1.

$2t_0$ = the distance a_0b_0.

$2t$ = the distance a_1b_1.

The lines Pb_0 and a_1b_1 are two parallel lines which define a plane in which the angle δ lies; hence,

$$\Delta = 2t \cos \delta. \tag{11-6}$$

But $2t = 2t_0 + a_1c \tan 2\varphi$, or, since $a_1c = D \tan i$,

$$t = t_0 + D \tan \varphi \tan i$$

to a sufficient degree of approximation since the angles are small. Substituting this value of t in eq. 11-6,

$$\Delta = (2t_0 + 2D \tan \varphi \tan i) \cos \delta. \tag{11-7}$$

But

$$\cos \delta = \frac{D}{Pa_1} = \frac{D}{\sqrt{D^2 + D^2 \tan^2 i + D^2 \tan^2 \theta}}$$

$$= \frac{1}{\sqrt{1 + \tan^2 i + \tan^2 \theta}}.$$

Hence,

$$\Delta = 2\frac{t_0 + D \tan \varphi \tan i}{\sqrt{1 + \tan^2 i + \tan^2 \theta}}. \tag{11-8}$$

Thus we see that the path, and hence the phase, difference between the two beams a_1P and b_1P may vary over the area of the wave front contributing to the fringes at P, and the phenomenon of interference may be obliterated. If the sizes of the angles φ, i, and θ are restricted sufficiently so that the maximum variation of Δ is $\lambda/2$ or less, one phase will predominate and the fringes will be distinct. In most cases the pupil of the eye places a sufficient restriction on i and θ, provided it is at a suitable distance from the interferometer, so that the fringes are easily seen. Sometimes the use of a pin-hole in front of the eye will improve the visibility of the fringes.

5. The Distinctness of the Fringes.—The fringes will be most distinct when $\partial\Delta/\partial\theta$ and $\partial\Delta/\partial i$ are both zero. Imposing on eq. (11-8) these two conditions gives

$$D = \frac{t_0 \tan i}{\tan \varphi}, \tag{11-9}$$

for the distance between P and the position of the surfaces for which the fringes will be most distinct. An examination of eq. 11-9 shows that if $t_0 = 0$ then $D = 0$, and the fringes will be best at the surface of B (Fig. 11-8). This means that if the eye is placed at normal reading distance from the mirror B, the fringes will appear distinct when the lengths of the optical paths in the two arms of the interferometer are the same. Equation 11-9 also says that when i is zero, D is zero, which is another way of saying that the area of the wave front is sufficiently restricted in a direction perpendicular to the intersection of the two wave fronts so that no troublesome confusion of phases exists. If φ is zero, the wave fronts are parallel, *i.e.*, the mirrors are at right angles; if also t_0 is zero, the optical paths in the two arms of the interferometer are the same and also the mirrors are perpendicular, and over the entire field the two wave fronts will cancel each other. If φ and i have the same sign, D is positive, and the fringes are formed in front of the mirror B; if they have opposite sign, D is negative and the fringes lie behind B.

6. The Form of the Fringes.—Any point on the plane where the fringes are formed may be described by the equations

$$\left.\begin{array}{l} x = D \tan i, \\ y = D \tan \theta. \end{array}\right\} \tag{11-10}$$

Substituting these values in eq. 11-8, we obtain the general equation for the form of the interference fringes,

$$\Delta^2 y^2 = (4D^2 \tan^2 \varphi - \Delta^2)x^2 + (8t_0 D^2 \tan \varphi)x + D^2(4t_0^2 - \Delta^2). \tag{11-11}$$

An analysis of this equation shows[1] that the fringes take the forms of straight lines, circles, parabolas, ellipses, or hyperbolas, depending on the values assigned to Δ and φ. The complete theory will not be discussed here; certain details are, however, worthy of attention since they bear directly upon the successful

[1] SHEDD, JOHN C., *Physical Review*, **11**, 304, 1900; also Mann, "Manual of Optics," Ginn.

use of the instrument.   For $\Delta = 0$, eq. (11-11) becomes

$$x = \frac{t_0}{\tan \varphi}, \tag{11-12}$$

which is the equation of a straight line.   This is the central fringe of the system of fringes obtained with a white-light source. Those on either side of it, corresponding to Δ very small, will be curved in opposite directions on either side of the central fringe, although the curvature is not noticed for the few fringes which occur with a white-light source.   The curvature is scarcely noticeable with a monochromatic source within the relatively small area of the field of the instrument unless Δ is large enough to correspond to about 100 fringes from the central fringe.   By moving the mirror B back and forth rapidly about the position for $\Delta = 0$, the change of curvature may be detected.   This maneuver constitutes one method of finding approximately the center of the fringe system.   With the limits of the position for B thus determined, white light may be substituted for the mono-chromatic source, and the mirror moved very slowly until the white-light fringes come into the field of view.

If $\varphi = 0$, eq. 11-11 becomes

$$x^2 + y^2 = \frac{D^2(4t_0^2 - \Delta^2)}{\Delta^2}, \tag{11-13}$$

which is the equation of a circle.   Hence, when the virtual source images are parallel, the fringes will be circular in form.   As Δ becomes small, the diameters of the circles will become large, until for $\Delta \doteq 0$, the entire field will be either dark or bright.   In theory it will be dark for $\Delta = 0$, since the reflection of the two beams at the dividing plate A introduces a difference of phase of π, and a difference of path of $\lambda/2$.   Actually, however, a field entirely dark is difficult to observe since very slight irregu-larities in the metallic coats, lack of planeness of the glass surfaces, or inhomogeneity in the glass may have an effect which is of maximum observability for this adjustment of the interferometer.   The field will in general be dark, with irregular streaks and patches of light showing.

7. The Visibility of the Fringes.   Visibility Curves.—Although the Michelson interferometer was originally designed as a refrac-tometer to measure the relative difference of path introduced into the two arms of the instrument by a change in the medium, it has been used with great success, especially by its inventor, in the analysis of complex spectral radiations. The method used depends upon the fact, already mentioned, that in its broadest sense the term "resolving power" does not necessarily imply the actual separation of the images of two sources, but rather the production of a pattern of light in the images which may be interpreted as indicating the presence of two separate sources with a determinable separation and ratio of intensities.

In the Michelson interferometer the entire pattern of light here referred to is in most cases not observable in the field of view at the same time but must be examined while the path difference between the two arms is changed. In order to outline the method, we may first consider the difference in the appearance of the fringes obtained with white light and with monochromatic light. Suppose mirrors A and B (Fig. 11-7) are placed so that the path difference at the middle of the field is zero. We may then indicate the two virtual wave fronts producing the interference by two crossed lines as shown in Fig. 11-10. If the source is white light, there will be a black fringe corresponding to the intersection, since at the half plate A (Fig. 11-7) one reflection is from a bounding surface of glass, the other from one of air, so that a difference of path of $\lambda/2$ is introduced between the two interfering beams. On either side of this will be fringes,

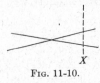

FIG. 11-10.

alternately light and dark. These will be colored, since at any position, such as X (Fig. 11-10), in the field of view where the difference of path is such as to produce a dark fringe for one wave-length, there will be light for other wave-lengths. The result will be that due to the superposition of an infinite number of fringe systems, one for each wave-length emitted by the white light source, all of which have different spacings. In consequence, only about a half dozen fringes will be seen on either side of the middle dark fringe, and beyond this range the field will be uniform. Another way of making the last statement is to say that the *visibility*[1] of the fringes will diminish gradually to zero,

---

[1] The visibility of the fringes is defined as the ratio $\dfrac{I_{max} - I_{min}}{I_{max} + I_{min}}$, where I_{max} is the intensity of a maximum, and I_{min} is the intensity of a minimum, of the fringe system.

so that beyond a half dozen on either side of the central minimum
none will be seen.   On the other hand, if strictly monochromatic

light is used, there will be no dimi-
nution of the visibility of the fringes,
no matter how far away from the
central dark fringe they are examined.   These details are illustrated
with a fair degree of exactness in
Fig. 11-11, in which (a), (b), and (c)
are photographs obtained with red,
green, and blue monochromatic
radiations, respectively, and (d) is
the photograph of the white-light
fringes due to the superposition of
all the radiations from a white-light
source.   Although the range of sensitivity of the eye is not the same
as that of the photographic plate,
Fig. 11-11d approximates closely
the visual appearance of white-light
fringes.

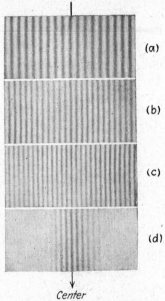

FIG. 11-11.—Interference fringes
with a Michelson interferometer.

Figure 11-12 illustrates the
effect produced by narrowing the
spectral range of white light.   In *a* are shown the fringes due
to the entire range of wave-length in a white-light source, while
in *b* are shown those obtained when a filter is interposed, which

(a)   (b)   (c)

FIG. 11-12.—(a) White light fringes.   The arrows point to the central dark
fringe.   (b) Fringes with white light through a filter which transmitted a band
of about 100 angstroms.   The arrows point to the central dark fringe.   (c)
Fringes with the green line of mercury, 5461 angstroms.

permits the passage of a band of light of only about 100 angstroms.   In Fig. 11-12c are shown the fringes, with the same

adjustment of the interferometer as in *a* and *b*, from the green mercury line, whose wave-length is 5461 angstroms.

If the light incident upon the interferometer is composed of two radiations, the visibility of the fringes will pass through alternations whose spacing will depend upon the ratio of the two wave-lengths. If this ratio is large, the alternations will occur rapidly, as illustrated in Fig. 11-13*a* and *b*. In *a* is shown the effect due to the superposition of the fringes of the two mercury lines 5461 and 4358 angstroms, and in *b* is shown the effect due to the mercury lines 5461, 5770, and 5790 angstroms. The

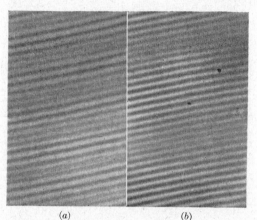

(a)   (b)

FIG. 11-13.—Interference fringes (*a*) with λ4358 and λ5461; (*b*) with λ5461 and the two yellow mercury lines λ5770 and λ5790.

last two are so nearly alike that in the field of view they have the effect of a single radiation.

Thus far in the discussion of visibility, the effect due to individual spectral lines has been treated as though each such radiation were monochromatic. Actually, however, there is no such thing as a completely monochromatic radiation, although in some the range of wave-length $d\lambda$ is extremely small. Owing to circumstances which depend on the nature of the radiating atoms or molecules and the conditions in the source, even the most nearly monochromatic radiations have a width $d\lambda$, so that with sufficient difference of path introduced between the two arms of the interferometer the visibility of the fringes will drop to zero. Moreover, most so-called single spectral lines, such as the mercury lines mentioned in the last paragraph, are composed of several

individual lines whose difference of wave-length is so small that
none but the highest resolving power will make it possible for
them to be observed directly as separate lines.   The Michelson
interferometer possesses theoretically unlimited resolving power;
although it does not enable the observer to see this *fine structure*
of spectral lines directly, the interpretation of the alternations of
visibility just illustrated makes it possible to determine the
presence and character of the fine structure.

No satisfactory method has been developed for determining
accurately changes in visibility by any but visual means.   Consequently, Michelson's method of analysis of spectral lines by
visibility curves, while it was the first to yield the structure of
many important radiations, has not progressed beyond the initial
stages developed by its inventor.   Other instruments of high
resolving power have taken its place, although the results
obtained by Michelson have in many cases not been surpassed in
accuracy.   His method consists essentially in plotting the
visibility graphically as a function of the difference of optical
path between the beams traversing the two arms of the interferometer.   This graph, however, may be regarded as the resultant intensity graph of a number of separate intensities.   By the
use of specially designed mechanical analyzers, these components
are found, and the wave-length ratios and relative intensities of
the corresponding individual lines determined.   A few of Michelson's visibility curves, taken from his published papers, are
shown in Fig. 11-14.

By means of this method, Michelson was able to show that the
red radiation from cadmium vapor was most nearly monochromatic of all those that he examined.   Accordingly he
used it as a primary standard of wave-length for comparison
with the standard meter, using interference methods.[1]   This
comparison was carried out first by Michelson, and later by
Benoit, Fabry, and Perot with the Fabry-Perot interferometer,
confirming Michelson's measurement.[2]   The value of the wave-

[1] "Détermination expérimentale de la valeur du mètre en longueurs d'onde
lumineuses."   Translated from the English by Benoit.   The details are
described briefly in Michelson, "Light Waves and Their Uses," and Michelson, "Studies in Optics," both published by the University of Chicago Press.

[2] BENOIT, FABRY, and PEROT, *Travaux et memoirs Bureau international*,
11, 1913.

length of the red cadmium line thus obtained in terms of the standard meter in dry air at 15°C. and 760 mm. Hg pressure is 6438.4696 angstroms. This value has been accepted by international agreement as a primary standard of wave-length.

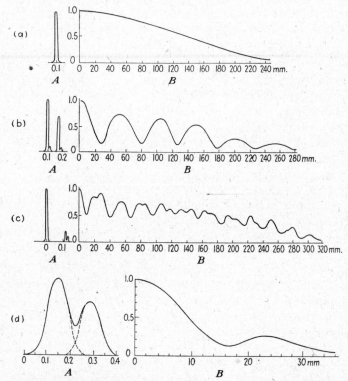

Fig. 11-14.—Michelson's visibility curves. In each case graph *B* shows the variation of visibility of fringes with path difference in millimeters, and *A* shows the interpretation of *B* in terms of intensity distribution in the spectral line used (*a*) The red cadmium line (primary standard) 6438.4696 angstroms; (*b*) the sodium lines 5890 and 5896 angstroms; (*c*) the mercury line 5790 angstroms; and (*d*) the red hydrogen line, H$_\alpha$, 6563 angstroms.

By the use of visiblity curves, Michelson was also the first to show that the red hydrogen line, 6563 angstroms, is really a very close double. His result is in good agreement with those obtained later by the use of instruments of direct resolving power, and with the structure of the line deduced theoretically by the application of the quantum theory to the analysis of spectra.

8. Multiple Beams. The Fabry-Perot Interferometer.—In general, the superposition of multiple beams results in higher resolving power than is obtained with a double-beam instrument. This is seemingly in contradiction to the fact already stated, that the Michelson interferometer has theoretically unlimited resolving power. The higher resolving power obtained with the Fabry-Perot interferometer, however, is due to a sharpening of the maximum of intensity in the interference pattern to the point where the existence of two separate images may be observed directly, while with double beams only, an analysis of the visibility of the interference fringes is required.[1] There is this difference also: While the resolving power of the Fabry-Perot

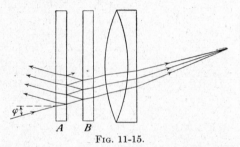

A B

FIG. 11-15.

interferometer is limited by the reflecting power of the surfaces, the limitation in the case of the Michelson interferometer is not in the instrument itself, but in the ability of the observer to distinguish and interpret correctly the variations in the visibility of the fringes.

The Fabry-Perot interferometer, illustrated in Fig. 11-15, is constructed of two plates, usually of glass or quartz, having their faces accurately plane, and mounted so that the adjacent surfaces are parallel. These parallel surfaces are coated with a metallic film capable of transmitting part of the light and reflecting a high proportion of the remainder. Consider light of a single wavelength, λ, incident upon the metallic coating of plate A, at an angle φ. Part of it is reflected and part is transmitted to surface B. At this latter surface, part of the incident light is reflected and part transmitted. Of the part reflected back and forth between the two surfaces, a fraction is transmitted through B at

---

[1] An analogous comparison may be made of the diffraction grating and the Michelson stellar interferometer. For details, see Chap. XII.

each incidence upon it. There are similar sets of reflections
due to the surfaces of the plates on which no metal is deposited,
but these surfaces have relatively low reflecting power. It is
customary to make each of the plates slightly wedge-shaped, so
that its two surfaces are at a small angle. This causes any
reflections at the outer, uncoated surfaces to be thrown to one
side so as not to be superposed upon the pattern of fringes
obtained with the inner metal surfaces. This wedge shape
introduces a slight amount of prismatic dispersion, but not
enough to cause serious difficulty. For angles of incidence

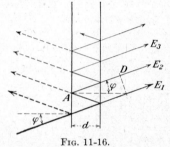

greater than zero, each beam undergoes a small sidewise displacement
owing to refraction, but this is the
same in both plates for all beams
having the same angle of incidence,
and so may be neglected.

We may thus consider the interferometer to be essentially a pair of
parallel surfaces of as high reflecting power as possible. By reference

Fig. 11-16.

to this simplified concept which is illustrated in Fig. 11-16, we
may readily see that

$$AD = p\lambda = 2d \cos \varphi, \qquad (11\text{-}14)$$

in which p is the number of wave-lengths in the common difference of path of consecutive rays such as E_1, E_2, etc., and d is the
separation of the surfaces. We may then call p the *order of
interference* between the successive beams E_1, E_2, etc. It should
be emphasized that the focal point of these parallel beams will be
the principal focus of the eye lens, in case of visual observation
of the fringes, or of the projecting lens, as shown in Fig. 11-15,
regardless of the manner in which the original beam of light is
projected upon the interferometer. The plane of incidence
represented by the page in Fig. 11-15 is one of an infinite number,
all containing the normal to the reflecting surfaces, hence there
will be a circle of focal points for each angle of incidence φ. If p
is a whole number, the difference of path between successive
elements will be an integral number of wave-lengths, and the
amplitudes of the successive beams will add to give a maximum

of intensity in the form of a circular fringe. Since there will be for any wave-length several values of φ for which p will be a whole number, there will correspond to each wave-length a number of concentric circles of maximum intensity.

At the center of the pattern, the intensity will depend on the difference of path for $\varphi = 0$. For this case, eq. 11-14 becomes

$$P\lambda = 2d, \tag{11-15}$$

where P is used to indicate the order of interference at the center of the ring system, while p is used to indicate the order of interference for a bright fringe. Except in an occasional instance,

FIG. 11-17.—Fabry-Perot fringes of the mercury line 5461 angstroms.

P is not a whole number, while p is always a whole number. Provided all wave-lengths undergo the same change of phase on reflection from the metallically coated surfaces, we may assume d to be constant, whereupon

$$P_1\lambda_1 = P_2\lambda_2 = \cdots = \text{constant}, \tag{11-16}$$

so that if the ratios of the P's can be found, the ratios of the wave-lengths may be calculated. If one of the observed radiations is either the primary standard, 6438.4696 angstroms, or else a suitable secondary standard of wave-length, the other wave-lengths may all be found with a high degree of accuracy. The use of the Fabry-Perot interferometer for the comparison of wave-lengths with primary or secondary standards has been adopted by international agreement for the establishment of wave-lengths of spectral lines throughout the visible, ultraviolet, and infrared spectral regions. For secondary standards, the spectra of iron, copper, and neon are principally used.

The use of the Fabry-Perot interferometer in the measurement of the length of the standard meter in terms of the wave-length of the red cadmium line has already been referred to in Sec. **11-7.** The instrument may also be adapted to a number of other uses, probably the principal one at the present time being the examination of the fine structure of spectral lines.[1] A photograph of the system of fringes of the green mercury radiation, 5461 angstroms, is shown in Fig. 11-17. The composite structure of the line, which can be found also by the visibility-curve method with the Michelson interferometer, is shown very well.

9. Intensity Distribution in Fabry-Perot Fringes.—From a consideration of Fig. 11-16, it is evident that the rate at which the intensity of the successive parallel beams E_1, E_2, E_3, etc., decreases depends upon the reflecting and transmitting powers of the metallically coated surfaces. Let Q and R represent respectively the fractional parts of the incident light intensity transmitted and reflected at each of the surfaces. Then the transmitted beam E_1 will have an intensity Q^2 and an amplitude Q; beam E_2 will have intensity Q^2R^2 and amplitude QR; beam E_3 will have intensity Q^2R^4 and amplitude QR^2, and so on. The amplitude of the nth beam will be QR^{n-1}. Neglecting the small change of phase on reflection which takes place at the surface of the metal, the constant difference in phase between successive beams is

$$(2d \, \cos \, \varphi) \cdot \frac{2\pi}{\lambda} = \delta. \qquad (11\text{-}17)$$

The disturbance at any point on the incident wave front may be represented by

$$S = a \, \cos \, 2\frac{\pi t}{T} = a \, \cos \, \omega t.$$

[1] For a fairly complete discussion of the uses of the Fabry-Perot interferometer, and an excellent bibliography, see Williams, "Applications of Interferometry."

It is possible, however, to use exponential instead of trigonometric expressions with some shortening of the labor involved. Since $e^{i\omega t} = \cos \omega t + i \sin \omega t$, the disturbance may be represented by the real part of $e^{i\omega t}$. If the difference of phase between the successive transmitted beams E_1, E_2, etc., is δ, the total amplitude of the sum of the beams at any instant will be the real part of

$$\Sigma = Qe^{i\omega t} + QRe^{i(\omega t - \delta)} + QR^2 e^{i(\omega t - 2\delta)} + \cdots \quad (11\text{-}18)$$

This can be put in the form

$$\sum = \frac{Q}{1 - Re^{-i\delta}} \cdot e^{i\omega t}. \quad (11\text{-}19)$$

where $\dfrac{Q}{1 - Re^{-i\delta}}$ is the amplitude factor. But the amplitude may be the real part of either $\dfrac{Q}{1 - Re^{-i\delta}}$ or of $\dfrac{Q}{1 - Re^{+i\delta}}$, and the intensity I put equal to the product of these two, or

$$\begin{aligned}
I &= \frac{Q^2}{(1 - Re^{i\delta})(1 - Re^{-i\delta})} \\
&= \frac{Q^2}{(1 - 2R \cos \delta + R^2)} \\
&= \frac{Q^2}{1 + 2R(1 - \cos \delta) - 2R + R^2} \\
&= \frac{Q^2}{(1 - R)^2 + 4R \sin^2 (\delta/2)} \\
&= \frac{Q^2}{(1 - R)^2} \cdot \frac{1}{1 + \dfrac{4R}{(1 - R)^2} \cdot \sin^2 \left(\dfrac{\delta}{2}\right)}. \quad (11\text{-}20)
\end{aligned}$$

When $\delta = 0$, 2π, 4π, etc., $\sin^2 (\delta/2) = 0$, and the *maximum* intensity of the fringes is $Q^2/(1 - R)^2$; when $\delta = \pi$, 3π, 5π, etc., $\sin^2 (\delta/2) = 1$, and the *minimum* intensity of the fringe system is $Q^2/(1 + R)^2$. It will be seen that the intensity never drops to zero although it may become very small.

The visibility of the fringes is defined as

$$V = \frac{I_{\max} - I_{\min}}{I_{\max} + I_{\min}}.$$

Hence for the Fabry-Perot fringes, the visibility is

$$V = \frac{2R}{1 + R^2},$$ (11-21)

and thus depends only on the reflecting power of the metal surfaces, and is independent of their transparency.

10. Resolving Power of the Fabry-Perot Interferometer.—By differentiation, from eq. 11-15, we obtain

$$P \, d\lambda + \lambda \, dP = 0,$$

from which it follows that the resolving power is

$$\frac{\lambda}{d\lambda} = -\frac{P}{dP};$$ (11-22)

or, the resolving power, defined as the ratio of the wave-length to the smallest difference of wave-length which may be detected, is equal to the order of interference at the center of the ring system divided by the smallest change of order dP which can be detected. Actually, since the value for p is different from that for P, for any given wave-length, by only a small number, provided one considers a bright fringe only a few rings outside the center, the actual measurement of dP may be more easily made on a fringe near the center instead of at the center itself, since at the center of the pattern the width of the rings is so large as to render estimates of intensity variation in them difficult. This point is taken up in detail in Sec. **11-11.**

The value of dP may be found from eq. 11-20. Consider two adjacent bright fringes in the interference pattern, belonging to two wave-lengths, λ and $\lambda + d\lambda$, between which the difference of order dP, corresponding to their difference of wave-length $d\lambda$, is to be found. It will be shown in the chapter on Diffraction that, according to an arbitrary criterion established by Rayleigh, two images are said to be just resolved when the maximum of intensity of one of them corresponds in position with the first minimum of intensity of the other, as illustrated in Fig. 11-18. This criterion, which agrees very well with experimentally determined measures of limit of resolution in optical imagery, was originally set up with regard to spectral-line images produced with diffraction gratings, and may be considered to hold sufficiently well in the present case. The intensity for either of the adjacent bright fringes in the Fabry-Perot ring system may be called I_{max}, and by the last section is equal to $Q^2/(1-R)^2$, while the intensity at the center of the pattern shown in Fig. 11-18 is, *for either image*, given by eq. 11-20.   Consequently we may write

$$\frac{I}{I_{max}} = \frac{1}{1 + \dfrac{4R}{(1-R)^2} \cdot \sin^2\left(\dfrac{\delta}{2}\right)}. \qquad (11\text{-}23)$$

It can be shown from diffraction theory that in case the images are equal in width and intensity and symmetrical, the intensity at a point c_2, midway between the images, will be $8/\pi^2$, or about

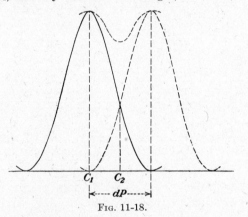

C_1 C_2

$\longleftarrow dP \longrightarrow$

Fig. 11-18.

0.81, times the maximum of either, so that the intensity of *each image* at the point c_2 is 0.405 times the intensity of either at its maximum.   Thus we may write

$$\frac{I}{I_{max}} = 0.405.$$

Substituting this value in eq. 11-23, there results

$$\sin^2\left(\frac{\delta}{2}\right) = \frac{(1 - 0.405)(1 - R)^2}{1.620R}.$$

It should be kept in mind, however, that the minimum intensity of the fringes, given by $Q^2/(1+R)^2$, never drops to zero, although for heavy metallic coats on the interferometer surfaces it may become so small that it is negligible for visual observations and correct photographic exposures.   Also, it is not always true that the fringes of two radiations to be resolved have even approximately the same intensity; consequently the Rayleigh criterion does not hold with great rigor. Moreover, the Fabry-Perot fringes are not symmetrical, but are unsymmetrically widened toward the center of the ring system. Since taking these exceptions into account would require a greater departure from simple theory than is justified in obtaining an expression for resolving power, which, after all, can only agree approximately with any observed value, we may disregard them. Then in the present case dP in eq. 11-22 may be said to correspond to a change in phase of π, since the difference of order of unity between two fringes corresponds to a difference of phase of 2π. Hence at the Rayleigh limit of resolution, $\delta = \pi \, dP$. Substituting this value of δ in eq. 11-23, we obtain

$$\delta = 2 \sin^{-1} \left[\frac{0.595(1 - R)^2}{1.62R} \right]^{1/2} = \pi \, dP,$$

so that the resolving power is

$$\frac{\lambda}{d\lambda} = -\frac{P}{dP} = -\frac{P\pi}{2 \sin^{-1} \left[\dfrac{0.367(1 - R)^2}{R} \right]^{1/2}}. \qquad (11\text{-}24)$$

From this equation the theoretical resolving power of the Fabry-Perot interferometer may be calculated. The negative sign in front of the right-hand member may be disregarded, as it means simply that a positive increase of wave-length corresponds to a negative change of order dP. For a wave-length of 5,000 angstroms and a mirror separation d of 10 mm., it follows from eq. 11-15 that P is 40,000. From eq. 11-24 are calculated the resolving powers shown in the following table:

Reflecting Power, Per Cent	Resolving Power
50	139,600
75	349,200
90	1,047,200

This shows that the resolving power increases very rapidly with the reflecting power of the metallic coating. Only the best metallic coats have reflecting powers of 85 per cent or better, and not all metals are satisfactory for the purpose. Those most useful for both the visible and near ultraviolet are aluminum, chromium, platinum, gold, nickel, and silicon. For the visible only, silver is very useful, but it possesses a band of almost complete transmission in the region of 3300 angstroms. Until recently it has been difficult to obtain uniform deposits, but the development of the modern evaporating process, outlined in Appendix V, has resulted in the production of deposits which are not only more uniform but more durable. In addition, the evaporating process has made it possible to obtain highly reflecting coats of metals not obtainable by earlier methods. The most useful metal for all-round purposes is probably aluminum, which is a good reflector over practically the entire available range of optical spectra and retains its reflecting power for very long periods.

11. The Shape of the Fabry-Perot Fringes.—In the last section it was stated that the fringes obtained with this interferometer are not symmetrical about their maxima. This may be shown in the following manner: Dividing eq. 11-15 by eq. 11-14,

$$\frac{P}{p} = \frac{1}{\cos \varphi} = \frac{1}{\cos (\alpha/2)},$$ (11-25)

in which α is the angular diameter of the pth fringe. The cosine term may be expanded into a series:

$$\cos\left(\frac{\alpha}{2}\right) = 1 - \frac{\alpha^2}{4 \cdot 2!} + \frac{\alpha^4}{16 \cdot 4!} - \cdots$$

For observations made with α sufficiently small, only the first two terms of the series are significant, hence eq. 11-25 may be written

$$P = \frac{p}{1 - \dfrac{\alpha^2}{8}}.$$ (11-26)

If D is the linear diameter of a fringe, and F is the principal focal length of a lens or mirror used to focus the fringes, then $\alpha = D/F$. Hence eq. 11-26 may be written

$$P = p\left(1 + \frac{D^2}{8F^2}\right).$$ (11-27)

For a given fringe p is a constant, so that differentiating eq.

11-27 with respect to D, we obtain

$$dP = pD \cdot \frac{dD}{4F^2}.$$

On substitution of this value for dP in eq. 11-22, it follows that

$$\frac{\lambda}{d\lambda} = \frac{-P}{dP} = -\frac{4PF^2}{p \cdot D \cdot dD},$$

whence

$$\frac{dD}{d\lambda} = -\frac{4PF^2}{p\lambda D}.$$

For any fixed separation of the interferometer surfaces the ratio P/p is constant for a given λ and is practically equal to unity provided a fringe not too far from the center is taken. We may therefore write

$$\frac{dD}{d\lambda} = \frac{K}{D} \tag{11-28}$$

where K is a constant depending on the wave-length and the principal focal length of the projecting lens or mirror. Equation 11-28 says that the change in diameter of a fringe with wave-length is inversely proportional to the diameter of the fringe. For fringes with very small diameters, *i.e.*, for fringes which lie very close to the center of the system, the change in D with small changes of λ will be very large. This means that the bright fringes in the pattern, for a single wave-length, will not be symmetrical in shape, but will be unsymmetrically broadened toward the center and sharper on the outer edge. Hence in determining the wave-lengths of spectral lines, it is desirable to avoid the use of the rings close to the center of the pattern unless great care is taken to set accurately on the maximum of intensity of the fringes rather than on the geometric center.

Problems

1. Describe a method by which Newton's rings could be used to determine the ratio of two wave-lengths 1000 angstroms apart, say 5000 and 6000 angstroms.

2. Between the convergent crown and divergent flint glass elements of an uncemented achromatic doublet Newton's rings are formed. When seen by reflection through the flint element there is a dark fringe at the center, and the fourth bright fringe has a radius of 1.16 cm. If the radius of curvature of the crown glass interface is 50 cm., and the incident light is nearly normal, what is the radius of curvature of the flint glass face next to it? Assume a wave-length of 5500 angstroms.

3. A Michelson interferometer is adjusted so that white light fringes are in the field of view. Sodium light is substituted and one mirror moved until the fringes reach minimum visibility. How far is the mirror moved?

4. A certain spectral line which is a close doublet has a mean wave-length of 3440 angstroms, and a separation between the components of 0.0063 angstrom. If the mirrors of a Fabry-Perot interferometer have a reflecting power of 85 per cent, what must be their separation to resolve the doublet? What resolving power is indicated? Assume the width of each component to be less than 0.002 angstrom.

5. What is the resolving power of a Fabry-Perot interferometer in which the separation is 15 mm., for a reflecting power of 75 per cent? For a reflecting power of 90 per cent? (Assume $\lambda = 5000$ angstroms.)

6. What will be the effect on the resolving power of a Fabry-Perot interferometer if one of the plates has a reflecting power of 60 per cent and the other 80 per cent? Will it make any difference which plate has the higher reflecting power?

CHAPTER XII

DIFFRACTION

In Sec. **9-9** it was shown that if a plane wave from a distant point S is incident on a slit of width a, the result will not be a sharply outlined single image of the slit but a series of images separated by regions of zero intensity, forming a *diffraction pattern*. The effect produced by diffraction is not to be confused with that obtained with an instrument fulfilling the conditions for interference proper. To be sure, the pattern of maxima and minima in diffraction is due to the reinforcement and cancellation of parts of wave fronts exactly as in interference, but by the principle of superposition it is shown that true interference may be obtained with no limitation whatever on the extent of the wave front. With certain types of interferometers, both true interference and diffraction are present.

1. Fresnel and Fraunhofer Diffraction.—Phenomena of this kind, *i.e.*, those which owe their appearance to a limitation of

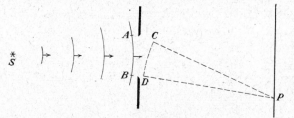

Fig. 12-1.—Fresnel diffraction at a slit.

the wave front, are divided into two general classes. When the wave front from a source, not necessarily at an infinite distance, passes one or more obstacles and then proceeds directly to the point of observation without modification by lenses or mirrors, the resulting phenomenon is known as *Fresnel diffraction*. When the wave front incident upon the obstacles is plane, either from a distant source or by collimation, and the diffracted light is focused by a lens or mirror, or is observed at a distance infinitely far from the obstacle, the result is known as *Fraunhofer diffrac-*

tion. The difference between these types of diffraction may be further illustrated by a comparison of the forms of the diffracted wave fronts. In Fig. 12-1 light from a source S is intercepted by a slit so that only the portion AB is transmitted. With P as a center, strike an arc CD. The effect at P, due to Fresnel diffraction, is the result of the summation of all the disturbances which occur along CD at the same time. While it must not be supposed that a wave front actually occurs at CD, it is possible to define the surface thus represented as the diffracted wave front with reference to the point P. In Fraunhofer diffraction both the real wave front incident on the obstacle and the diffracted wave front are plane, as shown in Fig. 12-2.

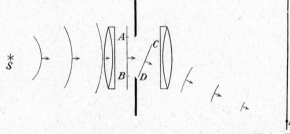

FIG. 12-2.—Illustrating the existence of a real wave front CD in Fraunhofer diffraction. The existence of CD may be deduced from the Huygens principle.

2. Fresnel Zones.—While many of the important applications of diffraction are of the Fraunhofer class, the methods developed by Fresnel constitute a simple approach to the theory of diffraction and will be considered first. From a consideration of the Huygens principle, Fresnel was led to the conclusion that light of a given wave-length from a point O (Fig. 12-3) will produce the same illumination at P, no matter whether it passes directly from O to P or is regarded as due to the summation of the effects at P of all the Huygens wavelets originating along W, a wave front proceeding originally from O. He divided the wave front into many elements in the following manner: Draw lines PM_1, PM_2, etc., in Fig. 12-3 such that

$$PM_1 = PM_0 + \frac{\lambda}{2}; \qquad PM_2 = PM_1 + \frac{\lambda}{2}; \text{ etc.}$$

Then if the figure is rotated about OP, each such pair of lines will enclose a zone whose distance from P is $\lambda/2$ smaller than the one outside it. While this would tend to lessen the amplitude at P for outer zones, it is offset by an increase in area of outer zones. Because of increasing obliquity of the wave-front, however, there is a decrease of amplitude for each succeeding zone from the center outward. We may write the total amplitude at P as the sum of a series, alternating in sign because of the alternation in phase from zone to zone, in the form

$$S = a_1 - a_2 + a_3 - a_4 + \cdots a_n,$$

in which each term of the sum is a little smaller than the one preceding it. It can be shown[1] that, taking into account the

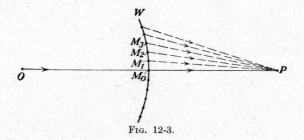

Fig. 12-3.

smallness of the differences between the terms and the regularity of their change, the sum is

$$S = \frac{a_1}{2} + \frac{a_n}{2},$$

and when a_n is very small, the effect is that of half the first zone. This brings the Huygens principle essentially into agreement with the rectilinear propagation of light, when the wave front is not limited by obstacles.

3. The Zone Plate.—If the light from a point source is passed through a circular aperture, the total effect of all the *half-period elements* passing through it to a point on the axis can be obtained. In Fig. 12-4 the circles are the boundaries of half-period elements whose distances to the point P differ by $\lambda/2$. The areas of the zones enclosed by these circles are

$$\pi r_1{}^2 = \pi(\overline{PM}_1{}^2 - \overline{PM}_0{}^2) = \pi\left[\left(s + \frac{\lambda}{2}\right)^2 - s^2\right],$$

[1] See Schuster, "Theory of Optics," Chap. V.

$$\pi(r_2{}^2 - r_1{}^2) = \pi(\overline{PM}_2{}^2 - \overline{PM}_1{}^2) = \pi\left[(s + \lambda)^2 - \left(s + \frac{\lambda}{2}\right)^2\right],$$

etc., where s is the distance from the zone plate to the image and r gives the radius of each circle, so that if λ is small enough compared to the other dimensions, λ^2 is negligible and the area of each zone is $\pi s \lambda$. Consequently the consecutive zones will, because of the approximate equality of their obliquity, almost cancel each other. But if alternate zones are blocked out so that they transmit no light, the remaining ones will give an image at P. A series of transmitting zone apertures of this sort is called a *zone plate*. If s is required to be 100 cm., for a wave-length of 0.00005 cm., the area of each zone will be about 0.0157 sq. cm.

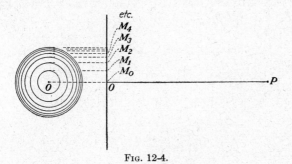

Fig. 12-4.

The radii of the zone boundaries are $r_1 = \sqrt{s\lambda}$, $r_2 = \sqrt{2s\lambda}$, etc., hence a zone plate may be constructed by first drawing on a large sheet concentric circles whose radii are proportional to the square roots of the consecutive integers 1, 2, 3, etc., and then blackening alternate zones. This drawing can be copied photographically in any desired size. The negative, or positive, thus obtained may be used to produce an image of a distant object, such as the sun, at a distance s from the plate. Thus the smaller the reproduction the shorter will be its "focal length." The intensity of the image produced with a zone plate will be greater if alternate zones are not blocked out but are left transmitting, with a phase difference of one half period introduced between them and adjacent zones. This can be done with some degree of success by covering a glass plate with a thin coating of wax which is then scraped away in the annular area corresponding to alternate zones. The plate is then etched slightly with dilute hydrofluoric acid to the proper depth.   Obviously this method is limited to the few zones which are of sufficient width to permit the treatment.[1]

4. Diffraction by a Circular Obstacle.—If a circular obstacle is interposed between a point source of light and the observer, all

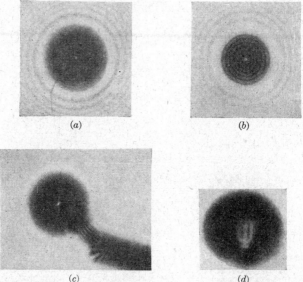

(a)   (b)

(c)   (d)

Fig. 12-5.—Diffraction of light by a circular obstacle.   (a) shows the bright image point at the center of the shadow.   (b) the same as (a) but with distances so chosen that distinct circular fringes also appear *in the shadow*.   The fringes *outside* the shadow are analogous to those in Fig. 12-7.   (c) the same as (a) and (b) but with a circular obstacle 20 cm. in diameter held in the hand, and the light condensed by a lens so as to make the virtual distance from source to screen equal to 7 km.   (d) was taken with the monogram of the letters I and U as a source instead of a point source.   (a), (b), and (c) copied from Arkadiew: Physikalische Zeitschrift, **14**, 832, 1913.   (d) copied from M. E. Hufford, Physical Review, **3**, 241, 1914.

the light due to a number of central zones will be obstructed.   In this case, by summing up the amplitudes due to the remaining zones in the way outlined in Sec. **12-2,** it will be found that the resulting disturbance is that due to one-half the first zone to pass the edge of the obstacle.   If the obstacle is not too large, there should be on the axis at the center of the shadow of the obstacle an image of the point source of practically the same

[1] Some interesting details on the construction of zone plates are given in Wood, "Physical Optics," Macmillan.   The subject is treated more fully in the edition of 1911 than in the later edition of 1934.

intensity as if the obstacle were not there.   This result was
deduced by Poisson, who considered it an argument against the
validity of Fresnel's theory.   Thereupon, Arago performed the
experiment, and showed that the image actually exists as predicted.   The effect is illustrated in Fig. 12-5.

5. Cylindrical Wave Front.—When the source is long and
narrow, as in the case of a hot filament or an illuminated slit, it
is convenient to consider the zones to be not concentric rings
but rather strips parallel to the source on a cylindrical wave
front.   Let O (Fig. 12-5A) represent such a source, and W a
cylindrical wave front whose axis is perpendicular to the page at
O.   Then as before on either side of M_0 points M_1, M_2, etc., may
be chosen such that the distances of the successive strips M_0M_1,

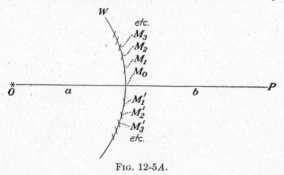

Fig. 12-5A.

M_1M_2, etc., from a point P differ by $\lambda/2$.   The adjacent strips
will differ in area, rapidly at first and then more slowly as strips
of higher number are considered.   Their distances from P and
their obliquity will also vary.   As in Sec. **12-2,** it may be shown
that the amplitude at P is due practically to the zone immediately
about M_0.   That point of the wave front nearest to the point
under discussion, as P, is known as the *pole of the wave front with
respect to P.*

5a. Diffraction at a Straight Edge.—Consider light from a line
source O perpendicular to the page in Fig. 12-6, passing a straight-
edged obstacle B to a screen.   It is required to find the illumination at any point on the screen.   Let us first consider a point P'
above P on the screen, well outside the geometrical shadow of
the obstacle.   A straight line drawn from O to P' intersects the
wave front at the point B', which is thus the pole of the wave
front with respect to P', and by the arguments of the preceding
section the amplitude at P' will be due only to the half-period

zones in the neighborhood of B'. If P' is sufficiently far away from P so that the obstacle imposes no limit on the elements effectively contributing to the amplitude at P', full illumination will exist, but if P' is a point on the screen near enough to P so that the effective half-period zones about the pole B' are partly obstructed, the amplitude at P' will suffer a modification depending, in the final analysis, upon whether or not there is an *odd* or an *even* number of zones between B and B'. If the number is even, their contribution to the amplitude at P' will be a minimum,

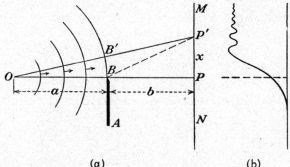

(a)   (b)

Fig. 12-6.—Diffraction at a straight edge.   The source is a slit at O perpendicular to the plane of the paper.

since alternate ones are opposite in phase; if the number is odd, the amplitude from them to P' will be a maximum, since all but one tend to cancel each other.

As points farther and farther into the region *below* P are considered, the farther will their poles lie along the wave front below the edge of the obstacle, and the smaller will be the number of zones contributing to the amplitude on the screen. Hence the intensity below P will fall off gradually to zero.

For a maximum at P', $BP' - B'P' = (2n + 1)\lambda/2$, and for a minimum, $BP' - B'P' = 2n\lambda/2$, where n is zero or any integer. Now if $OB = a$, $BP = b$, and $PP' = x$,

$$BP' = \sqrt{b^2 + x^2} = b\sqrt{1 + \frac{x^2}{b^2}} = \text{approximately } b\left(1 + \frac{x^2}{2b^2}\right),$$

$$OP' = \sqrt{(a + b)^2 + x^2} = \text{approximately } a + b + \frac{x^2}{2(a + b)},$$

$$B'P' = OP' - a = b + \frac{x^2}{2(a + b)}.$$

Hence for a maximum,

$$\frac{x^2}{2b} - \frac{x^2}{2(a+b)} = \frac{(2n+1)\lambda}{2},$$

or,

$$x = \sqrt{\frac{b(a+b)}{a}(2n+1)\lambda}, \qquad \text{for a maximum,}$$

$$x = \sqrt{\frac{b(a+b)}{a}2n\lambda}, \qquad \text{for a minimum,}$$

where n is zero or an integer. Thus the diffraction pattern will

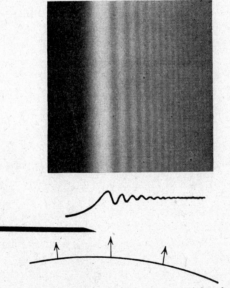

Fig. 12-7.—Photograph of diffraction at a straight edge.

be a series of maxima and minima as shown in Fig. 12-6b. A photograph of the pattern is shown in Fig. 12-7.

6. The Cornu Spiral.—The explanation of the intensity distribution observed in certain diffraction patterns of the Fresnel type which has been presented in the preceding sections is quite elementary, and is limited in its applicability. It serves, however, to furnish an introduction to a much more elegant method of representing the disturbance at any point in a diffraction pattern due to a straight edge, a long narrow slit, or any long obstacle. The analytical treatment, originally due to Fresnel, is given in Appendix VIII. Cornu made use of the *vector polygon* method of Sec. **9-5** to put Fresnel's treatment into graphical form.

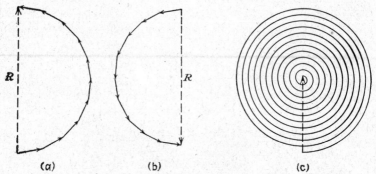

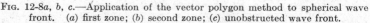

FIG. 12-8*a*, *b*, *c*.—Application of the vector polygon method to spherical wave front. (*a*) first zone; (*b*) second zone; (*c*) unobstructed wave front.

First, however, it is convenient and instructive to show the application of the vector-polygon method to the case of an unobstructed spherical wave front. Referring to Fig. 12-3, consider the first *zone*, of radius M_0M_1, to be divided into ten

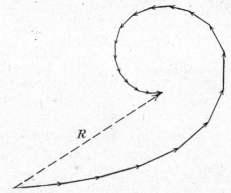

FIG. 12-8*d*.—Application of the vector polygon method to a straight obstacle. First two half-period strips, each divided into ten elements.

elements, slightly different in phase and amplitude at *P*. These can be represented vectorially as in Fig. 12-8*a*. It will be seen that the first and last of these elements have a phase difference that approaches π as the number of elements in the half-period zone is increased. For the half-period zone M_1M_2, the polygon is shown in Fig. 12-8b, in which the resultant is slightly shorter than in a. The summation of all zones, each of which has been divided into a very large number of elements, is shown in Fig. 12-8c. That figure shows the resultant amplitude to be one-half that for the first zone, as stated in Sec. **12-2.**

Passing to the case of a long narrow obstacle, the treatment must be modified because of the difference in the way the contributions of amplitude from successive *strips* vary. The vector

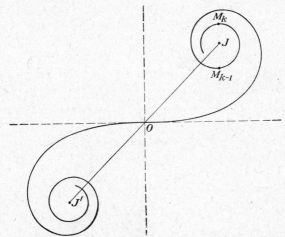

FIG. 12-9.—The Cornu spiral. The convolutions close up spirally to J and J'. The distance along the curve from M_{k-1} to M_k corresponds to a half convolution, representing a half-period zone. The distance from O to M_{k-1} represents two half-period zones opposite in phase.

polygon for the first two strips on one side of the pole of P, each divided into ten elements, is shown approximately by Fig. 12-8d. If the number of these elements in each strip is made very large, each vector will be correspondingly small, and the change of angle from one to the next will be slight. The succession of vectors representing all the elements will be a smooth curve. Representing an unobstructed wave front, this curve is known as the *Cornu spiral*, shown in Fig. 12-9, and also in more detail on page 441. The entire curve is not drawn, but the two arms are terminated in convolutions, of which only a few are shown, which become smaller and smaller and more nearly circular until they are finally asymptotic to circles of zero radius at J and J'. The straight line joining J and J' and passing through the origin represents the entire wave when it is unlimited by obstacles. Referring once more to Fig. 12-5A, in this case the point P will receive full illumination. Suppose, however, an obstacle is brought gradually in front of the source from one side so that as it advances, it cuts off more and more of the wave front. In doing so it will cut off successive half-period zones, each of which is represented in the Cornu spiral by a half convolution such as $M_k M_{k-1}$ (Fig. 12-9), and the vector representing the summation will no longer be the line joining J' and J, but will be a line joining J' and a point which moves along the spiral from J toward O. The corresponding illumination from the source will alternate between maximum and minimum. When half the wave front has been cut off, *i.e.*, when the obstacle is st the pole of the

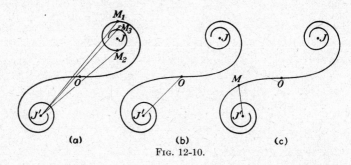

Fig. 12-10.

point P (Fig. 12-5A), the total amplitude will be represented on the Cornu spiral by the vector $J'O$.

Only two of the many graphical solutions of problems in diffraction will be mentioned; the case of the straight edge and the case of the single slit.

a. The Straight Edge.—Actually this case has just been described in considering an obstacle gradually brought in from the side so as to obscure more and more of the wave front, except that the alternations of intensity were considered as taking place at a single point on a screen as the obstacle advanced. If, instead, point P' in Fig. 12-6 is considered to move along the screen toward P, then the intensity at the moving point will alternate. On the Cornu spiral (Fig. 12-10a), a few alternations in amplitude will be in the order $J'M_3$ for a maximum, $J'M_2$ for a minimum, $J'M_1$ for a maximum, and thenceforth the amplitude will diminish until $J'O$ (Fig. 12-10b) represents the amplitude at the geometrical edge of the shadow on the straight line from

the source past the edge of the obstacle.   Thenceforth the amplitude vector $J'M$ (Fig. 12-10c), will reduce gradually in length
to zero, as M moves along the curve, representing the gradually
diminishing illumination on the screen in the shadow.

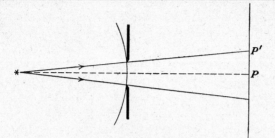

FIG. 12-11.

b. The Single Slit.—Consider a slit (Fig. 12-11) so narrow
that only the two central zones, one on each side of the pole of P,
contribute light to P.   The amplitude at P will then be given
by the vector $M_1'M_1$ (Fig. 12-12a).   As points above P are
considered, the amplitude will be given by a series of vectors

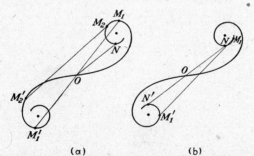

(a)   (b)

FIG. 12-12.—Amplitudes in Fresnel diffraction at a slit.

such as $M_2'M_2$ until when P' is reached, for which the edge of
the slit is the pole, the amplitude is given by ON.   Hence, when
the slit width is only two zones, the center of the pattern is a maximum.   Suppose, however, the slit is as wide as four zones.   Then
the amplitude at P (Fig. 12-11), is given by $N'N$ (Fig. 12-12b),
and for points just above P by M_1M_1', which is longer than
$N'N$, so that in this case the intensity at the middle of the
pattern is a minimum.   For cases where the aperture is smaller
than a single zone, the vector joining the two points in the spiral
is so short that it can be moved along the spiral in either direc-

tion without alternations in length, but with its greatest length when it extends equal distances on each side of O, indicating that there will be a maximum at the middle of the pattern.[1]

7. Fraunhofer and Fresnel Diffraction Compared.—While it is possible to make use of the graphical methods outlined in the preceding sections to describe diffraction effects of the Fraunhofer class, the difficulties involved in a mathematical analysis are far less than in the case of Fresnel diffraction. This is because in Fraunhofer effects the diffracted wave is plane, making possible a fairly simple method of summing up analytically

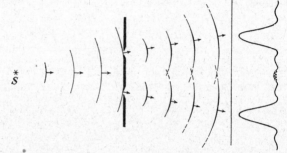

Fig. 12-13*a*.—Fresnel diffraction through two parallel slits. While interference fringes will appear across the entire field, their visibility will be greatest at the middle point.

the disturbances reaching any point, while in the Fresnel case the diffracted wave front is not plane.

The experimental advantages of Fraunhofer over Fresnel diffraction are really found in those cases where the effects to be observed are produced by the *interference* between two or more beams. The diffraction is present for the reason that these particular interference phenomena are without exception produced by apparatus belonging in class A (see Sec. **10-4**) in which a division of the wave front is made. In all apparatus such as the grating, the echelon, and the Michelson stellar interferometer, the elements recombined are relatively narrow sections of the wave front from a slit source or a source of small size, and the recombination necessary for interference is effected by focusing. A simple experiment will serve to illustrate the point. Figures

[1] For a more complete discussion of the Cornu spiral, see Meyer, "The Diffraction of Light, X-rays. and Material Particles," University of Chicago Press, 1934. There is also a comprehensive treatment in Preston, "Theory of Light," 4th ed., Macmillan. See also Appendix VIII of this text.

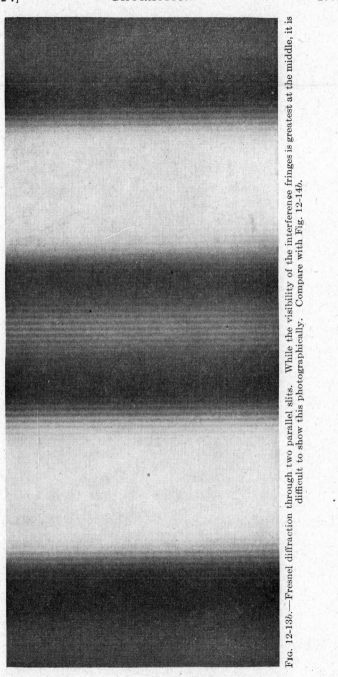

FIG. 12-13b.—Fresnel diffraction through two parallel slits. While the visibility of the interference fringes is greatest at the middle, it is difficult to show this photographically. Compare with Fig. 12-14b.

12-13*a* and *b* illustrate Fresnel diffraction through two slits. Obviously the effect due to the superposition of the two diffracted beams occurs in a region of poor illumination. It is true that by decreasing the width of each slit the regions of greatest intensity could be made to spread out until they overlapped, but this would be at the expense of illumination and little would be gained. If a lens system is used, as illustrated in Figs. 12-14*a* and *b*, the most intense portions of the diffraction patterns may be superposed at the focus, and the interference fringes will be observed in the

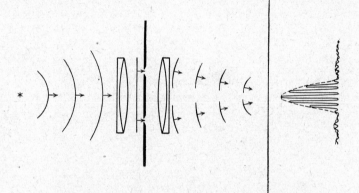

Fig. 12-14*a*.—Fraunhofer diffraction through two parallel slits. The visibility of the fringe system is highest in the region of maximum intensity.

brightest part of the field. This is the advantage which the Rayleigh refractometer has over Young's experimental apparatus (see Secs. **10-5** and **10-8**). The two are analogous, but the former uses Fraunhofer and the latter Fresnel diffraction. In Young's apparatus the two slits from which the interfering pencils of light come are so close together that it cannot be used for comparisons of optical path.

8. Fraunhofer Diffraction by a Single Slit.[1]—This is illustrated

---

[1] This is the first of a series of treatments, each of which gives the intensity distribution in a pattern due to diffraction. In many texts it is customary to adopt a standard method of derivation which is thereafter applied to each case in turn. The author feels that in an intermediate course the methods of analysis are often as valuable an acquisition for the student as an understanding of the phenomena themselves. Moreover, a variety of treatment often enhances the understanding of the entire field. For this reason different approaches have been made as often as feasible to the cases of diffraction treated in this chapter.

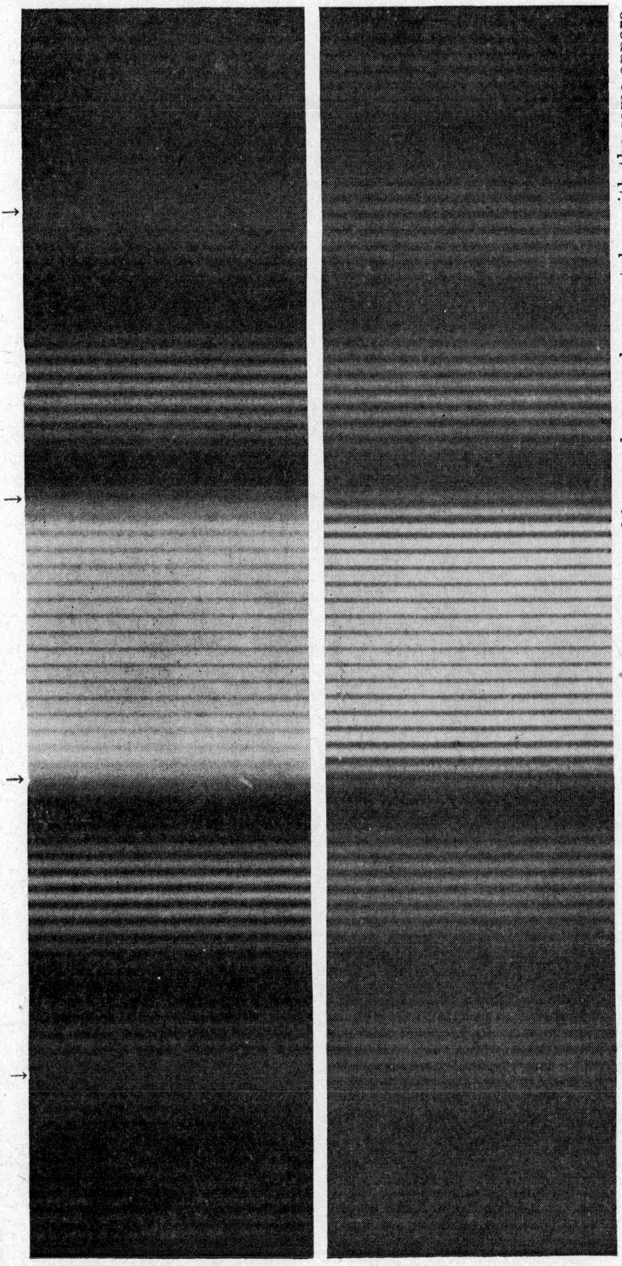

Fig. 12-14b.—Fraunhofer diffraction through two slits. The upper and lower photographs were taken with the same apparatus except that while the lower was taken with light of only the mercury line 5461 angstroms, the upper was taken with a mercury arc and a filter transmitting all its wave-lengths longer than 5000 angstroms. The arrows at the top indicate the resulting minima of visibility of the interference fringes. In both photographs the portion in the center is much overexposed and consequently difficult to reproduce properly.

by Fig. 12-2, but to assist in the derivation, a diagram showing more detail is desirable. In Fig. 12-15 a plane wave train of wave-length λ is incident upon a slit at an angle i to the normal to the slit. All parts of the incident wave are in the same phase of disturbance and can be represented by the expression

$$s = c \sin \frac{2\pi t}{T}.$$

Each part of the wave front passing through an element dx of the slit will be out of phase with that passing through the middle by an amount $2\pi\delta/\lambda$, where δ is the total difference of path $\delta_1 + \delta_2$ between that part of the wave front which traverses the center of the slit and that which traverses the element dx in passing to the diffracted wave front. By the geometry of the figure, it

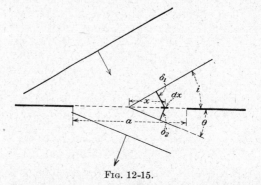

Fig. 12-15.

follows that $\delta = x(\sin i \pm \sin \theta)$, where x is the distance from the middle of the slit to the element dx and θ is the angle of diffraction. By convention the positive sign is used for $\sin \theta$ when the angle θ is as represented in the figure, and the negative sign for diffraction to the other side of the normal to the slit. The disturbance in the elementary pencil of light from dx will thus after diffraction be of the form

$$ds' = c \sin 2\pi \left[\frac{t}{T} - \frac{x(\sin i + \sin \theta)}{\lambda} \right] dx. \qquad (12\text{-}1)$$

In order to obtain the entire disturbance after diffraction, the function of x given in eq. 12-1 may be integrated between the limits $-\frac{a}{2}$ and $+\frac{a}{2}$:

$$S' = c \int_{-a/2}^{+a/2} \sin 2\pi \left[\frac{t}{T} - \frac{\varphi x}{\lambda} \right] dx, \qquad (12\text{-}2)$$

in which for convenience φ is substituted for the quantity $\sin i + \sin \theta$. Expanding the sine function in eq. 12-2

$$S' = c \sin 2\pi \frac{t}{T} \int_{-a/2}^{+a/2} \cos 2\pi \frac{\varphi x}{\lambda} dx - c \cos 2\pi \frac{t}{T} \int_{-a/2}^{+a/2} \sin 2\pi \frac{\varphi x}{\lambda} dx, \qquad (12\text{-}3)$$

in which the second term on the right-hand side, being an even function, is equal to zero. Hence

$$S' = c \sin 2\pi \frac{t}{T} \frac{\sin 2\pi \dfrac{\varphi x}{\lambda}}{2\pi \dfrac{\varphi}{\lambda}} \Bigg]_{-a/2}^{+a/2}$$

$$= ac \frac{\sin \pi \dfrac{\varphi a}{\lambda}}{\pi \dfrac{\varphi a}{\lambda}} \sin 2\pi \frac{t}{T}. \qquad (12\text{-}4)$$

Thus the disturbance in the diffracted wave is of the same form as in the incident wave but has instead of a constant amplitude c, the amplitude

$$\frac{ac \sin \pi(\varphi a/\lambda)}{\pi(\varphi a/\lambda)},$$

which depends upon the width of the opening, the wave-length, and the angles of diffraction and incidence. The intensity of the resulting diffraction pattern, after the light has been brought to a focus by a lens, is proportional to the square of the amplitude. Considering the proportionality factor to be unity, we have from eq. 12-4,

$$I = \frac{a^2 c^2 \sin^2 (\pi a \varphi/\lambda)}{(\pi a \varphi/\lambda)^2}. \qquad (12\text{-}5)$$

For simplicity, we may put this equal to $(\sin^2 u)/u^2$ and proceed to analyze the intensity pattern as follows:

a. When $u = 0$, $(\sin u)/u$ is an indeterminate quantity which evaluated gives unity. This corresponds to $\varphi = 0$, the middle of the diffraction pattern, and to $\theta = -i$, or, in other words, to a position directly opposite the source.

b. When $u = m\pi$, for $m = \pm 1, 2, 3$, etc., the intensity will be zero, representing a series of equidistant minima on either side of the central maximum given by case *a*. It should be noticed that the distance between the two minima corresponding to $m = +1$ and $m = -1$ is twice the distance between any other two adjacent minima.

c. Between the minima will exist a series of maxima whose positions cannot be found by inspection. To locate them we may put the first derivative of the intensity with respect to u equal to zero.

$$\frac{dI}{du} = \frac{2 \sin u}{u^3}(u \cos u - \sin u) = 0. \tag{12-6}$$

The first factor on the right-hand side gives the cases (*a*) and (*b*) already discussed. The second factor put equal to zero can be

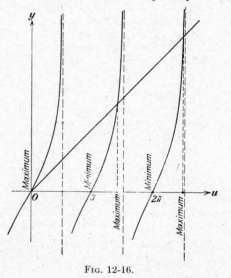

Fig. 12-16.

written $\tan u = u$. In order to find the values of u satisfying this equation, we may find the values which satisfy simultaneously the equations $y = \tan u$ and $y = u$. These graphs are shown in Fig. 12-16. The intersections of the solid lines are the required values of u. The dashed lines parallel to the y-axis give the values of u for which the angle is $\pi/2, 3\pi/2, 5\pi/2$, etc., and the dotted lines the values corresponding to the positions of maxima. It is apparent that the maxima do not lie midway between the minima but are displaced somewhat toward the middle of the pattern, the displacement being greatest for the maximum of lowest order. The values of u for the central maximum and the first six maxima on either side are given below, together with the relative intensities, the intensity for the central maximum being taken as unity.

Order of maximum	u	Intensity
0	0	1.0000
1	1.430π	0.0469
2	2.459π	0.0168
3	3.471π	0.0083
4	4.477π	0.0050
5	5.482π	0.0034
6	6.484π	0.0024

An examination of eq. 12-5 discloses that if the slit is made narrower the entire diffraction pattern will broaden. Since the

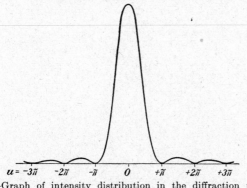

$$u = -3\pi \quad -2\pi \quad -\pi \quad 0 \quad +\pi \quad +2\pi \quad +3\pi$$

Fig. 12-17.—Graph of intensity distribution in the diffraction pattern of a single slit.

minima occur where $\pi a\varphi/\lambda = m\pi$, a smaller value of a corresponds, for any given value of m, to a larger value of φ, and hence of $\pm \sin \theta$. Increasing the angle of incidence will also result in a broadening of the pattern, since it will diminish the effective aperture, which is $a \cos i$. An increase in λ will also correspond to an increase in φ for both the maxima and the minima. Hence if light of more than one wave-length be incident on the slit each maximum except the central one will consist of a spectrum whose violet end will be closer to the middle of the pattern than the red and whose width will be proportional to the order of the maximum. A graph of the diffraction pattern of a single-slit opening with monochromatic light is shown in Fig. 12-17. A photograph of the diffraction pattern obtained with one slit is shown in Fig. 12-26.

9. Two Equal Slits.—If two parallel slits are used, the resulting disturbance after diffraction can be found analytically by the same procedure as followed in finding that for a single slit. For simplicity consider the two slits to be of equal width a, and separated by an opaque space b. Each part of the wave front passing through an element dx in *either slit* will, as before, be out of phase with that passing through the middle of the first slit by an amount $2\pi\delta/\lambda$. Consequently eq. 12-1 gives the disturbance ds' in each element of the diffracted wave, and to find the disturbance in the entire diffracted wave front, the integration over the entire wave front passing through two slits may be performed. The total disturbance will be

$$S' \text{ (two slits)} = \int_{-a/2}^{+a/2} ds' + \int_{+a/2+b}^{+3a/2+b} ds',$$

since the distances of the boundaries of the two slits are the limits of integration given. The result is

$$S' = 2ac\frac{\sin (\pi a\varphi/\lambda)}{\pi a\varphi/\lambda} \cdot \cos \frac{\pi(a + b)\varphi}{\lambda} \cdot \sin \frac{2\pi t}{T}, \qquad (12\text{-}7)$$

and the intensity, given by the square of the amplitude factor, is then

$$I = 4a^2c^2\frac{\sin^2 (\pi a\varphi/\lambda)}{(\pi a\varphi/\lambda)^2} \cdot \cos^2 \frac{\pi(a + b)\varphi}{\lambda}. \qquad (12\text{-}8)$$

As would be expected, a comparison of eqs. 12-5 and 12-8 shows that the intensity of the maximum for two equal openings is four times the intensity for a single opening of the same width, the amplitude being twice as great. Also, except for the factor 4, the expression for the intensity is the same as that for a single slit multiplied by the factor $\cos^2 \dfrac{\pi(a + b)\varphi}{\lambda}$, which varies between unity and zero for positive and negative values of φ, and hence for positive and negative values of θ. Two important features in the intensity pattern for two slits then follow: (1) The distribution of intensity due to a slit of width a, which will be a diffraction pattern like that shown in Fig. 12-17; and (2) superposed upon this a series of maxima and minima whose spacing is determined by the values of a and b, which will be a series of *interference fringes* in which the maxima are limited in intensity by the diffraction pattern. To show the result graphically we may first construct the graph of $4a^2c^2\dfrac{\sin^2{(\pi a\varphi/\lambda)}}{(\pi a\varphi/\lambda)^2}$, and under the

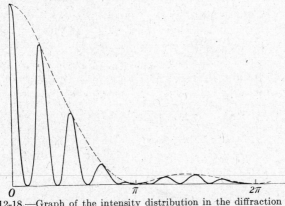
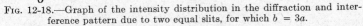

FIG. 12-18.—Graph of the intensity distribution in the diffraction and interference pattern due to two equal slits, for which $b = 3a$.

curve thus obtained, draw the graph of $\cos^2{[\pi(a + b)\varphi/\lambda]}$. By inspection of the latter function we see that there will be a series of minima when $\pi(a + b)\varphi/\lambda = (2m + 1)\pi/2$, and a series of maxima when $\pi(a + b)\varphi/\lambda = m\pi$, where $m = 0, 1, 2, 3$, etc., or

$$\begin{aligned}\varphi(\text{minima}) &= \frac{(2m + 1)\lambda}{2(a + b)} = \sin i + \sin \theta, \\ \varphi(\text{maxima}) &= \frac{2m\lambda}{2(a + b)} = \sin i + \sin \theta.\end{aligned} \qquad (12\text{-}9)$$

Hence the maxima will be evenly spaced and midway between the minima. The intensity of a maximum for a particular value of m will in all cases be limited by the value of $\dfrac{\sin^2{(\pi a\varphi/\lambda)}}{(\pi a\varphi/\lambda)^2}$, but it will depend also upon the relation between b and a. If b is equal to an integer times a, there will be a value of m corresponding to a *maximum* of the two slit *interference* pattern which will be located at the *minimum* of the *diffraction* pattern. The graph shown in Fig. 12-18 is for the case where $b = 3a$.

The pattern obtained with two or more openings is an interference pattern since it is due to the superposition of separate beams, originally from the same source, in such a manner that a regular distribution of maxima and minima of intensity is the result.

10. Limit of Resolution.—According to Rayleigh's criterion, the *limit of resolution* with a single opening is reached when the two objects are such a distance apart that the central maximum of the diffraction pattern of one object coincides with the first minimum of the diffraction pattern of the other. We may consider the two objects to be two parallel incandescent filaments, or two slits close together and illuminated, or, in fact, any two sources of light parallel to the diffracting slit. In Sec. 12-8 it was shown that the first minimum of the diffraction pattern of a single object occurs when $u = \pi a \varphi / \lambda = \pi$, or when $\varphi = \lambda / a$. But $\varphi = \sin i + \sin \theta$, so that for normal incidence, and provided φ is not too large (*i.e.*, provided a is not too small),

$$\varphi = \theta = \frac{\lambda}{a}. \tag{12-10}$$

If, however, the intensity pattern is due to two slits, it follows from eqs. 12-9 that the limit of resolution is reached when

$$\theta = \frac{\lambda}{2(a + b)}. \tag{12-11}$$

If a has the same value in both eqs. 12-10 and 12-11, it follows that the angular separation of two objects which are just resolved is less than half that for a single slit, the exact ratio between the two angular separations depending on the value of b. The larger b is, the smaller will be the angle for the *limit of resolution* with two slits and the greater will be the *resolving power*. If, moreover, the a in eq. 12-11 is a', much smaller than a in eq. 12-10, and the value of $a' + b$ is the same as that of a, the resolving power of the two slits will be twice that of the single opening. This condition is approximated in the case of the stellar interferometer which will be discussed later. In the simplest form of this instrument, the central part of a lens of width a is covered up, permitting the light to pass only through two narrow openings at the edge, whose separation is $a' + b$, where a' is the width of each opening and b is the width of the cover.   In this case, $a' + b$ is approximately equal to a.

There is a difference, however, in what is observed with one and with two slits.   If diffraction images of two objects are obtained with a single slit, at the limit of resolution the graphical representation of the result is that given in Fig. 12-19a.   Here the central images are so much greater in intensity than the others that in most cases they are the principal observable features, especially if the slit is wide.   If two slits are used, at the limit of resolution the graphical representation is that given in Fig.

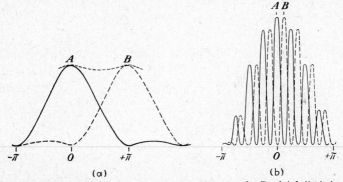

Fig. 12-19.—The difference between superposition at the Rayleigh limit in the case of (a) diffraction by a single slit, and (b) interference by two slits.

12-19b, where for each image there are several maxima not differing much in intensity.   The resulting effect of the superposition of the two interference patterns with the separation shown in the figure is a *disappearance* of the fringes.   If the superposition is not at the limit of resolution, some alternations of intensity will be visible, the maximum visibility of the fringes being when the dotted curve is exactly superposed on the one represented by the solid line, but with a separation between points A and B equal to the distance between two adjacent maxima   The test for limit of resolution is then determined by the degree of *visibility* of the fringes.   This principle is made use of in Michelson's stellar interferometer.

11. The Stellar Interferometer.—It now remains to show that the angular separation between the diffraction (or interference) maxima is the angular separation between the objects.

This may be done with the aid of Fig. 12-20.   Points O_1 and O_2 represent two very distant objects, and the straight lines connecting them to I_1 and I_2 are the chief rays of the rays collected by the lens which focuses the light at the image plane.   The distance between I_1 and I_2 in the case of one opening is, for the limit of resolution, the distance between the principal maximum of I_1 and the first minimum in its diffraction pattern.

In the case of two slits, the situation requires a more complicated diagram.   At the limit of resolution, given by the disappearance of the interference fringes, the angle θ is, in this case, the angle between the two central maxima of the inter-

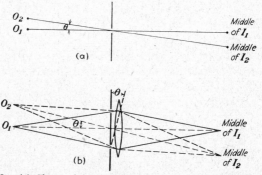

Fig. 12-20.—(a) Shows the relation between the angular separations of the two objects and the two images with one slit.   The lens has been omitted.   (b) Shows the corresponding case for two slits.   The distance $a + b$ is from center to center of the slits and the distance e is from the upper slit to the inclined dotted line.   There is no relation between the scales used in the two diagrams.

ference pattern, these maxima being indicated by A and B in Fig. 12–19b.   The angle θ, subtended at the slit plane by the distance between the maxima A and B, is the same as that subtended at the slit plane by the distance between the two point objects. From Fig. 12-20b

$$\sin \theta \doteq \theta = \frac{e}{a + b},$$

but by eq. 12-11,

$$\theta = \frac{\lambda}{2(a + b)},$$

when the limit of resolution is reached.   These two values of θ will be the same when $e = \lambda/2$, but since this is true when the fringes disappear, it follows that for a separation of the two slits such that the visibility of the fringes is a minimum as shown, the separation s of the two objects is given by

$$\frac{s}{D} = \frac{\lambda}{2(a + b)}.$$

Similarly, the disappearance of the fringes, or, rather, the adjustment of the separation between the slits so that the visibility of the fringes is a minimum, may be made use of to measure the *diameters* of stellar objects whose distances are known. The application of the principle in this case may by illustrated by considering the case of a distant slit considered as a source. Let 1, 2, 3, 4, 5, . . . n (Fig. 12-21) represent elements in the plane of the source parallel to its sides. For each of these elements there will be, because of the double slit, a pattern of equidistant maxima and minima. Patterns from elements 1, 2, 3 . . . n will be superposed as shown graphically in Fig. 12-22. It is evident that unless the angular separation of elements 1 and n at the plane of the double slit is $\theta = \lambda/2(a + b)$, alternations of intensity will still be observed,

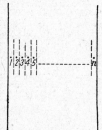

FIG. 12-21.—For two point sources the zones 1, 2, 3, . . . n each give an interference pattern of the type illustrated in Fig. 12-22 by the intensity curves correspondingly numbered.

i.e., the visibility of the fringes will not be a minimum. If, however, the angular separation of elements 1 and n is $\lambda/2(a + b)$, the visibility will be a minimum, and zero in case the intensity is uniform across the source.

An analytic treatment of the visibility of the fringes may be based on further consideration of eq. 12-8. In this equation, the quantity $(a + b)\varphi$ is the total difference of path for light diffracted at a particular angle θ through the two openings, and $(a + b)\varphi/\lambda$ is consequently the number of wave-lengths n in that difference of path. Also, since in practice the angles i and θ are very small, we may substitute the angles for their sines, so that $\varphi = i + \theta$. Thus for an element of the source of width di, considering that for small angles $\sin (\pi a\varphi/\lambda) = \pi a\varphi/\lambda$, we may write eq. 12-8 in the form

$$I_{(di)} = 4B^2 \cos^2 \pi n(i + \theta) \qquad (12\text{-}12)$$

where B is the amplitude for a particular point in the diffraction

pattern from either opening, and n is the number of wave-
lengths difference of path.   The total intensity will be

$$I = \int_{-\alpha/2}^{+\alpha/2} 4B^2 \cos^2 \pi n(\theta + i)di, \qquad (12\text{-}13)$$

where α is the angular width of the source as seen from the position of the double slit.   Since the double slit is in front of the
objective of a telescope, α is the angular width subtended at the
telescope.   If the intensity is uniform over the source, the value

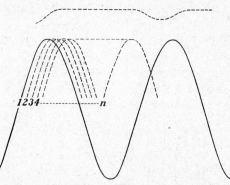

Fig. 12-22.—Each of the curves 1, 2, 3, ... n indicates a maximum of an
interference pattern from a line element in the source, due to two slits.   The
dotted curve at the top of the picture indicates that, unless the two slits have a
suitable separation, there will be maxima and minima of intensity in the composite pattern.

of B will be the same for all elements di, so that eq. 12-13 may be
written

$$I = 2B^2\left[\int_{-\alpha/2}^{+\alpha/2} di + \int_{-\alpha/2}^{+\alpha/2} \cos 2\pi n\theta \cos 2\pi ni \, di \right.$$
$$\left. - \int_{-\alpha/2}^{+\alpha/2} \sin 2\pi n\theta \sin 2\pi ni \, di \right].$$

Putting

$$\begin{aligned}
2B^2 \int di &= P, \\
2B^2 \int \cos 2\pi ni \, di &= C, \\
2B^2 \int \sin 2\pi ni \, di &= S,
\end{aligned} \qquad (12\text{-}14)$$

there results

$$I = P + C \cos 2\pi n\theta - S \sin 2\pi n\theta. \qquad (12\text{-}15)$$

The condition for maxima and minima of intensity is

$$\frac{dI}{d\theta} = 2\pi n(C \sin 2\pi n\theta + S \cos 2\pi n\theta) = 0,$$

hence the intensity of the pattern of interference fringes varies between

$$I_{max} = P + \sqrt{C^2 + S^2}$$

and

$$I_{min} = P - \sqrt{C^2 + S^2},$$

and the visibility of the fringes is given by

$$V = \frac{I_{max} - I_{min}}{I_{max} + I_{min}} = \sqrt{\frac{C^2 + S^2}{P^2}}. \qquad (12\text{-}16)$$

If the source is symmetrically placed with respect to the axis of the telescope, S is an even function and becomes zero, whereupon

$$V = \frac{C}{P} = \frac{2B^2 \int_{-\alpha/2}^{+\alpha/2} \cos 2\pi n i \, di}{2B^2 \int_{-\alpha/2}^{+\alpha/2} di} = \frac{2B^2 \sin n\pi\alpha}{2B^2 n\pi\alpha}. \qquad (12\text{-}17)$$

Thus the visibility is independent of B, which relates to a particular place on the interference pattern under observation, *i.e.*, V is a constant across the pattern, provided, of course, monochromatic light is used. Since $n = (a + b)/\lambda$ and $\alpha = w/D$, where w is the width of the source and D is its distance from the telescope,

$$V = \frac{\sin \pi\dfrac{a + b}{D} \cdot \dfrac{w}{\lambda}}{\pi\dfrac{a + b}{D} \cdot \dfrac{w}{\lambda}}. \qquad (12\text{-}18)$$

From this it is evident that the visibility will be zero, *i.e.*, the interference fringes will disappear, when $\dfrac{a + b}{D} \cdot \dfrac{w}{\lambda}$ is equal to any integer m. That is, the width w of the source is given by

$$w = \frac{mD\lambda}{a + b},$$

where $m = 1, 2, 3$, etc.
The first-order disappearance of the fringes will be for $m = 1$, or when

$$w = \frac{\lambda D}{d}, \qquad (12\text{-}19)$$

where d is the separation of the two openings in the double slit. The disappearances of higher order will in general be more difficult to observe, since they correspond to larger values of b, the separation between the two slits, for which the fringes become very narrow.

Should the focal plane of the eyepiece not be exactly at the focal plane of the objective of the telescope, the fringes will still be visible, provided the relation expressed in eq. 12-19 does not hold. In any case there is a separate diffraction pattern for each of the slits in front of the objective, and these two patterns will overlap in some part of their extent. The only effect of absence of correct focusing of the telescope eyepiece will be that the fringes may not be observed in the most intense portion of the field of view; they will in any case be present. Moreover, since the width of the two openings is inversely proportional to the widths of the resulting diffraction maxima, the fringes will still be seen (provided eq. 12-19 does not hold), even if each of the fringes has appreciable width. If white light is used, all of the fringes except the central one will be slightly colored at the edges, owing to the small amount of dispersion present. Since this dispersion is quite small, the disappearance of the fringes, or, at least, the reduction of the visibility to a minimum, may still be observed. In this case, the value of λ in eq. 12-19 will depend on the sensitivity of the eye to color. For most eyes the wave-length for maximum sensitivity is approximately 5700 angstroms.

If the distance between two illuminated objects is to be measured, their separation is given by

$$s = \frac{\lambda D}{2d}, \qquad (12\text{-}20)$$

a result which may be derived by the preceding analysis.

If the source is a circular disk of uniform luminosity, a series of strip elements on its surface will decrease in height as the edge of the disk is approached. For this reason the angle subtended at the telescope by the disk must be somewhat larger than the angle for the disappearance of the fringes. Theory shows that in this case the diameter of the disk is given by

$$L = \frac{1.22\lambda D}{d}. \qquad (12\text{-}21)$$

Similarly, in case the separation s of two stars is to be measured, it is given by

$$s = \frac{0.61\lambda D}{d}, \tag{12-22}$$

where s is the distance between the centers of the stars. In eqs. 12-20, 12-21, and 12-22, d is the separation between the two slits.

Observations by this method of the diameters and separations of celestial objects are usually made with a telescope whose

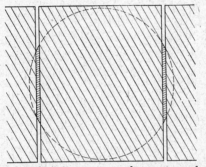

FIG. 12-23.—The dotted circle represents the aperture of an objective; the two heavily shaded portions represent that part of the objective through which light passes.

central portion is covered by a shield, so that there is used only light which passes through two narrow slots whose distance apart can be changed. From the four preceding equations, it will be seen that the angular diameter of an object is proportional to w/D, and the angular separation of two objects to s/D. Hence the smaller these quantities are, the larger must be the value of d, the linear distance between the slots, so that the measurement of diameters or separations of very distant celestial objects, or those with relatively small dimensions, would be impossible

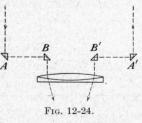

FIG. 12-24.

except with a telescope objective of enormous size. For such objects, instead of having two movable slots over the objective as illustrated in Fig. 12-23, an arrangement of total reflection prisms is mounted on a crossarm placed in front of the objective, as illustrated in Fig. 12-24. While the prisms B and B' are primarily for the purpose of reflecting the two interfering beams into the objective, it follows from the third condition for interference given in Sec. **10-2** that with this arrangement the fringes are sensibly wider and hence more easily observed than if the angle between the beams were larger.

12. Many Slits.   The Diffraction Grating.—If the diffraction is by more than two equidistant slits of equal width, the equation for the disturbance after diffraction may be obtained by integrating 12-1 between successive limits $-\dfrac{a}{2}$ to $+\dfrac{a}{2}$, $\dfrac{a}{2} + b$ to $\dfrac{3a}{2} + b$, $\dfrac{3a}{2} + 2b$ to $\dfrac{5a}{2} + 2b$, etc.   This procedure is so long and involved that it is likely to mask the significance of the final result.   Therefore a more descriptive method of accounting for the resulting diffraction pattern will be used.

In the case of two slits it was shown that interference maxima will occur at values of φ for which the elements of disturbance from corresponding points in the two slits have path differences of $m\lambda$, where $m = 0, 1, 2, 3$, etc., *i.e.*, phase differences of $2m\pi$. Similarly there will be minima at values of φ for which the difference of path is $(2m + 1)\lambda/2$, and the difference of phase is $(2m + 1)\pi$. Let us now consider the case of three slits.   Obviously maxima will occur for the same values of φ as for two slits, *i.e.*, where the difference of path through *successive* slits is $m\lambda$. These are called *principal maxima*.   But the minima will not occur midway between these as in the case of two slits.   The reason is that, the difference of phase between corresponding elements of disturbance from successive slits being at the midpoint $(2m + 1)\pi$, two of the elements will cancel each other, and the third will give rise to a maximum.   This series of maxima, midway between the principal maxima for three slits, will not have an intensity comparable to that of the principal maxima, and are called *secondary maxima*.   On either side of these secondary maxima will occur minima at values of φ for which the disturbances from all three slits have a phase difference such that their sum is zero.

These results can be described graphically by an adaptation of the vector polygon method described in Sec. **6** of this chapter. Consider each slit to be the source of a Huygens wavelet which has the usual characteristic of sending light in all directions, but with a maximum intensity in the direction of the incident wave. Thus each slit contributes an element of amplitude to the disturbance in a particular part of the diffraction pattern. For each element e_1, e_2, e_3, let amplitude vectors v_1, v_2, v_3 be drawn, with the angles between them corresponding to a difference of phase which will be different at different points in the pattern. Then the results are as shown in Fig. 12-25. At point D of the diffraction pattern, for instance, at which the path difference between successive elements is λ, and the phase difference 2π, the vectors are all in the same straight line, and add up to give the resulting amplitude of the first-order maximum. This

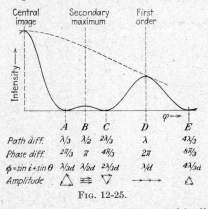

FIG. 12-25.

amplitude squared gives the intensity graphically represented above D. Similarly, at point A the path difference between successive elements is $\lambda/3$, and the phase difference is $2\pi/3$, so that the vectors form a closed polygon. This corresponds to zero amplitude and intensity. At B, the path difference between successive elements is $\lambda/2$ and the phase difference π, hence three such vectors give a resultant amplitude corresponding to the disturbance due to one element. As the angle φ increases, the intensity diminishes, the graph of the entire pattern being enclosed by a diffraction curve exactly as in the case of two slits. Similar results may be obtained for more than three slits. In Fig. 12-26 are photographs of the patterns for 1, 2, 3, 4, 5, and 6 equal and equidistant slits. These photographs were made with gratings in which the ratio of opaque to open space was 3:1. Theory predicts that when this ratio is a whole number, there will be missing interference maxima which will occur at points corresponding to values of φ for which the enclosing diffraction curve has zero height. This can be seen from eq. 12-8 for two slits, but it will be equally true for any number of equi-

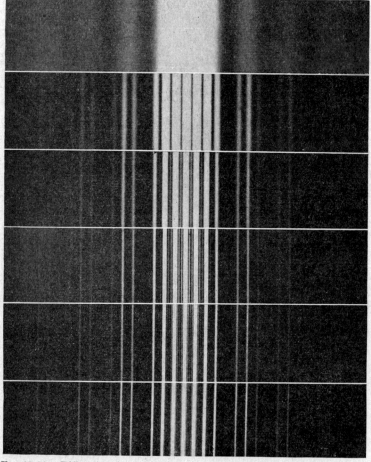

Fig. 12-26.—Diffraction through 1, 2, 3, 4, 5, and 6 slits. In each case the central bright portions are much overexposed.

distant slits when the ratio of opaque to open space is a whole number. In eq. 12-8 when $b = 3a$,

$$\cos \frac{\pi(a + b)\varphi}{\lambda} = \cos \frac{4\pi a \varphi}{\lambda}.$$

The condition for a *minimum* in the enclosing diffraction pattern is that $\pi a \varphi / \lambda = \pi$, but in this case $\cos (4\pi a \varphi / \lambda) = \cos 4\pi$, which corresponds to a *maximum* in the interference pattern. These orders are actually missing in the photographs. Also the number of secondary maxima is $N - 2$, where N is the number of openings. Their intensity relative to the principal maxima decreases as N increases. This is not clearly evident in the photographs, which were printed from the negatives so as to suppress the principal maxima, the latter being much overexposed in the negative. The most important thing illustrated in this series is that as N increases the principle maxima, or *orders* become increasingly sharp. For very large values of N, the intensities of the secondary maxima are practically zero, and each principal maximum (with a perfect grating) is a sharp image of the slit.

These results are for monochromatic light. If more than one wave-length is present in the source, each order will consist of a spectrum. Since $\varphi = m\lambda / (a + b)$, it is evident these the spectra will have the blue end nearer the central image, *i.e.*, at smaller values of φ, than the red end.

Diffraction gratings in practice are made by ruling lines close together with a diamond on polished metal or glass surfaces. In most cases the entire surface retains its reflecting qualities, the rulings serving merely to create a surface with a periodic structure. It might seem at first as if the fundamental concept of diffraction does not hold in such a case, since the incident waves are not interrupted or cut off by obstacles in the form of opaque spaces. However, the periodicity of the reflecting surface

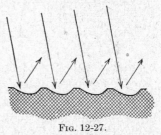

Fig. 12-27.

consists of regularly spaced strips, of a width appropriate to the wave-lengths of the diffracted light, which are as effective in giving rise to regularly spaced elements of disturbance as in the case of a transmission grating. This is illustrated in Fig. 12-27. Moreover, by shaping the diamond tool with which the grating is ruled, it is possible to send a preponderance of light into particular orders.

13. The Dispersion of a Grating.—In eq. 12-9 the position of a maximum was given by

$$\frac{m\lambda}{a+b} = \sin i + \sin \theta.$$

While this equation was derived for the case of two equal slits, it holds equally well for the positions of the *principal maxima* in the case of many equal and equidistant slits, since, as shown in the preceding paragraphs, the effect of increasing the number of slits is to sharpen the principal maxima, or orders. If the grating is made up of equidistant openings, or rulings on a reflecting surface a distance s apart, we may write

$$\sin i + \sin \theta = \frac{m\lambda}{s}. \tag{12-23}$$

In Sec. **8-2,** the dispersion D of a prism was defined as $di'/d\lambda$, where di' is the difference of angle of dispersion of two spectral lines obtained with a prism. Similarly we may express the dispersion of a grating by

$$D = \frac{d\theta}{d\lambda},$$

$d\theta$ being the difference of angle of diffraction between two close spectral lines. Differentiating with respect to λ the function in eq. 12-23, it follows that for i constant,

$$D = \frac{d\theta}{d\lambda} = \frac{m}{s \cos \theta}, \tag{12-24}$$

by which it appears that the dispersion of a grating is *directly proportional to the order of the spectrum and inversely proportional to the grating space.* That it is independent of the number of rulings has already been shown.

14. Resolving Power of a Grating.—By definition, the resolving power of any dispersive instrument is given by $\lambda/d\lambda$, where $d\lambda$ is the smallest difference of wave-length which can be observed at the wave-length λ. According to Rayleigh's criterion for limit of resolution, this smallest observable $d\lambda$ corresponds to the angle between the maximum of a spectral line of wave-length λ and the maximum of one of wave-length $\lambda + d\lambda$, when the latter coincides in position with the first minimum on either side of the maximum of λ. But we have seen that as the number of grating elements (slit openings or rulings, as the case may be) is increased, the maxima become narrower, and the position of the minimum on either side of the principal maximum (a spectral line) becomes closer to the center of the maximum. For instance, in the case of six slits the distance between one principal maximum and the next is the same as for two slits, but the distance between each principal maximum and the adjacent minimum is one-third as great as for two slits. For N slits, the distance between a principal maximum and an adjacent minimum may be seen to be $2/N$ times the corresponding distance for two slits, the latter being $\lambda/2s$ when $a + b$ in eq. 12-9 is replaced by s. Thus the angle of diffraction corresponding to this distance becomes, for N slits,

$$\frac{2}{N} \cdot \frac{\lambda}{2s} = d(\sin \theta) = \cos \theta \, d\theta. \tag{12-25}$$

The resolving power may now be obtained from the relations in eqs. 12-24 and 12-25; *i.e.*,

$$R = \frac{\lambda}{d\lambda} = \frac{d\theta}{d\lambda} \cdot \frac{\lambda}{d\theta} = \frac{m}{s \cos \theta} \cdot Ns \cos \theta = mN. \tag{12-26}$$

Thus the resolving power of a grating is the product of the order of interference m and the number of rulings N on the grating, and is independent of the grating space.

The resolving power may also be obtained by applying the general principle illustrated in Sec. **8-3**, wherein it was shown that the resolving power of a prism may be obtained by multiplying the dispersion by the width a of the beam of light intercepted by the prism, or, by putting $R = aD$. Applying this principle to the case of the grating, for which, if w be used for the width of the diffracted beam and l the length of the grating,

$$w = l \cos \theta.$$

Thus,

$$R = w \cdot D = l \cos \theta \, \frac{m}{s \cos \theta},$$

in which l/s is the number of rulings on the grating, so that

$$R = mN.$$

15. The Echelon.—This instrument, invented by Michelson, is an interesting illustration of the application of the principles of both diffraction and interference. Like the diffraction grating, it is an "interference spectrometer," belonging to class A (see Sec. **10-4**), in which there is a division of the wave front. It consists of a pile of plane-parallel plates of equal thickness, arranged as illustrated in Fig. 12-28, each plate projecting beyond the one following it by a small width w. Consider a plane wave front F, advancing toward the right. Upon reaching any one of

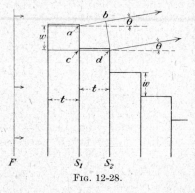

FIG. 12-28.

the surfaces such as S_1, an element of the wave front of width w passes through air, while another element of the same width traverses the thickness t of the glass plate between surfaces S_1 and S_2. The diffraction pattern will be spread over a very small area if, as in practice, w is of the order of magnitude of 1 mm. At an angle of diffraction θ with the normal

to the face of the glass plate the path difference between the light through glass and that through air is $n(cd) - ab$. But

$$ab = t \cos \theta - w \sin \theta,$$

which for small angles may be written

$$ab = t - w\theta. \tag{12-27}$$

The path difference at angle θ is thus

$$(n - 1)t + w\theta = m\lambda, \tag{12-28}$$

where m is the order of interference for a single plate at angle θ. The dispersion $d\theta/d\lambda$, obtained from eq. 12-28 is given by

$$D = \frac{m}{w} - \frac{t}{w}\frac{dn}{d\lambda}. \tag{12-29}$$

In order to express D in terms of measurable quantities, it is desirable to eliminate m between eqs. 12-28 and 12-29. Since θ is small, we may for this purpose write eq. 12-28 in the form

$$m = \frac{(n - 1)t}{\lambda}.$$

Substituting this value of m in eq. 12-29, we obtain

$$D = \left[(n - 1) - \lambda \frac{dn}{d\lambda} \right] \frac{t}{w\lambda}. \qquad (12\text{-}30)$$

The resolving power is given by the product of the total aperture and the dispersion (see Sec. **8-3**). The total aperture a is the product of the number of plates N and the width w of each step, so that

$$R = aD = \frac{Nwt}{w\lambda} \left[(n - 1) - \lambda \frac{dn}{d\lambda} \right]. \qquad (12\text{-}31)$$

For small angles, $(n - 1) = m\lambda/t$. Substituting this value of $(n - 1)$ in eq. 12-31, we obtain

$$R = mN - Nt \frac{dn}{d\lambda}. \qquad (12\text{-}32)$$

The second term on the right-hand side is small compared to the first, so that to a high degree of approximation, $R = mN$, the same as for the grating.

The appearance of the spectrum will, however, be totally different from that ordinarily obtained with a grating. For, note that the *smallest* difference of path obtainable is that introduced by *one* of the plates. For small θ, $m = (n - 1)t/\lambda$, so that if $t = 1$ cm., $\lambda = 5 \times 10^{-5}$ cm., and $n = 1.5$, then $m = 10,000$. Thus the orders observed are always very high, and since the angle of diffraction is small they will be very close together, *i.e.*, the orders will overlap in such a way as to make observations on an extended region of the spectrum impossible. In order to avoid the overlapping of orders, auxiliary dispersion with a prism is used to isolate a spectrum line to be examined. The prismatic and echelon dispersions are in this case parallel, instead of at right angles, as in the case of the Fabry-Perot interferometer. It is customary to pass the light first through the slit, collimator and prism of an ordinary spectrometer, and then through the echelon, which is inserted between the prism and the camera or telescope objective. Since the intensity is distributed over a very narrow region, because of the small width of the central diffraction minimum (*i.e.*, large w), only a few orders are seen at one time. For instance, with the dimensions given above, a 30-plate echelon would yield only three orders of comparable intensity, their numerical values being of the order of magnitude of 300,000, say, 299,999, 300,000, and 300,001. Because of the extremely high order of interference possible, the echelon is particularly useful in the analysis of fine structure of spectral lines (see Chap. XIV).

If made of glass, the echelon cannot be used to examine the ultraviolet below 3500 angstroms. A quartz echelon will give fair transmission to 1800 angstroms. In recent years, reflection echelons have been constructed, the steps being coated with reflecting metal, so that the instrument may be used for very short wave-lengths. For regions below 2200 angstroms it is, of course, necessary to place the entire instrument in an evacuated chamber.

The principal drawback to the echelon is the practical difficulties involved in its construction. The plates must be of glass of highest optical quality, if used for transmission, and their thicknesses must be as nearly the same as it is possible to make them. Another obvious disadvantage is that it is capable of no modifications in dimension to suit special conditions, as are the Michelson and the Fabry-Perot interferometers.

16. Rectangular Opening.—The analytical expression for the diffraction of a slit of width a derived in Sec. **12-8** took no account of the length of the slit, that dimension being considered to be so great that the resulting diffraction was negligible. If the opening, instead of being very long, has a length comparable to its width, the expression for the elements of disturbance after diffraction must contain terms taking account of both directions. Instead of eq. 12-1, we may write

$$ds' = c \sin 2\pi \left[\frac{t}{T} - \frac{\varphi_1 x + \varphi_2 y}{\lambda} \right] dx\, dy, \qquad (12\text{-}33)$$

where $\varphi_1 = \sin i_1 + \sin \theta_1$, and $\varphi_2 = \sin i_2 + \sin \theta_2$, the subscripts referring to the width a and length b of the opening. Then

$$S' = c \sin 2\pi \frac{t}{T} \int_{-a/2}^{+a/2} \int_{-b/2}^{+b/2} \cos 2\pi \left(\frac{\varphi_1 x + \varphi_2 y}{\lambda} \right) dx\, dy$$

$$- c \cos 2\pi \frac{t}{T} \int_{-a/2}^{+a/2} \int_{-b/2}^{+b/2} \sin 2\pi \left(\frac{\varphi_1 x + \varphi_2 y}{\lambda} \right) dx\, dy. \quad (12\text{-}34)$$

Since the integral of the sine between limits with the same value but opposite sign is zero, we can write

$$S' = c \sin 2\pi \frac{t}{T} \int_{-a/2}^{+a/2} \int_{-b/2}^{+b/2} \cos \frac{2\pi\varphi_1 x}{\lambda} \cdot \cos \frac{2\pi\varphi_2 y}{\lambda} \cdot dx \, dy$$

$$- c \sin 2\pi \frac{t}{T} \int_{-a/2}^{+a/2} \int_{-b/2}^{+b/2} \sin \frac{2\pi\varphi_1 x}{\lambda} \cdot \sin \frac{2\pi\varphi_2 y}{\lambda} \cdot dx \, dy. \quad (12\text{-}35)$$

The second term is equal to zero, and the first is

$$S' = abc \sin 2\pi \frac{t}{T} \frac{\sin \frac{\pi\varphi_1 a}{\lambda}}{\pi\varphi_1 a/\lambda} \frac{\sin \frac{\pi\varphi_2 b}{\lambda}}{\pi\varphi_2 b/\lambda}; \quad (12\text{-}36)$$

the intensity is given by

$$I = a^2 b^2 c^2 \cdot \frac{\sin^2 \frac{\pi a\varphi_1}{\lambda}}{(\pi a\varphi_1/\lambda)^2} \cdot \frac{\sin^2 \frac{\pi b\varphi_2}{\lambda}}{(\pi b\varphi_2/\lambda)^2}. \quad (12\text{-}37)$$

The resulting diffraction pattern for monochromatic light is shown in Fig. 12-29.

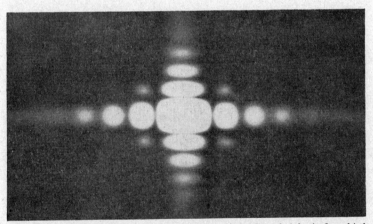

Fig. 12-29.—Diffraction by a rectangular opening whose height is five-thirds its width. The brightest central image and those next to it are much over-exposed.

17. Diffraction by a Circular Opening.—While the resolving power for a long slit opening of width a is given by $\theta = \lambda/a$, that for a circular opening is given by $\theta = 1.22 \, \lambda/a$, where in each case θ is the angle between the center of the diffraction pattern of a point object and the first minimum of intensity. This can be shown in the following manner: Consider a plane wave advancing in a direction normal to the plane of a circular opening AB, of radius r (Fig. 12-30a).   It is required to find the expression for the intensity in the diffraction pattern at an angle θ.   The resulting diffraction will be like that obtained by a lens which brings all rays diffracted at a common angle θ to a focus. The disturbance at this point will be due to the addition of all

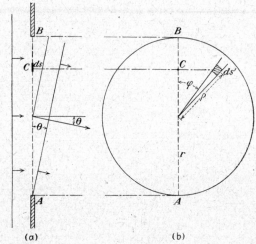

FIG. 12-30.—Diffraction through a circular opening.   (a) Side view of opening with wave-front advancing in a direction normal to the screen.   (b) Front view of the opening.

the elements over the area of the opening.   The path difference between the element ds at C and that at A will be $AC \sin \theta$, and the phase difference, $(2\pi AC \sin \theta)/\lambda$, so that if the disturbance at A is $S = \sin (2\pi t/T)$, after diffraction that due to an element ds at C will be

$$ds' = \sin 2\pi\left(\frac{t}{T} - \frac{AC \sin \theta}{\lambda}\right)ds. \qquad (12\text{-}38)$$

But light diffracted at the angle θ through an element ds' (Fig. 12-30b) has the same path difference as regards the light from A as has that from ds, since ds' lies on a perpendicular to the line AB at C.   Since $AC = r + \rho \cos \varphi$, and since also the element ds' has an area $\rho \, d\varphi \, d\rho$ in polar coordinates, the disturbance from ds' may be written

$$ds' = \sin 2\pi\left(\frac{t}{T} - \frac{r \sin \theta}{\lambda} - \frac{\rho \cos \varphi \sin \theta}{\lambda}\right)\rho \, d\rho \, d\varphi, \quad (12\text{-}39)$$

and the total disturbance at the angle θ is

$$S' = \int_0^{2\pi} \int_0^r (\sin 2\pi M \cos 2\pi N - \cos 2\pi M \sin 2\pi N) \, \rho \, d\rho \, d\varphi, \quad (12\text{-}40)$$

in which $M = \left(\dfrac{t}{T} - \dfrac{r \sin \theta}{\lambda}\right)$ and $N = \dfrac{\rho \cos \varphi \sin \theta}{\lambda}$. The integral of the second term, being an even function, is zero, so that

$$S' = \sin 2\pi\left(\frac{t}{T} - \frac{r \sin \theta}{\lambda}\right)\int_0^{2\pi} \int_0^r \cos 2\pi \frac{\rho \cos \varphi \sin \theta}{\lambda}\rho \, d\rho \, d\varphi. \quad (12\text{-}41)$$

The integration with respect to φ must be carried out in series and that with respect to ρ by parts,[1] giving as the final result for the intensity:

$$I = \pi^2 r^4\left[1 - \frac{1}{2}n + \frac{1}{3}\left(\frac{n^2}{2!}\right)^2 - \frac{1}{4}\left(\frac{n^3}{3!}\right)^3 + \frac{1}{5}\left(\frac{n^4}{4!}\right)^4 -, \text{etc.}\right]^2,$$

in which $n = (\pi r/\lambda) \sin \theta$. The series in the brackets, which may be denoted by s, is convergent for all values of n, and goes through positive and negative values alternately as n increases. There will accordingly be maximum values corresponding to $ds/dn = 0$, and zero values when $s = 0$. The maxima and minima in the resulting circular diffraction pattern, whose center will be on the normal to the opening, are thus at positions for which $\sin \theta = n\lambda/\pi r$, where for given values of r and λ, n/π takes the values in the following table:

	n/π	Intensity
1st max......	0	1
1st min......	0.61	0
2d max......	0.819	0.0174
2d min......	1.116	0
3d max......	1.333	0.0041
3d min. etc...	1.619	0

[1] For the steps in the integration see Preston, "Theory of Light," 4th ed., Macmillan. A discussion is also to be found in Meyer, "Diffraction of Light, X-Rays, and Material Particles," Appendix C, University of Chicago Press.

Since n is inversely proportional to λ, the minima for shorter wave-lengths will be rings of smaller diameter. Likewise, since n is proportional to r, the radius of the opening, the minima will become smaller in diameter as the aperture is increased in size. Thus the size of the ring for the first minimum of intensity will be very small for a large telescope, and the resolving power will be correspondingly large. The resolving power, according to

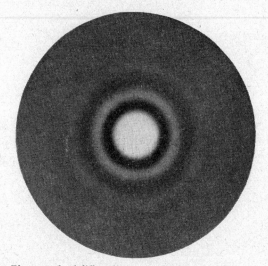

Fig. 12-31.—Photograph of diffraction pattern obtained with a circular opening. The central image is much overexposed.

Rayleigh's criterion, is given by $\sin \theta = n\lambda/\pi r$, in which the value $n/\pi = 0.61$ is substituted, giving for small angles

$$\theta = 0.61\frac{\lambda}{r}.$$

Problems

1. What is the diameter of the central image, *i.e.*, the diameter of the first dark ring, formed on the retina of the eye, of a distant point object? Assume the wave-length 5500 angstroms, and consider the diameter of the exit pupil of the eye to be 2.2 mm. and its distance from the retina to be 20 mm.

2. Because of atmospheric disturbances, it is rarely true that the diffraction pattern of a star is seen distinctly; instead, the star image may be twice the size of the central image of the diffraction pattern predicted by theory. If this is true, how far from the center of the field of the 100-in. telescope will the effects of coma first become visible? The focal length of the telescope is to be taken as 45 ft.

3. In making the upper half of Fig. 12-14*b*, a yellow filter was used which transmitted all wave-lengths greater than 5000 angstroms, a mercury arc being used. In making the lower half, only the green line, 5461 angstroms was used. Count the number of interference fringes between the points of minimum visibility and calculate the mean wave-length of the additional radiations effective in making the upper half of the illustration.

4. How must a grating of alternate transmitting and opaque spaces be constructed so that every third order will be "missing"?

5. A diffraction grating has 15 cm. of surface ruled with 10,000 rulings per centimeter. What is its resolving power? What would be the size of a prism of glass for which $B = 1.1 \times 10^{-10}$ cm. which would give the same resolving power at 5500 angstroms? If the mirrors of a Fabry-Perot interferometer have a reflecting power of 80 per cent, what must be their separation to obtain the same resolving power as the grating?

6. The spectrum lines formed by the concave diffraction grating are astigmatic images of the slit. The equations for the primary and secondary focal distances from the grating may be obtained from eqs. 6-8, for a single surface, by putting $n = 1$, $n' = -1$, and changing the signs of s_1', s_2', and r. In place of the angle of refraction i' is to be used the angle of diffraction θ. Find the values for s_1', s_2', and the value of the astigmatic difference $s_2' - s_1'$. Show that on the normal the length of the astigmatic spectral lines is given by $l \sin i \cdot \tan i$, where l is the length of the rulings on the grating.

7. Describe four ways of obtaining the absolute value of a wave-length of light.

8. Describe four methods for obtaining the ratio of two wave-lengths.

9. Using the tabulated values on pages 183 and 205 draw superposed graphs to scale of the distributions of intensity by diffraction (1) with a long narrow slit of width a, (2) with a circular opening of radius $r = a/2$. Other things being equal, which pattern would be harder to photograph? Discuss the relative resolving powers.

CHAPTER XIII

POLARIZATION OF LIGHT

Thus far for none of the phenomena described has it been necessary to assume that the light is a wave motion of a particular sort. The explanations given for diffraction and interference will hold equally well for longitudinal waves, in which the oscillatory motion is in the direction of propagation; for transverse waves, in which the oscillations are at right angles to the direction of propagation; and for waves having a composite motion like that of surface waves in water. The phenomenon of polarization, however, requires for its explanation the hypothesis that the vibrations are transverse.

1. Polarization by Double Refraction.—Although double refraction of light in crystalline media was observed by Bartholinus in 1669, the first comprehensive investigation of the phenomenon was made by Huygens in 1690. He observed that on passing through a crystal of Iceland spar (calcite), light was doubly refracted, *i.e.*, the beam was divided into two, whose separation depended upon the thickness and orientation of the crystal. From certain elementary experiments he concluded that the two rays had properties related to two planes at right angles to each other, one of them containing the crystallographic axis. Huygens gave to the phenomenon the name polarization.

The property of double refraction is possessed by all except cubic crystals. It is also a property of some organisms under strain. Since Iceland spar shows the property to a marked degree it is used extensively for experimental purposes, and offers a convenient medium for study. Calcite (crystallized calcium carbonate) has planes of cleavage in three directions, forming a rhombohedron. Each obtuse angle in each plane is 101° 55' and each acute angle 78° 5'. The form of the crystal is shown in Fig. 13-1. At each of the opposite corners A and A' are three equal obtuse angles. The line AC is an axis of symmetry with respect to these three faces and its direction through the crystal is associated with important optical properties Suppose the crystal to be placed with its face $A'B'$ on a screen with a pinhole in it to admit light from beneath. On looking down into the face AB not one image but two will be seen. Obviously these are due to two beams which travel in the crystal with different angles of refraction. More conveniently a black dot on a sheet of white paper may be used instead of the pinhole. The following observations may be made:

a. No matter how the crystal is turned about an axis perpendicular to the paper, a line drawn through the two images of

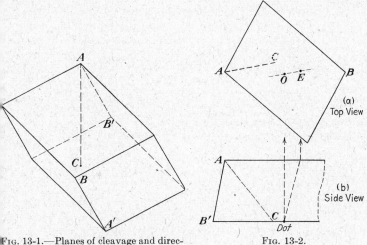

Fig. 13-1.—Planes of cleavage and direction of optic axis of calcite.

Fig. 13-2.

the dot will be parallel to the projection of AC (Fig. 13-2) on the surface of AB, as shown in Fig. 13-2a, in which the obtuse angles are the same in Figs. 13-1 and 13-2. Figure 13-2b shows the manner in which the two beams pass upward through the crystal.

b. As the crystal is turned about a vertical axis, the image toward A remains stationary. This image corresponds to the *ordinary ray*, for which the crystal acts like an isotropic medium such as glass or water. The other image rotates about the first as the crystal is turned, and its position is such that the ray must be bent away from the normal in contradiction to the ordinary law of refraction. This ray is called the *extraordinary ray*.

c. The dot corresponding to the ordinary ray appears closer to the top of the crystal than that for the extraordinary ray.

d. If the crystal is tilted up on the corner A' (Fig. 13-1), the two dots draw together. If the two corners A and A' were flattened and polished in planes perpendicular to AC, only one image would be seen when viewed perpendicularly, no matter how the crystal was rotated about AC, as if the light were in an isotropic medium. The direction AC is called the *optic axis* of the crystal; it is not a particular line, but a direction through the crystal.

e. If the crystal were to be flattened and polished in two planes parallel to the optic axis and the dot viewed perpendicularly through these, in general only one image would be seen as in *d.*

f. If two calcite crystals are placed one above the other above the dot, and the top one rotated about a vertical axis as indicated in Fig. 13-3*a*, *b*, and *c*, the images will appear as shown.

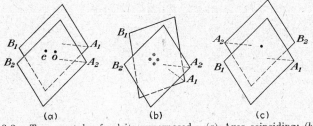

Fig. 13-3.—Two crystals of calcite superposed.   (*a*) Axes coinciding; (*b*) axes at an acute angle; (*c*) axes opposite.

These observations may be explained as follows: Consider a section through the crystal which contains both the ordinary and extraordinary rays. It will also contain the optic axis and will be perpendicular to the upper and lower cleavage planes. This section is called a *principal plane.*[1] In Fig. 13-4 is shown a principal plane as the plane of incidence, the line AC being the same direction as in Fig. 13-1 and 13-2. A parallel beam of ordinary light passing up through the crystal from a dot on the lower cleavage plane is divided into two beams which travel through the crystal in different directions and with different velocities.

For the ordinary ray traversing the crystal in any direction, the Huygens wavelets will be spherical in shape. In Fig. 13-4

[1] In optical mineralogy a principal section or plane is one containing the ray and the optic axis of the mineral.

these wavelets are represented by small circles, the common tangent of which will be the wave front. The perpendicular to the wave front is the direction of the ordinary ray. The extraordinary ray travels through the crystal with a velocity which is the same as that of the ordinary ray in the direction of the optic axis, and which becomes increasingly greater as its direction of propagation makes larger angles with the axis, until its maximum velocity occurs perpendicular to the axis. This is shown by the variation in the appearance of depth of the two refracted images which is described in experiment (c) above. In order to represent the propagation of the

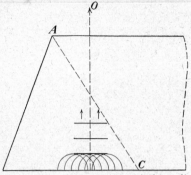

Fig. 13-4.—The passage of the ordinary ray through calcite.

extraordinary ray, the Huygens wavelets must be drawn as ellipses, as in Fig. 13-5, with the long axis perpendicular to the optic axis of the crystal. The wave front of the extraordinary ray will be the common tangent of the ellipses. While the wave

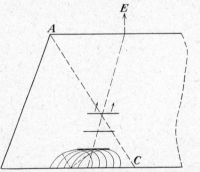

Fig. 13-5.—The passage of the extraordinary ray through calcite.

front remains parallel to itself, the ray is not normal to it, thus acting in a manner contradictory to the ordinary laws of refraction. If the light should be incident upon the crystal at such an angle that its direction through the crystal is parallel to the optic axis, there will be only one ray.

2. The Wave-velocity Surface.—In the foregoing it is supposed (1) that the light is incident normally to the surface of the

crystal, and (2) that the optic axis is parallel to the plane of
incidence.   If (2) holds but (1) does not, the resulting refraction
is as illustrated in Fig. 13-6.   Here the plane of the paper is the
plane of incidence.   The optic axis is parallel to this plane, and
MN indicates the intersection with the surface of the crystal
which is perpendicular to that plane.   To find the path of a
plane wave, MM', incident obliquely on the face of the crystal,
we may proceed as follows: By the usual Huygens construction
a circle is drawn with the center at M and a radius equal to
$M'N/n_0$, where n_0 is the index of refraction of the ordinary ray.
The line drawn from N tangent to this circle will be the refracted

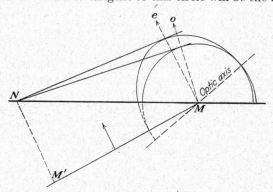

FIG. 13-6.—Optic axis not in refracting surface of crystal.

wave front for the ordinary ray, and MO drawn through the
point of tangency is the direction of the ray.   Since the velocity
of the extraordinary ray is greater than that of the ordinary in
directions other than that of the axis, the Huygens construction
will be an ellipse touching the circle at the axis and having a
semimajor axis equal to $M'N/n_e$.   The tangent from N to this
ellipse is the extraordinary wave front, and Me drawn to the
point of tangency is the ray.

The laws of refraction in *ordinary isotropic media* were first
stated by Descartes as follows: "The incident and refracted
rays (*a*) are in the same plane with the normal to the surface,
(*b*) they lie on opposite sides of it, and (*c*) the sines of their inclina-
tions to it bear a constant ratio to one another."   It is evident
that for the case just described (*c*) is not obeyed, for the ratio of
the sines of the angles for the extraordinary ray will vary with the
angle of incidence.   If the optic axis is not in the plane of inci-

ence but making an angle with it, in general the point of
tangency of the extraordinary wave front to the ellipse will not
be in the plane of incidence and (a) will also be violated.

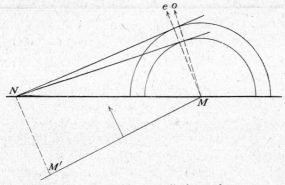

FIG. 13-7.—Optic axis perpendicular to the page.

A special case is illustrated in Fig. 13-7.   Here the optic axis
is perpendicular to the plane of incidence.   Since the velocity
of the extraordinary ray is a maximum in every direction per-

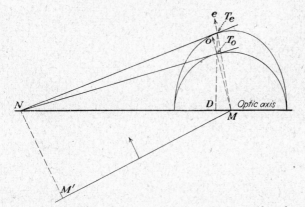

FIG. 13-8.—Optic axis parallel to the refracting surface and to the page.

pendicular to the axis, the Huygens construction for each ray is a
circle.   In this case all the ordinary laws are satisfied.

If the optic axis is parallel to the face of the crystal and also
parallel to the plane of incidence, as shown in Fig. 13-8, an interesting relation exists.   A line dropped from T_e, the point of
tangency of the extraordinary wave front, perpendicular to MN,

will pass through T_0, since the polar[1] of any point such as N on the chord of contact of a circle and an ellipse is the same for both curves. When an ellipse is projected into a circle, the ratio of two lines such as T_eD and T_0D is the same as the ratio of the semimajor to the semiminor axis; hence it follows that

$$\frac{\tan r_0}{\tan r_e} = \frac{T_eD}{T_0D} = \frac{n_0}{n_e}, \qquad (13\text{-}1)$$

where n_e is understood to correspond to the maximum velocity of the extraordinary ray through the crystal. This relation and

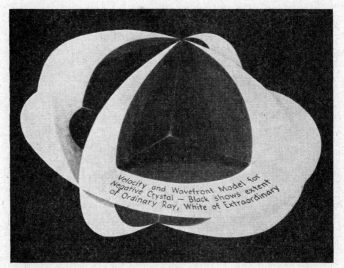

Fig. 13-9.

others which may be found by similar constructions have been experimentally verified, supporting the assumption that the surface of the Huygens wavelet for the extraordinary ray is an ellipsoid of revolution formed by revolving an ellipse about its minor axis, which is parallel to the optic axis.

Of great assistance to an understanding of the manner in which the two rays traverse the crystal is a model of the *ray-velocity surface*. In the case of calcite this will consist of a sphere inside an ellipsoid and tangent to it at the extremities of the minor axis. A very satisfactory model, illustrated in Fig. 13-9,

[1] See any good text on projective geometry.

may be made of three pieces of cardboard, one circular, the other two elliptical, fitted together at right angles. On these may be indicated by circles or colored areas the ray-velocity surface of the ordinary ray. The model represents, of course, the distances traversed in a given time by the light from a point source inside the crystalline medium.

3. Positive and Negative Crystals. Uniaxial Crystals.— Calcite is one of a group of crystals which possess a single direction in which the wave-velocity surfaces are tangent to one another. These are called *uniaxial crystals*. Crystals in which the common tangent to the two wave fronts corresponds to more than one direction through the crystal are called *biaxial*. Uniaxial crystals may be further divided into two groups, depending on whether the velocity of the extraordinary ray is greater or smaller than that of the ordinary. Calcite belongs to the former class and is called a *negative* crystal, while those of the latter are called *positive*. The most useful positive uniaxial crystal is quartz, since it occurs in abundance in many places, is hard, and transmits a considerable portion of the near ultraviolet in the spectrum. The wave model for a positive crystal will consist of a sphere *outside* an ellipsoid of revolution about the major axis of the ellipse, which would be equal to the diameter of the sphere.

The indices for a partial list of positive and negative crystals are given in Table II at the end of the book.

In addition to the property of double refraction, some crystals also absorb the two rays unequally. In tourmaline, an aluminous silicate of boron containing sodium, magnesium, or iron, one of them is absorbed completely, so that if two plates are cut from it with their faces parallel to the optic axis, they will, when crossed, extinguish the light completely. Recently some success has been achieved in the preparation of crystals of quinine-iodine sulphate in thin sheets of transparent material. These have properties similar to those of tourmaline, so that pieces cut from the same sheet and crossed may be used with considerable success in experiments in polarized light. This material, called polaroid, is also useful for the reduction of glare due to light reflected from polished surfaces, since such light is often polarized.

4. Polarization by Reflection.— In 1808 Malus discovered that after reflection from the surface of a transparent substance such as glass the light exhibited the same properties of polarization as the separate beams transmitted through doubly refracting crystals. This can be demonstrated in the following way: From a source S (Fig. 13-10a) allow a beam of light to pass through a horizontal slot about 5 mm. high to a clean glass plate P_1 at an angle of incidence of about 57 deg. Above P_1 place another glass plate P_2 which can be rotated about a vertical axis. It is convenient to exclude light from other sources by laying beneath P a piece of black cloth or paper. If possible, P_2 should be made of black glass, but if this is not available, a backing of black paper may be gummed to it, or it may be coated on the back with optical black. On looking into P_2 from the position indicated in

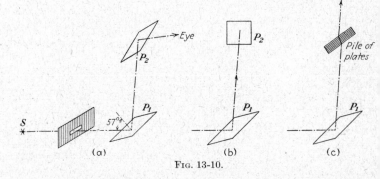

Fig. 13-10.

Fig. 13-10a, no great change in intensity will be observed in the light from S as P_2 is rotated about a *horizontal* axis, but if it is turned through 90 deg. about a *vertical* axis, it will be found that afterward a rotation about a horizontal axis will cause the light to change in intensity. When the angle of P_2 is such that the plane of incidence upon it is at right angles to the plane of incidence upon P_1, and the angle of incidence of the ray upon P_2 is about 57 deg., the light from S will be extinguished. The angle of incidence upon either mirror is then called the *polarizing angle.*

This experiment can be explained by certain assumptions as to the nature of the light and the effect upon it of reflection at the two mirrors. Let us suppose that the light is a transverse wave motion, composed of vibrations in all possible orientations in planes perpendicular to the direction of propagation. Then these vibrations may be resolved into two sets of component perpendicular to each other, as shown in Fig. 13-11, in which the short bars crossing the rays represent components of vibration

in the plane of incidence and the dots, components perpendicular
to that plane. Let us assume also that, upon reaching the glass,
the light passes into it, has its direction changed by refraction,
is partly absorbed and a part of the absorbed light is re-emitted
in the reflected ray. If the angle between the refracted and
reflected rays is 90 deg., then no part of the components of vibration parallel to the plane of incidence in the former can be
re-emitted in the latter, since light is assumed to be a transverse
vibration. At the mirror P_2 in the position of Fig. 13-10b none
of the plane-polarized light will be
reflected, provided the angle is
the polarizing angle, since its direction of vibration is parallel to the
plane of incidence in P_2.

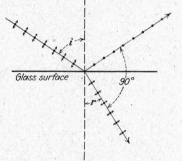

The ray refracted into the glass,
however, will consist of light re-
solvable into both components
of vibration just as was the original beam, but with a reduction
of the amplitude of the component
perpendicular to the plane of incidence. This s u g g e s t s another
experiment. For, if instead of a
single plate of glass a pile of plates
is used, then at each succeeding
refraction there will be a reduction
of amplitude of the component per-
pendicular to the plane of incidence, provided the pile is at the
polarizing angle or nearly so. Twelve or fifteen plates with
clean and sensibly plane surfaces will extinguish that component
of the refracted light completely. In Fig. 13-10c is shown a
pile of plates which is set for extinction.

FIG. 13-11.—Schematic representation of polarization by reflection.
The light in the incident beam is not
actually broken up into two components as represented, but, since
upon reflection the amplitudes parallel and perpendicular to the plane
of incidence are to be discussed
separately, these components are
also indicated in the incident beam.

In a sense, however, the term "extinction" is a misnomer here,
for the intensity of the light is ordinarily only reduced to a
minimum at the polarizing angle. Jamin found that only for
certain glasses whose index is about 1.46 is the polarization ever
complete. In general, it may be said that the polarizing angle
is the *angle of most complete polarization.*

These experiments support the theory that light is a transverse
vibration. No analogous results can be obtained with longi-

tudinal sound waves. The hypothesis which has been introduced concerning the nature of the mechanism of reflection has been found by other experiments to be sound and is supported by accepted theories of the nature of light.

5. Brewster's Law.—It is evident that if the mirror P_1 (Fig. 13-10b) is set at angles other than the angle of polarization, the reflected beam will contain a considerable proportion of light whose direction of vibration contains a component parallel to the plane of incidence. At the polarizing angle, this is reduced to a minimum, and the reflected and refracted rays are perpendicular to each other. Then Snell's law becomes

$$n = \frac{\sin i}{\sin r} = \frac{\sin i}{\sin (90 - i)} = \tan i. \qquad (13\text{-}2)$$

This result is known as *Brewster's law*, after its discoverer. The polarizing angle thus depends upon the transparent substance used, and to a small extent upon the wave-length of the light. The polarizing angles for the orange and blue for two representative kinds of glass are given below:

λ	Color	Ordinary crown		Heavy flint	
		n	i	n	i
5893	Orange	1.518	56° 38′	1.717	59° 47′
4358	Blue	1.529	56° 49′	1.749	60° 15′

For polished metallic surfaces Brewster's law does not hold, although some degree of polarization occurs upon reflection.

6. Direction of Vibration in Crystals.—We are now in a position to determine the direction of vibration of the two rays in calcite. Let P_1 (Fig. 13–10a) be placed at the polarizing angle and in place of P_2 be placed a section of calcite split along cleavage planes, with a dot of ink on its lower surface. It will be observed that when the calcite is held with the cleavage faces horizontal and is turned about a vertical axis, there is a position where the ordinary ray disappears. This will be when the principal section of the crystal, containing the optic axis, is perpendicular to the plane of incidence. If the crystal is turned through an angle of 90 deg. the extraordinary ray disappears. Because of some inaccuracy in adjustment of the apparatus the disappearance in either case may not be complete, but the reduction to almost zero intensity will be evident. From this experiment it is clear that the ordinary ray corresponds to a vibration in a plane *perpendicular to the principal section,* while the extraordinary ray corresponds to a vibration *in the principal section.* At an angle of the crystal about halfway between the two positions the dots will be approximately of equal intensity. This experiment throws additional light upon the experiment (*f*) in the first section in this chapter, where the number and intensity of the images changed as one crystal was rotated above another.

7. Plane of Polarization.—From his observations on double refraction in calcite Huygens concluded that the ordinary and extraordinary rays must in some way be related to the principal plane and the optic axis. He differentiated between the two rays by postulating that the ordinary ray was polarized in the principal plane and the extraordinary perpendicular to it. The existence of these so-called *planes of polarization* is substantiated by further consideration of polarization by reflection. In Sec. **13-4** it was pointed out that only when the two mirrors P_1 and P_2 (Fig. 13-10*a*) are arranged so that the planes of incidence and reflection at both mirrors coincide is the light which reaches the eye a maximum in intensity. This may be interpreted in the form of a conventional statement that the plane of incidence thus described is the plane of polarization of the reflected light. Actually, however, from the results of experiments, some of which have been outlined in the preceding paragraphs, it appears that the direction of vibration in every case is perpendicular to this plane of polarization. The original phraseology of Huygens still persists in treatises on the subject, and *plane of polarization* is still referred to, rather than *plane of vibration*; in fact, frequently both terms are used. There seems to be no reason for using both terms in an elementary discussion of the phenomena of polarization of light. This text will avoid further description of the phenomena in terms of the plane of polarization and will continue to refer to the direction of vibration of polarized beams. It is not denied that something of importance may be taking place in directions other than the direction of vibration; whatever it may be, however, does not come within the scope of the present discussion.

8. The Cosine-square Law of Malus.—When P_1 (Fig. 13-10a) is set at the polarizing angle, a ray of ordinary light incident upon it and the polarized ray reflected from it define the *plane of reflection* at the mirror. If P_2 is also set at the polarizing angle so that the plane of reflection from it is at right angles to that from P_1, extinction will take place. For positions of the two mirrors in which their respective planes of reflection are not at right angles, the light will be partly reflected. These facts were summed up by Malus in the statement that with the two mirrors set at the polarizing angle the intensity of the twice reflected beam varies as the square of the cosine of the angle between the planes of reflection. For instance, if P_1 and P_2 have the positions shown in Fig. 13-10a, the intensity is I, but if P_2 is oriented to a position making an angle intermediate between those shown in Fig. 13-10a and b, say, 60 deg. from that in a, then the intensity of the light reflected from P_2 is

$$I' = I \cos^2 60° = I/4.$$

At the position shown in Fig. 13-10b, $I' = 0$.

9. The Nicol Prism.—As a device for producing or examining plane-polarized light, the glass plate used at the polarizing angle is lacking in convenience. Also, to obtain plane polarization over any considerable area it is necessary to collimate the light. It is usual to employ some prism of double-refracting crystal arranged so that light vibrations in only one plane are transmitted. One of the most convenient prisms is the nicol, named after William Nicol, who first described its construction in 1828. The original form was made of a rhombohedron of calcite about three times as long as it was wide. As shown in Fig. 13-12a, this is cut along a plane perpendicular to the shorter diagonal of the end face, which is diamond-shaped. The two pieces are then cemented together again with Canada balsam, which has an index of refraction intermediate between n_o and n_e for calcite. Since the natural angle of the end faces is slightly altered, light incident upon the nicol parallel to the long sides will be refracted so that the extraordinary ray is incident upon the interface at an angle less than the critical angle of refraction, and will thus be transmitted with no appreciable loss of intensity, while the ordinary ray is incident at an angle greater than the critical angle of refraction and so is totally reflected. The direction of vibration of the transmitted extraordinary ray is in the plane containing the ray and the short diagonal of the end face, as illustrated in Fig. 13-12c.   Nicol prisms are often made in other shapes, to admit beams of wider angle or greater cross-sectional area, but the effect is the same, *i.e.*, to transmit light with vibrations in only one plane.   It is usual in examinations of polarized light to make use of two nicols.   The one nearer the source,

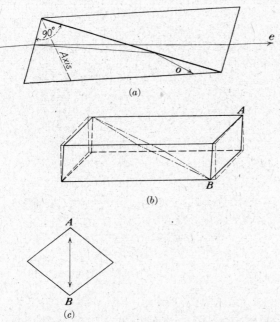

Fig. 13-12.—The Nicol prism.   (*a*) Principal section; (*b*) side view; (*c*) end view, the arrow showing the direction of vibration of the transmitted light.

called the *polarizer*, is for the purpose of producing the plane-polarized beam; the other, nearer the eye, called the *analyzer*, is for the purpose of examining the state of polarization of the transmitted light.

10. Double Image Prisms. The Wollaston Prism.—While the nicol transmits light vibrations in a single plane and eliminates the vibrations perpendicular to that plane by total reflection, it is sometimes necessary to retain both components so that the two separate images, polarized perpendicularly to each other, are in the field of view.   This can be done for objects with limited area by the use of an ordinary crystal of calcite, but with the disadvantage that the emerging beams are parallel and cannot be easily separated to any greater extent.   There are several polarizing devices which will give two diverging beams, the most useful probably being the *Wollaston prism*.   Its construction and use are illustrated in Fig. 13-13.   The light is incident normally on a compound prism of quartz with parallel faces made of two prisms cemented together, whose optic axes are perpendicular to the direction of propagation but also perpendicular to each other.   The ordinary and extraordinary beams will thus traverse the first prism in the same direction but with different velocities.   Since the second prism is cut with its optic axis perpendicular to that of the first, the ordinary beam in the first prism will become the extraordinary in the second, and *vice versa*.   At the interface between the two prisms,

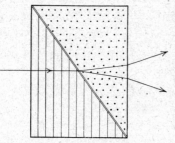

FIG. 13-13.—The Wollaston prism.

the beam traveling faster in the first than in the second has an angle of refraction which is smaller than the angle of incidence.   Likewise, the beam which travels slower in the first prism than in the second has an angle of refraction which is larger than its angle of incidence.   The interface is cut at such an angle that the two plane-polarized beams traversing the second prism are equally inclined to the emergent face.   Thus each beam will undergo the same amount of bending by refraction, and the two will emerge into the air at the same angle to the normal but oppositely inclined.   The larger the distance from the prism, the farther apart will be the two images.

If to a Wollaston prism is added a nicol used as an analyzer, the combination is known as a *Cornu polariscope*.   The nicol may be rotated to an angle such that the two plane-polarized images are transmitted with the same intensity, in which case the ratio of the intensities incident upon the nicol is proportional to the square of the tangent of the angle.   The Cornu polariscope is a useful device for the detection of small amounts of polarization, since a small change of angle of the nicol results in a large change of the relative intensities of the two images.

11. Elliptically Polarized Light. Wave Plates.—Suppose a beam of plane-polarized light is incident, as in Fig. 13-14a, upon a thin section of crystal whose faces are parallel to each other. For convenience suppose also that the optic axis is parallel to the faces but makes an angle α with the plane of vibration of the incident beam. Then the original vibration will be divided in the crystal into two components as illustrated in Fig. 13-14b. The component of vibration parallel to the axis (extraordinary ray) will have an amplitude $A \cos \alpha$, and that perpendicular (ordinary ray), an amplitude $A \sin \alpha$, where A is the amplitude of the incident vibration. If the plate is thin and the source of appreciable area, there will be no detectable

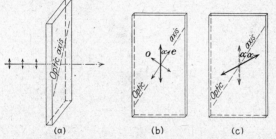

(a)   (b)   (c)

FIG. 13-14.—The heavy arrow in (b) indicates the original plane of vibration of a plane-polarized beam, and in (c) the plane of vibration after passing through a half-wave plate.

separation between the two beams, but since their velocities are not the same, they will emerge from the crystal with a difference in phase. If the retardation of phase (of the ordinary in a negative crystal, the extraordinary in a positive) corresponds to an even number of half wave-lengths difference of path, the plane of vibration of the emergent beam will be the same as that of the incident beam. If the retardation corresponds to an odd number of half wave-lengths, the two components will after emergence have the relative positions shown in Fig. 13-14c, and their combined effect will be that of a plane vibration in a plane making an angle 2α with that of the incident beam. A plate which thus effects a turn of the plane of vibration of the light is called a *half-wave plate*. If the angle α is 45 deg., the emergent vibration will be in a plane at right angles to the incident plane-polarized beam.

If the retardation corresponds to an odd number of quarter wave-lengths, the emergent components will combine to form, not a plane vibration, but one which in general is elliptical in form. An analogue is the motion of a particle which executes an elliptical motion in a plane which is moved normal to its surface. If in addition the angle α is 45 deg., *circularly polarized light* results. A plate of crystal which produces these results is called a *quarter-wave plate.*

The effect upon the passage of plane-polarized light through thin crystals can be best treated analytically. Let OP (Fig. 13-15) represent the amplitude and direction of vibration of a plane-polarized beam traveling perpendicular to the page, and OX the direction of the optic axis of a double-refracting crystal,

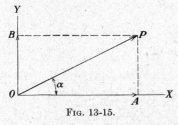
Fig. 13-15.

of which the plane cutting OX perpendicular to the page is a principal section. In the crystal the incident vibration will be separated into two, one parallel, the other perpendicular, to the principal section. After passage through a crystal whose thickness is such that a path difference of δ is introduced between the ordinary and extraordinary rays, the amplitude of the X- and Y-components is given by

$$x = a \cos 2\pi\frac{t}{T}, \left.\begin{array}{c} \\ \\ \\ \end{array}\right\} \quad (13\text{-}3)$$
$$y = b \cos 2\pi\left(\frac{t}{T} + \frac{\delta}{\lambda}\right).$$

If these two equations are combined so as to eliminate t, the result will be[1]

$$\frac{x^2}{a^2} + \frac{y^2}{b^2} - \frac{2xy \cos (2\pi\delta/\lambda)}{ab} = \sin^2 \frac{2\pi\delta}{\lambda}, \quad (13\text{-}4)$$

which is the equation of an ellipse, representing in general the character of the vibration after emergence from the crystal. This ellipse may be inscribed in a rectangle whose sides are $2a$ and $2b$, the ratio of the sides depending on the angle α between the original plane of vibration and the principal section OA.

[1] This may be done by solving the first equation for $\cos 2\pi t/T$, expanding the second and solving it for $\sin 2\pi t/T$; squaring and adding, making suitable substitutions.

The particular character of the transmitted light will depend upon the values of δ and α.

Case 1. $\delta = n\lambda$, $n = 0, 1, 2, 3$, etc., eq. 13-4 becomes

$$\frac{x}{a} - \frac{y}{b} = 0.$$

The emergent light is plane-polarized, the vibrations being in the same direction as in the original beam.

Case 2. $\delta = (2n + 1)\lambda/2$, $n = 0, 1, 2, 3$, etc., eq. 13-4 becomes $\frac{x}{a} + \frac{y}{b} = 0$. The emergent light is plane-polarized in a direction making an angle 2α with the original beam. The original beam is in the first and third quadrants, the emergent is in the second and fourth quadrants. If $\alpha = 45°$, the vibrations

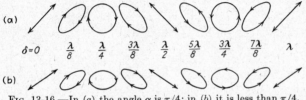

(a)

$\delta = 0 \qquad \frac{\lambda}{8} \qquad \frac{\lambda}{4} \qquad \frac{3\lambda}{8} \qquad \frac{\lambda}{2} \qquad \frac{5\lambda}{8} \qquad \frac{3\lambda}{4} \qquad \frac{7\lambda}{8} \qquad \lambda$

(b)

Fig. 13-16.—In (a) the angle α is $\pi/4$; in (b) it is less than $\pi/4$.

in the emergent beam will be in a plane perpendicular to those in the incident beam.

Case 3. $\delta = (2n + 1)\lambda/4$, $n = 0, 1, 2, 3$, etc., eq. 13-4 becomes $\frac{x^2}{a^2} + \frac{y^2}{b^2} = 1$. The emergent beam is elliptically polarized with the axes of the ellipse parallel and perpendicular, respectively, to the principal section of the crystal. If $\alpha = 45°$, $a = b$ and $x^2 + y^2 = a^2$, and the emergent light is circularly polarized. For $\delta = \lambda/4$ the vibration corresponds to the motion of a particle moving in a clockwise direction in a circle of radius a; for $\delta = 3\lambda/4$ the circular vibration will be in the opposite sense, *i.e.*, counterclockwise.

Case 4. If δ is other than an integral multiple of $\lambda/4$, and therefore does not come under one of the three cases above, the light will in general be elliptically polarized.

For $\alpha = \pi/4$, these results may be represented graphically as in Fig. 13-16a. The straight line on the left represents the plane of the emergent vibration for a plate of thickness zero, or the plane of vibration of the incident beam. The others represent the effect on the state of polarization of the emergent light by passage through such crystal thicknesses as to introduce additional path differences of $\lambda/8$. The arrows indicate the direction of rotation in the cases of circular and elliptical polarization. If the angle α is less than 45 deg., the resulting vibrations will be as in Fig. 13-16b. If α is greater than 45 deg., the effect will be to increase the vertical axis instead of diminishing it.

It will be noticed that except for $\alpha = 0$ or $\pi/2$ it is possible to produce elliptically polarized light with wave plates which introduce a retardation of an odd number of quarter wavelengths, the difference between this case and case 4 above being that with the quarter-wave plate the axes of the ellipse are parallel and perpendicular to the principal section of the crystal. It should also be noticed that it is impossible to obtain circularly polarized light with a quarter-wave plate unless the angle between the optic axis and the plane of vibration of the incident light is 45 deg.

In practice it is customary to make quarter-wave plates and half-wave plates of mica. Although mica is not uniaxial but biaxial, two of its three indices are nearly the same. Mica splits easily along planes of cleavage which are perpendicular to the bisector of the angle made by the optic axes. Because of the strains introduced when it is made into thin sheets, cellophane is also anisotropic, and may be used for making quarter-wave plates by superposing two pieces at a suitable angle.

In the preparation of wave plates it is customary to mark with an arrow the plane of vibration of the slower component through the crystal; if the plate is made of calcite or some other uniaxial negative crystal, this is also perpendicular to the direction of the optic axis. In mica, it indicates only the plane of vibration of the slower component, or the principal section in which that component vibrates.

12. The Babinet Compensator.—In the production or analysis of elliptically polarized light the quarter-wave plate is limited to a narrow band of wave-lengths. There are several devices which do not have this limitation, the compensator of Babinet being the most useful. As illustrated in Fig. 13-17, it is made of two wedges of quartz with their optic axes perpendicular to each other, and both perpendicular to the direction of propagation of

the transmitted light.   As improved by Jamin, one of the wedges
is arranged to slide with respect to the other, the amount of
motion being controlled by a micrometer screw.   In the figure
the angles of the wedges are much exaggerated.   It is apparent
that for the ray traversing equal thicknesses in the two wedges
there is no difference in phase introduced since each plate produces an identical amount of retardation of the slower com-

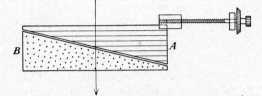

FIG. 13-17.—Diagram of Babinet-Jamin compensator.

ponent of plane-polarized light.   Where the thicknesses traversed
are not equal, there will be a phase difference introduced between
the two components.   The compensator is therefore at every
point equivalent to a wave plate, and introduces a relative
retardation between the components vibrating in planes parallel
to the optic axes of the two wedges.   Zero at the point where
equal thicknesses are traversed in the two wedges, this retarda-

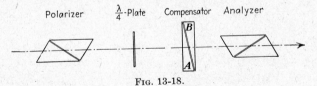

FIG. 13-18.

tion increases uniformly on either side, and is of opposite sign on
the two sides of the zero point.

Let us suppose that the light incident on the compensator is
monochromatic and plane-polarized, with its plane of vibration
neither parallel nor perpendicular to the plane of incidence.
This may be effected by means of the polarizer (Fig. 13-18).
In case it is desired to change the state of polarization of the
light incident on the compensator, a quarter-wave plate may be
inserted, as shown.   In the first wedge, A, the light is resolved
into an ordinary and an extraordinary beam.   If the thickness
traversed in wedge A is t_1, the relative retardation of the two

beams is $t_1(n_e - n_0)$, while for thickness t_2 traversed in wedge B the relative retardation is $-t_2(n_e - n_0)$. The total retardation will be

$$\delta = (t_1 - t_2)(n_e - n_0). \qquad (13\text{-}5)$$

For the light traversing equal thicknesses of A and B, $\delta = 0$. At distances from this middle position having retardations λ, 2λ, 3λ, etc., the light is plane-polarized and vibrating parallel to the original plane, as at the middle position. At positions midway between these, where the retardation is $\lambda/2$, $3\lambda/2$, $5\lambda/2$, etc., the transmitted light is plane-polarized but vibrating in a plane making an angle 2θ with the original plane of vibration,

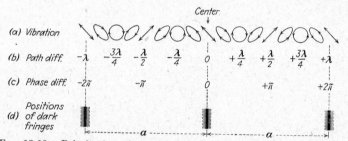

Fig. 13-19.—Polarizations due to a Babinet compensator with its axes at 45 deg. to the direction of vibration of an incident plane-polarized beam. The fringe pattern (d) really has an intensity distribution similar to that of double-beam interference fringes and only the *positions* of the minima are indicated.

where θ is the angle between that plane and the direction of the optic axis in the first wedge. Thus there is a set of equidistant positions at which the light is plane-polarized, and in any adjacent pair of such positions the planes of vibration are parallel to, and at an angle of 2θ to, the original plane of vibration. At all other positions the light will in general be elliptically polarized.

If $\theta = 45°$, the alternate plane-polarized beams transmitted by the compensator will consist of vibrations at right angles to each other. Midway between these the retardation will be like that of a quarter-wave plate with its principal section at 45 deg. to the plane of vibration of the incident light, and the transmitted light will be circularly polarized. At other positions, the retardation will be that of a fractional-wave plate producing elliptically polarized light. This situation is illustrated in Fig. 13-19a, in which the arrows on the circles and ellipses represent the direction of rotation introduced. If the field of the compensator now be

viewed through a nicol (analyzer) set so as to extinguish the light
transmitted at the middle position, there will be seen a set of dark
fringes crossing the field perpendicular to the long edge of the
compensator. These are indicated in Fig. 13-19*d*. Only the
central fringe will be black if white light is used; the others will
be colored. If $\theta \neq 45°$, the fringes will be dark, but not black,
with monochromatic light. The distance apart of the fringes
will correspond to phase differences of 2π, or path differences of λ.
If the analyzer is rotated through 45 deg., these fringes will
disappear and the entire field will become uniform in intensity,
since the analyzer will have no effect at the positions of circular

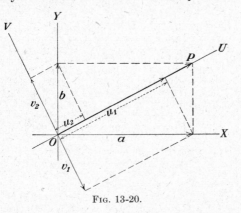

Fig. 13-20.

polarization, and at all other positions will effect a retardation
changing plane or elliptical vibrations to circular ones.

It is thus evident that the compensator will in general transmit
elliptically polarized light for which the ellipticity will depend
upon the δ in eq. 13-5 and which will, for $\theta = 45°$ and also
for certain values of δ be plane or circularly polarized. It is
possible to obtain an equation representing the form of the
emergent vibration for any value of δ. Let the plane and amplitude at any instant of a plane-polarized beam incident on the
compensator be represented by *OP*, (Fig. 13-20) and the *X*- and
Y-directions represent the directions of the optic axes of the
wedges *A* and *B*, respectively. The components of *OP* in the
X- and *Y*-directions are, respectively,

$$a = OP \cos \theta,$$
$$b = OP \sin \theta,$$

the values of a and b used here being the *maximum* amplitudes of the vibration components in the X- and Y-directions. The vibrations themselves may be represented by

$$x = a \cos 2\pi \frac{t}{T} \left. \begin{array}{c} \\ \\ \end{array} \right\}$$
$$y = b \cos 2\pi\left(\frac{t}{T'} + \Delta\right) \qquad (13\text{-}6)$$

in which $2\pi\Delta$ is the difference of phase angle between the components after transmission through the compensator. It has already been shown by the detailed discussion that for $\theta = 45°$ the axes of the elliptical vibration will be parallel and perpendicular to OP, so that, in order to find the analytical form of the vibration, we must obtain equations analogous to eqs. 13-6 for the vibrations in these directions. From Fig. 13-20 it is seen that a may be resolved into two components, u_1 in the direction of OP and v_1 perpendicular to OP; likewise b may be resolved into u_2 and v_2. As u_1 and u_2 are not in general in the same phase, they cannot be added algebraically, nor can v_1 and v_2 be so added; the additions can only be made with the proper phase relations assigned. This may be done by writing for the components of vibration in the U- and V-directions the general expressions

$$u = u_1 \cos 2\pi \frac{t}{T} + u_2 \cos 2\pi\left(\frac{t}{T} + \Delta\right),$$
$$v = v_1 \cos 2\pi \frac{t}{T} + v_2 \cos 2\pi\left(\frac{t}{T} + \Delta\right),$$

taking into account a phase difference $2\pi\Delta$, and substituting in them the values of u_1, u_2, v_1, and v_2 for the case under discussion. From above

$$u_1 = a \cos \theta = OP \cos^2 \theta,$$
$$u_2 = b \sin \theta = OP \sin^2 \theta,$$
$$v_1 = -a \sin \theta = -OP \sin \theta \cos \theta,$$
$$v_2 = b \cos \theta = OP \sin \theta \cos \theta,$$

so that

$$u = OP\left[\cos^2 \theta \cos 2\pi \frac{t}{T} + \sin^2 \theta \cos 2\pi\left(\frac{t}{T} + \Delta\right)\right]$$
$$v = OP\left[\sin \theta \cos \theta \cos 2\pi\left(\frac{t}{T} + \Delta\right) - \sin \theta \cos \theta \cos 2\pi \frac{t}{T}\right].$$

The phase number Δ is δ/λ, or the number of wave-lengths difference of path in the distance δ given in eq. 13-5, so we may write

$$2\pi\Delta = \frac{2\pi}{\lambda}(t_1 - t_2)(n_e - n_0). \tag{13-7}$$

For the special case, $\theta = 45°$, the equations for u and v reduce to

$$u = \frac{OP}{2}\left[\cos 2\pi\frac{t}{T} + \cos 2\pi\left(\frac{t}{T} + \Delta\right)\right],$$
$$v = \frac{OP}{2}\left[\cos 2\pi\left(\frac{t}{T} + \Delta\right) - \cos 2\pi\frac{t}{T}\right],$$

which by a simple trigonometric transformation become

$$\left.\begin{array}{l}\dfrac{u}{\cos \pi\Delta} = OP \cos 2\pi\left(\dfrac{t}{T} + \dfrac{\Delta}{2}\right), \\[2mm] \dfrac{v}{\sin \pi\Delta} = -OP \sin 2\pi\left(\dfrac{t}{T} + \dfrac{\Delta}{2}\right).\end{array}\right\} \tag{13-8}$$

On squaring and adding, these reduce to

$$\frac{u^2}{\cos^2 (\pi\Delta)} + \frac{v^2}{\sin^2 (\pi\Delta)} = OP^2. \tag{13-9}$$

This gives the form of the vibrations for different values of Δ, *i.e.*, for different positions in the field of view. If the light transmitted at the position $\Delta = 0$ is extinguished by a nicol, the intensity at all other positions is given by $v^2 = OP^2 \sin^2 (\pi\Delta)$.

If the light incident upon the compensator is changed from plane to elliptically polarized light by means of a quarter-wave plate inserted between the polarizer and the compensator, in general there will be a shift of the fringes by an amount depending on the ratio of the major and minor axes. There will also be a change in their blackness since nowhere will the light be plane-polarized in the plane extinguished by the analyzer. A rotation of the analyzer to the angle of extinction will restore the blackness of the fringes.

The value of $2\pi\Delta$ given in eq. 13-7 may be found experimentally. The entire fringe system may be moved to bring successive dark fringes under the cross hairs by moving wedge B. If the actual distance between the fringes is s, the wedge must be moved a distance $2s$ to move the fringe system through the distance s.

If the change from plane to elliptically polarized incident light shifts the fringe system a distance x, the corresponding difference of phase introduced is $\pi x/s$. This is, however, the amount by which the phase difference is changed by passage through the compensator. Hence,

$$2\pi\Delta = \frac{\pi x}{s}. \tag{13-9}$$

The positions of the axes of the incident polarized light may also be found. To do this let plane-polarized light fall on the compensator and move wedge B through a distance $s/2$, having previously calibrated the micrometer driving the wedge in terms of the distance $2s$ between the dark fringes. Then the cross hairs will be over a position at which the phase difference is $\pi/2$, corresponding to a retardation of $\lambda/4$. Now let the elliptically polarized light fall once more on the compensator. In general the middle black band will not be under the cross hairs, but it may be brought there by rotating the compensator. It will usually be necessary to rotate the analyzer also to obtain maximum distinctness of the fringes. The axes of the incident elliptically polarized light are now parallel to the axes of the wedges.

The situation is now as shown in Fig. 13-21. OA and OB are parallel to the axes of the two wedges, OC is the direction of the principal section of the analyzer, and the direction of vibration of the light which is extinguished at the central fringe is DD'. If the analyzer is rotated through the angle θ, the fringes will disappear, since for this position the compensator will act like a quarter-wave plate. The tangent of θ will be the ratio of the axes of the incident elliptical polarization. In the illustration the longer axis is in the direction OA.

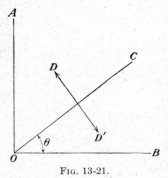

Fig. 13-21.

13. The Reflection of Polarized Light.—The electromagnetic theory of light tells us that if a plane wave is incident upon the boundary between two media, the character of the reflected and

refracted waves will depend upon the state of polarization of the
wave as well as upon the character of the two media and the angle
of incidence.   Consider a vector (Fig. 13-22) representing an
electric force at an angle with the plane of incidence to be resolved
into components of amplitude a and b perpendicular and parallel,
respectively, to that plane.   Then for an isotropic transparent
medium the components of amplitude
a_1 and b_1 in the reflected wave are
shown to be given by·

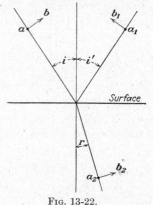

$$a_1 = -a\frac{\sin (i - r)}{\sin (i + r)}, \quad (13\text{-}10)$$

$$b_1 = b\frac{\tan (i - r)}{\tan (i + r)}. \quad (13\text{-}11)$$

These equations were originally
derived by Fresnel for the transmission of light on the assumption of an
elastic-solid medium.   Although certain of his assumptions have not been
able to withstand the test of experi-

FIG. 13-22.

ment, the equations themselves have been experimentally proved
correct.

An examination of eqs. 13-10 and 13-11 discloses that no matter
what i may be, a_1 never becomes zero, while for $i + r = 90°$,
$b_1 = 0$.   This corresponds to the condition for maximum polarization, in agreement with *Brewster's law*.

If the second medium has a higher index of refraction than
the first, $i > r$, and by eq. 13-10, a_1 and a are of opposite sign,
which can be interpreted as meaning that on reflection there is a
change of phase π in the vibrations perpendicular to the plane of
incidence.   The vibrations b_1 and b parallel to the plane of
incidence are alike in sign if $i + r < 90°$, and different in sign
if $i + r > 90°$.   In Fig. 13-22, where $i + r$ is taken less than
90 deg. this sign convention, which may also be interpreted as a
change of phase, is illustrated.

For normal incidence, the sine and the tangent may be replaced
by the angle and, in the limit, eqs. 13-10 and 13-11 become, on
combining with $i = nr$ (Snell's law)

$$a_1 = -a\frac{n - 1}{n + 1}, \quad\quad\quad (13\text{-}12)$$

and

$$b_1 = b\frac{n-1}{n+1}. \qquad (13\text{-}13)$$

Since a change of phase occurs on reflection, it follows that for the case of normal incidence, provided $n > 1$, there will be a node at the surface and standing waves set up if the reflection takes place at the surface of a denser medium. Actually the node will be at the surface only if $n = \infty$, *i.e.*, if the reflected and incident waves are equal in amplitude; for reflection at ordinary media there is only a minimum at the surface. From the postulates of the electromagnetic theory it follows also that in the equation similar to eq. 13-13 for the *magnetic* force, like signs in the two sides really mean no difference in phase in the incident and reflected amplitudes. In order to determine whether the light is the electric force or the magnetic force in an electro-

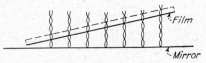

Fig. 13-23.—Fringes appear on the film where it intersects loop.

magnetic wave, Wiener, Drude, and others performed experiments in which the standing waves were recorded on extremely thin transparent photographic or fluorescent films on plates inclined at small angles to a mirror surface, as illustrated in Fig. 13-23. These experiments proved conclusively that what we have described as transverse light vibrations consist of the electric disturbance in an electromagnetic wave of light frequency. The experiments also showed that the node at reflection was not at the surface, but a very small distance below it.

14. Rotation of the Plane of Vibration on Reflection.—If the light incident on a surface is a plane-polarized beam of amplitude A vibrating in a plane making an angle α with the plane of incidence, the vibration can be resolved into two components, one of amplitude $a = A \sin \alpha$ perpendicular to, and one of amplitude $b = A \cos \alpha$ parallel to, the plane of incidence. For a transparent isotropic medium the reflected light will thus have components of amplitude

$$a_1 = -A \sin \alpha \frac{\sin (i - r)}{\sin (i + r)} \qquad (13\text{-}14)$$

perpendicular to, and

$$b_1 = A \cos \alpha \, \frac{\tan (i - r)}{\tan (i + r)}, \qquad (13\text{-}15)$$

parallel to, the plane of incidence. The reflected plane-polarized vibration will in general lie in a plane inclined to the plane of incidence at an angle β, and the components of the reflected beam may therefore also be written

$$a_1 = B \sin \beta, \qquad (13\text{-}16)$$
$$b_1 = B \cos \beta, \qquad (13\text{-}17)$$

perpendicular and parallel, respectively, to the plane of incidence. From eqs. 13-14, 13-15, 13-16, and 13-17 it follows that

$$-\tan \alpha \, \frac{\cos (i - r)}{\cos (i + r)} = \tan \beta. \qquad (13\text{-}18)$$

When the light is incident normally, then $-\tan \alpha = \tan \beta$. As the angle of incidence increases, β becomes greater than α until, when the angle of complete polarization is reached, $\tan \beta = \infty$, and $\beta = 90°$, in accordance with *Brewster's law*. For greater angles of incidence, $\beta > 90°$, $(90 - \beta)$ becomes negative and finally equals $-\alpha$ when $i = 90°$. Equations analogous to those above may be developed for the case of refraction, and for the reflection and refraction of elliptically polarized light. The conclusions thus reached have been tested by experiment and found to be valid.

15. The Nature of Unpolarized Light.—The descriptive mechanism employed in the discussion of polarized-light phenomena often leads the student to infer that the nature of ordinary light, which has suffered no reflection from, nor transmission through, material media, is disclosed by a dogged application of the mechanical picture of linear vibration components. A typical question which arises is, "What is the form of the transverse vibration in ordinary (unpolarized) light in, say, some unit element of the beam?" It seems worth while to clarify this point by indicating the limits to the use of the descriptive mechanism of the phenomena of polarization. In order to explain these phenomena, it is found convenient to consider separately the components of transverse vibration perpendicular and parallel to a given plane. In many cases, experiment proves that the transverse light vibration is actually decomposed by a medium into two such components; an illustration is the birefringence of ordinary calcite.   The error occurs if an attempt is made to extend this form of representation to explain the nature of the original unpolarized beam.   Thus we find that either by implication or explicit statement, ordinary (unpolarized) light from a source is sometimes spoken of as being actually made up of innumerable transverse *linear* vibrations with all possible orientations in a plane perpendicular to the direction of propagation. There is not the slightest experimental evidence for this point of view.[1]   Such evidence tells us only that if ordinary (unpolarized) light is broken up into plane components by some sort of polarizing device, the amplitudes in all orientations in the original beam are shown to be equal.[2]

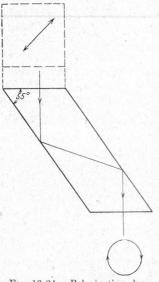

Fig. 13-24.—Polarization by Fresnel rhomb.

16. The Fresnel Rhomb.—From a consideration of the change in phase suffered by light reflected inside isotropic media such as glass, Fresnel concluded that when plane-polarized light is totally reflected internally in ordinary glass the components undergo a relative phase change of $\pi/4$.   The rhomb constructed by him, and shown in Fig. 13-24, provides for two such internal reflections, thus introducing a phase change of twice $\pi/4$, or $\pi/2$ between the two components, as does a quarter-wave plate.[3] Plane-polarized light incident upon the rhomb with its plane of vibration at 45 deg. to the plane of incidence will emerge as

---

[1] There *is* evidence of the existence of plane-polarized light *of particular frequency* in the Zeeman effect (see Chap. XVI), but this is another matter.

[2] An interesting experiment dealing with this question has recently been performed by Langsdorf and DuBridge, *Jour. Optical Soc. Amer.*, **24**, 1, 1934.   See also subsequent comments by R. W. Wood, *Jour. Optical Soc. Amer.*, **24**, 4, 1934, R. T. Birge, *Jour. Optical Soc. Amer.*, **25**, 179, 1935, and L. DuBridge, *Jour. Optical Soc. Amer.*, **25**, 182, 1935.

[3] For a detailed description of the Fresnel rhomb see Drude's "Theory of Optics."

circularly polarized light. Moreover, the effect is the same for all wave-lengths, since the variation of index of refraction with wave-length is insufficient to cause any trouble. The disadvantage of the Fresnel rhomb is that the emergent beam, while in the same direction as the incident, is displaced sideways with respect to it so that a rotation of the rhomb causes a movement of the image which is difficult to follow with other apparatus.

17. General Treatment of Double Refraction.—Thus far the subject of double refraction has been confined to uniaxial crystals. These are characterized by possessing a single direction through the crystal for which there is a common tangent to the wave fronts of two vibrations in planes perpendicular to each other. In biaxial crystals, however, the mechanism of wave propagation is not so simple. In order to explain in a most general way the optical properties of transparent crystalline media, Fresnel developed a theory which, though founded on assumptions which may be criticized, gave an accurate representation of the experimental facts. The intention here is simply to give the conclusions reached by the theory as to the form of the light waves propagated through crystals, and their state of polarization.[1] We may suppose that at any instant many plane waves are traveling in different directions through a point O (Fig. 13-25) in a crystal. For each such plane wave there will be, in general, directions of maximum and minimum velocities of

FIG. 13-25.—The origin is at O. The form of the wave surface is given by the curved line.

propagation at right angles to each other. The form of the *wave surface* after a given time is represented by the curved line in Fig. 13-25; it is the common tangent to the plane waves at that instant. Since in any direction there are in general two wave velocities, this wave surface consists of two surfaces or sheets, only one being shown in the figure. The equation of the wave surface derived by Fresnel is

[1] For an extended treatment of Fresnel's theory see Preston, "Theory of Light"; or Schuster, "Theory of Optics." For a complete treatment of the subject from the standpoint of the electromagnetic theory of light see Born, "Optik."

$$\frac{a^2x^2}{r^2 - a^2} + \frac{b^2y^2}{r^2 - b^2} + \frac{c^2z^2}{r^2 - c^2} = 0, \qquad (13\text{-}19)$$

where a, b, and c represent the velocities of propagation through the crystal of the vibrations which are respectively parallel to the x-, y-, and z-axes, and $r^2 = x^2 + y^2 + z^2$. We may consider that $a > b > c$. Equation 13-19 may be written

$$r^2(a^2x^2 + b^2y^2 + c^2z^2) - a^2(b^2 + c^2)x^2 - b^2(c^2 + a^2)y^2$$
$$- c^2(a^2 + b^2)z^2 + a^2b^2c^2 = 0.$$

The properties of this surface are more easily examined by studying its projections on the three planes, each of which is defined by a pair of the coordinate axes.

By putting $x = 0$, we obtain the intersection of the wave surface and the yz-plane. The equation of this intersection is

$$(r^2 - a^2)(b^2y^2 + c^2z^2 - b^2c^2) = 0,$$

since in the yz-plane $r^2 = y^2 + z^2$, and is satisfied by

$$y^2 + z^2 = a^2,$$

a circle of radius a, and

$$\frac{y^2}{c^2} + \frac{z^2}{b^2} = 1,$$

an ellipse with semiaxes b and c, lying entirely within the circle. Similarly, putting $z = 0$, the intersection with the xy-plane is shown to be

$$x^2 + y^2 = c^2,$$

a circle of radius c, and

$$\frac{x^2}{b^2} + \frac{y^2}{a^2} = 1,$$

an ellipse with semiaxes a and b, lying outside the circle. The intersection with the xz-plane, obtained by putting $y = 0$, is

$$x^2 + z^2 = b^2,$$

a circle of radius b, and

$$\frac{x^2}{c^2} + \frac{z^2}{a^2} = 1,$$

an ellipse with semiaxes a and c which is cut by the circle at four points.

These sections are illustrated in Figs. 13-26a, b, and c. The form of the entire wave surface is illustrated in Fig. 13-27. The differences between the velocities a, b, and c are exaggerated.

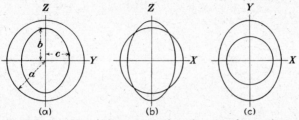

(a)   (b)   (c)

FIG. 13-26.—Intersections of the wave-surface by: (a) the yz-plane; (b) the xz-plane; (c) the xy-plane.

In accordance with the fundamental assumptions upon which the theory is based, a plane-polarized wave in which the vibrations are parallel to the x-direction is thought of as traveling through the crystal in any direction with the velocity a. For such waves the index of refraction is V/a, where V is the velocity of light in a vacuum. Similarly, the indices for plane-polarized waves in which the vibrations are parallel to the y- and z-directions, respectively, are V/b and V/c. These three ratios, V/a, V/b, V/c, are called the *principal indices of refraction of the crystal.* The use of Fig. 13-27 will enable the reader to understand more precisely the manner in which the velocities correspond to the directions of vibration. It shows the intersections of the wave surfaces with the three coordinate planes in one quadrant. Consider the xz-plane: Vibrations perpendicular to it, *i.e.*, parallel to y, have velocity b, no matter in which direction they travel through the crystal; vibrations in the xz-plane parallel to the x-direction travel in the z-direction with velocity a, and vibrations parallel to the z-direction travel in the x-direction with velocity c. Vibrations oriented otherwise in the plane do not have velocities intermediate between a and c,

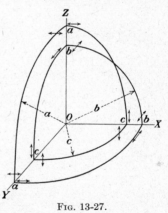

FIG. 13-27.

but are transmitted as though decomposed into component vibrations parallel to the x- and z-directions which travel with the velocities a and c, respectively.

The transmission velocities of vibrations parallel and perpendicular to the two other coordinate planes may be obtained from the figure in the same way. The double-headed arrows represent the directions of vibration.

It is to be noted that the ray through the crystal is not in general normal to the corresponding wave front but is the line from the point of incidence drawn to the point of contact of the tangent plane to the wave surface.

18. Optic Axes in Crystals.—There are two directions in a biaxial crystal along which plane waves may be transmitted with a single wave velocity, no matter what the directions of vibration in their wave fronts may be. These are called the *optic axes*. In Fig. 13-28 they are OM and OM', since tangents to the circle at M and M' are also tangent to the ellipse at N and N'. That is, a wave front which after refraction is parallel to MN (or $M'N'$) is

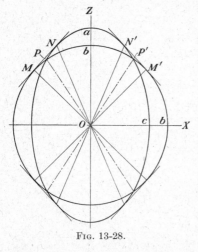

Fig. 13-28.

propagated as a single wave in the direction OM (or $O M'$), whatever the direction of the vibrations in the wave front may be, but the *rays corresponding to the vibrations with different orientations have different directions.* For instance, for waves vibrating in the xz-plane the ray lies in the direction ON, while for waves vibrating perpendicularly to the xz-plane and in the tangent plane the ray has the direction OM. The tangent plane, however, which intersects the plane of incidence in

MN, touches the wave surface in a ring, with the point P in the middle of a slight depression in the surface.

Consequently, if a narrow bundle of ordinary light is incident on a section of a biaxial crystal so that after refraction the wave normal proceeds along the optic axis, a single ray may have any one of the infinite number of directions represented by a line from O to a point on the circle of contact, depending on the particular direction of its vibration, and the rays of the entire bundle spread out so that each ray becomes a line in the surface of the circular cone whose apex is at O and whose base is the circle MN. This is shown by the phenomenon of *internal conical*

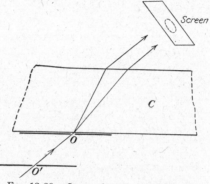

Fig. 13-29.—Internal conical refraction.

refraction. A crystal C (Fig. 13-29) is cut with its faces perpendicular to the bisector of the angle between the optic axes, and a narrow pencil of light is allowed to fall on a limited area of the surface. In general there will be two images of the hole on the screen, but for a certain direction $O'O$ of the incident beam there is a ring of light which has the same diameter for different distances from the screen. The angle of the cone of refraction agrees with that predicted by theory.

19. Axes of Single Ray Velocity.—The two directions OP and OP' are called the *axes of single ray velocity*. At the points P and P' there is an infinity of tangents to the surface, two of which, in the plane of incidence, are illustrated in Fig. 13-30. This is another way of saying that there is an infinity of wave normals at P. Since the

Fig. 13-30.

direction of emergence of the light into the air depends upon the direction of the wave normal in the crystal, there will be, corresponding to a ray traversing the crystal in the direction OP (or OP') a hollow cone of rays leaving the crystal. This phenomenon, called *external conical refraction*, can be demonstrated by the use of the same crystal that is used for demonstrat

ing internal conical refraction. A convergent beam of light is
focused on a small hole O in a screen covering one surface, as in
Fig. 13-31.   In a screen over the other surface is another hole O',
for which a position may be found so that a hollow cone of rays
is refracted into the air.   The direction OO' is the axis of single
ray velocity.   Actually, of course, only the light in a similar
hollow cone on the incident side is thus refracted through O'.

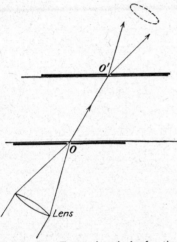

The rest of the light which
passes through O is refracted in
other directions and is stopped
by the screen.

The meaning of the phrase
"single ray velocity" is made
clear by this experiment, for it
is obvious that while the ray
OO' (or, rather, a narrow bundle of rays) is made up of waves
vibrating in any plane whatever, these all have the same
velocity through the crystal.
Thus along the directions OP
and OP' (Fig. 13-28) is fulfilled
the condition that a difference
in optical length between two

FIG. 13-31.—External conical refraction.

points on the ray is independent of the plane of vibration.
The relation between this characteristic in biaxial and uniaxial
crystals is now apparent, for the optic axis in a uniaxial crystal is
that direction through the crystal for which the condition just
stated is fulfilled.   The mechanics of wave propagation in uniaxial
crystals is thus seen to be a special case of the more general
mechanics of wave propagation in biaxial crystals, and is, in
effect, that case for which the ellipse of Fig. 13-28 is tangent to
the circle.   If the ellipse is inside the circle and tangent to it at
two points, the wave surface represented is that of a positive
uniaxial crystal; if the ellipse is outside the circle and tangent to
it at two points, the wave surface represented is that of a negative
uniaxial crystal.   In either case, the line through the crystal
connecting the points of tangency is the optic axis of the crystal.

20. Rotatory Polarization.—If a pair of nicols is crossed so as
to extinguish the incident light, an ordinary isotropic substance

placed between them will produce no effect.   The same thing is true if a thin section of calcite with its faces perpendicular to the optic axis is placed between the nicols, provided the light is a parallel beam.   But if a thin section of crystal quartz so cut is used, light will be transmitted by the analyzer.   The analyzer may then be rotated to an angle at which the light will once more be extinguished, proving that after passing through the quartz plate, it is still plane-polarized but vibrating in a plane different from that of the light incident on the quartz.   From the ordinary laws of double refraction the failure of the calcite to produce any effect was to have been expected, since both the ordinary and extraordinary rays traverse the crystal in the direction of the optic axis with the same velocity, and no difference of phase is introduced between them.   From these considerations also the same result might have been expected with the quartz plate, but instead there is definite evidence that a rotation of the plane of vibration has taken place.   The use of thicker plates of quartz will show that the angle of this rotation is proportional to the thickness traversed.

Crystal quartz and other substances which have this power to turn through an angle the plane of vibration of a polarized beam transmitted along the optic axis are said to be *optically active*. This property is quite distinct from that possessed by half-wave plates in effecting a change in the plane of vibration by a relative retardation between the ordinary and extraordinary plane vibrations, for, as has been seen, the result may be produced when the light traverses the crystal in a direction along which these two vibrations have the same velocity.   Some crystals rotate the plane of vibration in a right-handed (clockwise) direction and others in a left-handed (counterclockwise) direction, and are accordingly called right-handed or dextrorotatory and left-handed or levorotatory.   Quartz occurs in both forms, the crystal symmetry of one being the mirror image of that of the other.   A rotation is said to be right-handed when the observer looking toward the light source sees the plane of polarization rotated in a clockwise direction.   If the crystal is turned around so that the light traverses it in the opposite direction, no change in the direction of rotation of the plane of polarization is observed. Destruction of the crystal state, as in the case of fused quartz, destroys the optical activity of the substance.

Many liquids and organic substances in solution have been found to be optically active. A solution of an active substance in an inactive one possesses a power of optical rotation which is proportional to the amount of active substance present in a given quantity of solution. While this rule is generally true, in some cases the rotation is found to vary slightly with the nature of the solvent. An approximate formula for the rotation ρ, *in degrees*, is given by

$$\rho = A + Bs + Cs^2, \tag{13-20}$$

where s represents the weight of the solvent in 100 parts by weight of solution, and B and C are empirical constants. A is defined as the *molecular rotation* of the pure substance, for $s = 0$, molecular rotation in turn being defined as the amount of rotation of the plane of polarization produced by a column 10 cm. in length containing 1 gm. of the substance per cubic centimeter, or, as the amount of rotation produced by a thickness of 10 cm. of the pure substance divided by the density of the substance. For most purposes the second two terms on the right-hand side of the equation are negligible. The molecular rotation, sometimes called the *specific rotation*, of sucrose (cane sugar) for the D-line of sodium (5893 angstroms) is $+66.67$ deg., the positive sign indicating that the substance is *right-handed*. The almost complete dependence of the angle of rotation on the density of the optically active substance in solution has made the rotatory power an extremely useful means of determining the purity of sugar. The effect produced by a given thickness of a particular sample may be compared with that of one of standard purity, and the percentage of foreign substance may thus be determined.

The angle of rotation of the plane of vibration in optically active substances is nearly proportional to the reciprocal of the wave-length squared. If the proportionality were exact, the law could be written $\rho = K/\lambda^2$, where K is a constant. A better agreement with experiment is obtained if to the right-hand side of the equation are added terms whose values depend on natural free periods of vibration in the crystal.[1] The relation between the rotation and wave-length is called *dispersion of the rotation*.

21. Fresnel's Theory of Rotatory Polarization.—Fresnel assumed that the incident plane-polarized light upon entering the

[1] For a more complete discussion of this topic, see Drude, "Optics."

quartz was broken into two beams circularly polarized in opposite directions and propagated through the crystal with different velocities. In Fig. 13-32a and b are represented two opposite circular vibrations in which, when they are superposed, the linear components in the X-direction will neutralize each other, leaving only a plane vibration in the Y-direction as in Fig. 13-32c. But if the left-handed vibration travels through the crystal faster

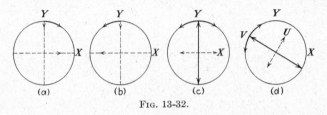

FIG. 13-32.

than the right-handed, after emergence from the crystal the components in a direction represented by U (Fig. 13-32d) will neutralize each other, leaving only a plane vibration in the V-direction. The angle between the Y- and V-directions depends on the relative velocities of the two circular vibrations and the thickness of crystal traversed.

If this explanation is correct, then the two vibrations, since they travel with different velocities, should undergo different

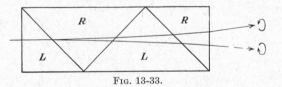

FIG. 13-33.

amounts of bending by refraction at an oblique surface. Fresnel found that the resulting separation of the beams, while very small, could be detected if a narrow beam is passed through a block made of alternate prisms of right- and left-handed quartz, as illustrated in Fig. 13-33, the prisms being cut so that the light traversed them in the general direction of the optic axis. While in the first prism the left-handed circularly polarized beam travels faster than the right-handed, in the second it travels slower. Since the light is incident upon each oblique face at a large angle, refraction of the two components takes place at slightly different angles at each face, thus increasing the separation of the beams.

Upon examination with a quarter-wave plate and an analyzer, the two beams may be shown to be circularly polarized in opposite directions.

The rotation of the plane of vibration can be described analytically as follows: Let

$$X_1 = a \cos \frac{2\pi}{T}\left(t - \frac{d}{v_1}\right)$$

$$Y_1 = a \sin \frac{2\pi}{T}\left(t - \frac{d}{v_1}\right)$$

represent a left-handed circular vibration, and

$$X_2 = a \cos \frac{2\pi}{T}\left(t - \frac{d}{v_2}\right)$$

$$Y_2 = -a \sin \frac{2\pi}{T}\left(t - \frac{d}{v_2}\right)$$

a right-handed circular vibration, the two having the same period and amplitude and traveling in the same direction with velocities v_1 and v_2, respectively, through a crystal of thickness d. Superposition of the two can be represented by adding the X-components and the Y-components separately, *i.e.*,

$$X = X_1 + X_2 = a\left[\cos \frac{2\pi}{T}\left(t - \frac{d}{v_1}\right) + \cos \frac{2\pi}{T}\left(t - \frac{d}{v_2}\right)\right],$$

$$Y = Y_1 + Y_2 = a\left[\sin \frac{2\pi}{T}\left(t - \frac{d}{v_1}\right) - \sin \frac{2\pi}{T}\left(t - \frac{d}{v_2}\right)\right],$$

which may be changed to the form

$$\left.\begin{array}{l} X = 2a \cos \dfrac{2\pi}{T}\left[t - \dfrac{d}{2}\left(\dfrac{1}{v_1} + \dfrac{1}{v_2}\right)\right] \cos \dfrac{\pi d}{T}\left[\dfrac{1}{v_2} - \dfrac{1}{v_1}\right], \\[2ex] Y = 2a \cos \dfrac{2\pi}{T}\left[t - \dfrac{d}{2}\left(\dfrac{1}{v_1} + \dfrac{1}{v_2}\right)\right] \sin \dfrac{\pi d}{T}\left[\dfrac{1}{v_2} - \dfrac{1}{v_1}\right], \end{array}\right\} \quad (13\text{-}21)$$

according to which the X- and Y-components of the combined vibration have the same phase, hence the result is a plane-polarized vibration. The plane of this vibration is given by

$$\frac{Y}{X} = \tan \frac{\pi d}{T}\left(\frac{1}{v_2} - \frac{1}{v_1}\right), \quad (13\text{-}22)$$

which varies with d, the thickness of the crystal traversed.   The angle of rotation corresponding to any thickness d is therefore

$$\rho = \frac{\pi d}{T}\left(\frac{1}{v_2} - \frac{1}{v_1}\right). \qquad (13\text{-}23)$$

22. The Cornu Double Prism.—Since crystal quartz transmits ultraviolet radiations of wave-length as short as about 1800 angstroms, it is extremely useful in the construction of lenses and prisms for spectrographs.   But in the preceding section it was shown that ordinary light incident obliquely upon the surface of a quartz prism suffers double refraction, even if the light traverses the prism in the direction of the optic axis. This not only results in double images in a single quartz prism, but the rotation of the plane of polarization is a disadvantage in spectroscopic observations in which the measurement of polarization is involved.

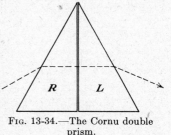

Fig. 13-34.—The Cornu double prism.

The Cornu prism, designed to eliminate these double images, is constructed of two 30-deg. prisms, one of right-handed, the other of left-handed quartz, cut so that the light travels in the direction of the optic axis in each.   The two are placed together, as illustrated in Fig. 13-34.   The amount of rotation in the first prism is exactly neutralized by the rotation in the opposite direction in the other.   This arrangement is

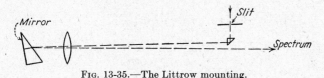

Fig. 13-35.—The Littrow mounting.

unnecessary if the spectrograph is of the Littrow type, illustrated in Fig. 13-35.   In this instrument a single lens serves for both collimator and camera, and the light is reflected back through the prism from a coat of metal deposited on its rear face.   Since for either right- or left-handed quartz the angle of rotation is the same no matter in which direction the light travels along the axis, the rotations produced in the incident and reflected paths neutralize each other.

23. Half-shade Plates and Prisms.—Measurements of rotatory polarization may be made by setting a pair of nicols for extinction, interposing the optically active substance between them, and recording the angle through which the analyzer is turned to produce extinction once more. This method is not very accurate, because it is difficult to tell just when the light is completely cut off. Since a determination of equality of intensity of two parts of the field may be made with greater accuracy, it is customary to introduce into the optical path some device for substituting this setting for the setting for extinction. One of these, the *Laurent half-shade plate*, consists of a semicircular half-wave plate of quartz or other crystal set between the polarizer and analyzer and close to the former, with its optic axis at a small angle θ with the principal section of the polarizer. In order to compensate for the absorption and reflection of this plate, the other half of the field is covered with a piece of glass of appropriate color and thickness. The smaller the angle θ, the greater the change in relative intensity of the two halves of the field of view when the analyzer is rotated. For small values of θ, however, the intensity in both halves will be small. For this reason it is customary to mount the half-wave plate to permit its adjustment over a small range of angle. The observations are made by turning the analyzer until the two halves of the field are equally bright. In some instruments a small nicol covering one half of the field is substituted for the Laurent plate.

Another device which serves the same purpose as the Laurent plate is the *Cornu-Jellet prism*. This is made by splitting a

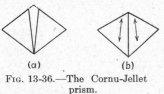

nicol in a plane parallel to the direction of vibration of the transmitted light, and removing a section, as illustrated in Fig. 13-36a. When the two pieces are joined together, as shown in Fig. 13-36b, the planes of vibration of the light

(a)   (b)

Fig. 13-36.—The Cornu-Jellet prism.

transmitted by the two halves make a small angle with each other, and extinction takes place for different settings of the analyzer. When the beam through one half is extinguished, a small amount of light is transmitted through the other. In making observations of the rotation of the plane of polarization in a substance, it is customary to set the analyzer with its plane of transmission so that the two halves are equally bright. When the plane of rotation of the incident light is rotated through a given angle by the substance under examination, the analyzer may be set with great accuracy to the new angle at which the two halves of the field once more appear equally bright.

Problems

1. How thick must a quarter-wave plate be if it is made of quartz? In what direction must its faces lie with regard to the optic axis?

2. What is the refractive index of a piece of glass if the light of the green mercury line (5461 angstroms) is plane-polarized when reflection is at an angle of 57°47'?

3. A Wollaston prism is made of quartz, each prism having an angle of 45 deg. If it is used so that the incident light is normal to the surface of the prism, what will be the angle between the two emerging beams?

4. A plate of quartz 0.54 mm. thick is cut with its faces parallel to the axis. If a beam of plane-polarized light of wave-length 5461 angstroms is incident normally on the plate, what will be the phase difference between the two emergent beams?

5. If the direction of vibration of the incident plane-polarized beam of Prob. 4 makes an angle of 30 deg. with the optic axis of the quartz, what will be the character of the polarization of the emergent beam? Give full details.

6. A solution of camphor in alcohol in a tube 20 cm. long is found to effect a rotation of the plane of vibration of the light passing through it of 33 deg. What must be the density of the camphor in grams per cubic centimeter in solution? The specific rotation of camphor is +54 deg. at 20°C.

7. Consider the experiments described in Secs. **13-1***d* and *e*. A slight tilting of the crystal in either case will reveal that in light transmission *along* the axis the two dots appear to be at *different* depths in the crystal, while in transmission *perpendicular* to the axis they appear almost at the same depth. This is contrary to theory. Explain the apparent contradiction, considering the light to be divergent.

CHAPTER XIV

SPECTRA

1. Kinds of Spectra.—In general there are three kinds of spectra:

a. Bright Line Spectra.—These have their origin in incandescent gases at low pressure as in a partly evacuated discharge tube, in flames, in the glowing gas between the terminals of an electric arc or spark, and in certain so-called gaseous nebulae such as the irregular nebula in Orion, and in the tails of comets. The spectrum seen when only the *edge* of the sun is observed through a spectroscope is a bright line spectrum. In the majority of cases, bright line spectra are those of monatomic gases, although certain of them called band spectra are due to molecules.

b. Continuous Spectra.—These are due to incandescent solids or liquids, such as a lamp filament, the poles of an electric arc, molten metals of high melting point, and also to incandescent gases at high pressure such as exist in lower levels in stars.

Gases at low pressures for which the most conspicuous spectrum is one of bright line emission may under certain circumstances also emit a spectrum which is continuous over a given spectral range. The manner in which spectral theory explains this type of emission will be given in later sections.

c. Absorption Spectra.—These are in general of two sorts: continuous absorption, and line absorption. A type of continuous absorption, *i.e.*, over a considerable range of wave-length, will be discussed briefly in the sections on dispersion. Line-absorption spectra commonly occur when the light from a source *emitting* a continuous spectrum is observed with a spectroscope after passing through gases at low pressure and lower temperature than that of the source. For the production of this type of spectrum, it is necessary that the atoms or molecules of the intervening gas be in a condition to *absorb* energy of radiation which strikes them. The mechanism of this *line absorption* is explained on the basis of the quantum theory of spectra.

2. Early Work on Spectra.—Although the dispersion of light into a spectrum by a prism had been studied by Kepler and others,

Newton was the first to formulate the precise laws of dispersion. He invented the word "spectrum" for the band of color obtained from the sun's light with a prism.   Fraunhofer's discovery of the significance of the absorption lines in the solar spectrum[1] was the beginning of what might be called the first pioneering era in spectroscopy, which lasted for about 30 years after Fraunhofer's discovery.

The relationship existing between laboratory and celestial spectra was first clearly stated by Kirchhoff in 1859.   By exhaustive experiments carried out in collaboration with Bunsen, he showed that if a burning salt is placed between *any* hotter source of a continuous white-light spectrum and the spectroscope, there will be seen a spectrum crossed by absorption lines whose positions coincide with the bright lines obtained from the burning salts alone.   His conclusion was that the cooler flame absorbs light of the same wave-length as it will emit.   He inferred therefore that the Fraunhofer lines in the solar spectrum are due to the presence of a solar atmosphere cooler than the underlying body of the sun, and *containing the same elements which give rise to corresponding bright lines in the laboratory.*   A year or two after the announcement of these conclusions he published the fundamental law of radiation and absorption: *The ratio between the absorptivity and emissive power is the same for each kind of rays for all bodies at the same temperature.*

3. The Balmer Formula for Hydrogen.—The half century following Kirchhoff was a period of accelerated accumulation of experimental data and technique, much of which was in the field of astrophysics.   Engrossing as the story of these developments may be, it cannot be told here.[2]   The first step toward precise knowledge of the origin of spectra was made in 1885 by Balmer, who showed that with a high degree of approximation the wave-lengths of the hydrogen lines could be fitted into the formula

$$\lambda = 3645 \, \frac{n^2}{n^2 - 4},   \tag{14-1}$$

[1] See Sec. **6-14**.

[2] The reader is referred to Crew, "Rise of Modern Physics," Scheiner, "Astrophysical Spectroscopy," and Lockyer, "Inorganic Evolution as Studied by Spectrum Analysis," for the history and background of spectroscopy during this period.

where n is an integer equal to or greater than 3, and λ is in angstroms.

4. The Rydberg Number.—It is a little easier to connect this formula with developments to be described later if a change is made from wave-length (λ) to wave number ($\bar{\nu}$), the number of waves in a centimeter *in vacuo*. We then have

$$\bar{\nu} = R\left(\frac{1}{2^2} - \frac{1}{n^2}\right). \tag{14-2}$$

in which $n = 3, 4, 5 \ldots$, and R has the approximate value 109,700. In 1890, Rydberg discovered that the number R is with slight variations common to all elements. For any particular element the formula is

$$\bar{\nu} = Z^2 R\left(\frac{1}{n_1{}^2} - \frac{1}{n_2{}^2}\right). \tag{14-3}$$

For instance, with this formula the wave numbers of certain lines in the helium spectrum are given with the atomic number[1] of helium $Z = 2$, $n_1 = 3$, $n_2 = 4, 5, 6$, etc. It may be perplexing to the student that in illustrating eq. 14-3 by choosing $n_1 = 3$ instead of 2, for helium, nothing is said to indicate the reason for that choice. That reason will appear in the following sections.

5. Series in Spectra.—The lines of the hydrogen spectrum given by the Balmer formula (eq. 14-1) constitute what is called a series. Several years before Balmer's discovery it was noticed that in the spectra of several elements, notably those of sodium and potassium, most of the lines could be fitted into series. In these spectra there is not a single series of lines, as in hydrogen, but several series, each of which is extended throughout the spectrum. Also, the series themselves consist of doublets, triplets, or higher multiple groups. Since the lines in different series for a given element are different in appearance, some being predominantly strong, others diffuse, others sharp, etc., it became customary to classify series as *principal, sharp, diffuse, fundamental*, etc., the letters P, S, D, F, etc., being used for convenience. Because of the existence of a real physical significance to these differences of appearance, the letters have remained in the nota-

---

[1] By "atomic number" is meant the ordinal number of the atom in the periodic table of the elements, beginning with hydrogen as number one.

tion of spectral theory.   In Fig. 14-1 is a reproduction of the
sodium spectrum showing members of three series.[1]

6. The Hydrogen Series.—It occurred independently to two
workers in this field, Rydberg and Ritz, that in the Balmer
formula (eq. 14-3) n_1 might be a running integer as well as n_2.
For instance, if, as in the Balmer formula, $n_1 = 2$, $n_2 = 3$, 4,

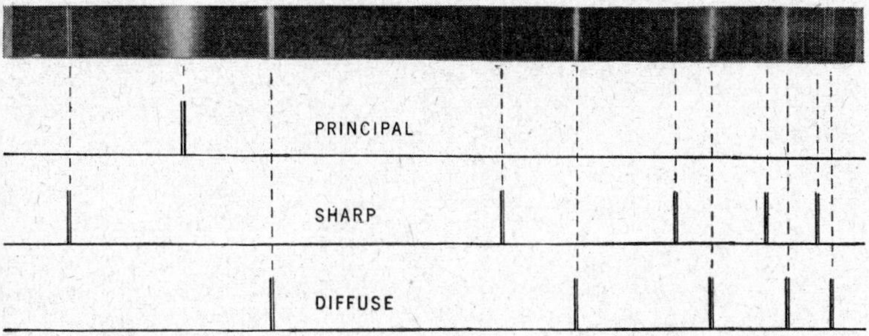

FIG. 14-1.—The spectrum of sodium, showing the *principal* series doublet and
some members of the *sharp* and *diffuse* series.   The principal series doublet
(5890 and 5896 angstroms) is overexposed and surrounded by Rowland ghosts
due to imperfections in the diffraction grating used.   The other lines in the
spectrum are due to impurities in the source.

5, . . . , etc., the series of wave-lengths represented is 6563,
4861, 4340 angstroms, . . . , etc., while if n_1 is put equal to 1,
and n_2 put equal to 2, 3, 4, 5, etc., successively, the calculations
yield the wave-lengths 1216, 1026, 972 angstroms, . . . , etc.,
fractional parts of angstroms being omitted.   These lines, lying
in the far ultraviolet, were observed by Lyman.   Thus far, five
series of hydrogen spectra have been observed.   These are listed
below, designated in accordance with custom by the names of
the original observers.   The values of n_1 and n_2 are given in
each case.

HYDROGEN SERIES OF ATOMIC SPECTRA

Lyman series:

$$\bar{\nu} = R\left(\frac{1}{1^2} - \frac{1}{n^2}\right), \qquad n = 2, 3, 4, 5, \text{ etc.}$$

[1] For summary of the work in this subject see Fowler, "Report on series
in Line Spectra," Fleetway Press, 1922; or White, "Introduction to Atomic
Spectra," McGraw-Hill.

Balmer series:

$$\bar{\nu} = R\left(\frac{1}{2^2} - \frac{1}{n^2}\right), \qquad n = 3, 4, 5, 6, \text{ etc.}$$

Paschen series:

$$\bar{\nu} = R\left(\frac{1}{3^2} - \frac{1}{n^2}\right), \qquad n = 4, 5, 6, 7, \text{ etc.}$$

Brackett series:

$$\bar{\nu} = R\left(\frac{1}{4^2} - \frac{1}{n^2}\right), \qquad n = 5, 6, 7, 8, \text{ etc.}$$

Pfund series:

$$\bar{\nu} = R\left(\frac{1}{5^2} - \frac{1}{n^2}\right), \qquad n = 6, 7, 8, 9, \text{ etc.}$$

The last three of these series lie in the infrared, as can be verified by calculation.

It is now evident that for *any element* a fair approximation to the wave numbers of series is given by eq. 14-3, and that the illustration at the end of Sec. **14-4** gives only one of the series of the helium spectrum. Others will correspond to different values of n_1 and n_2, in accordance with the rules laid down. It must be kept in mind, however, that only the simplest of series formulas have been presented here. Others which give a closer approximation to the wave-lengths may be found in treatises on the subject of line spectra.

7. The Quantum Theory of Spectra.—The attention of many spectroscopists was focused upon series relations in spectra from the time of Balmer's discovery, but it was not until the announcement of the Bohr theory about 30 years later that the physical significance of these relations was disclosed. Series relations still are spectroscopic tools of tremendous power, for, by their aid, if several lines of a spectral series are experimentally identified, the wave-lengths of the rest can be predicted. During the quarter century following Balmer's discovery, however, there remained unsolved the riddle of spectra: What, precisely, is the connection between the wave-lengths of the radiation and the changes in the atoms or molecules from which that radiation is emitted? The answer to this question did not follow from series relations in spectra. Several lines of investigation converging to a common end, and brought together by the insight of Niels

Bohr, gave us a theoretical explanation which later was expanded into what might be called the *quantum theory of spectra*. The lines of investigation contributing to this end will now be taken up in detail.

8. Kirchhoff's Law of Emission and Absorption.—In order to trace the events' leading to modern theories of spectra, it is necessary to outline the developments in the field of radiation which followed the work of Kirchhoff.[1]

The relation between emission and absorption deduced by Kirchhoff and mentioned in Sec. **14-2** rests on more extensive grounds than observations on solar aborption. A study of their characteristics shows that certain substances such as lampblack, deep-piled velvet, etc., absorb a greater amount of the radiation that falls upon them than other substances, while at the same time they also act as good radiators. Experiments with such surfaces led to the theoretical concept of a *perfect black body*, which may be defined as one whose surface absorbs *all* the radiation falling upon it. Obviously this (ideal) surface does not reflect at all. For any surface, the fraction of the radiation falling upon its surface, which is absorbed is called the *absorptivity* of the surface. Similarly, the *emissive power* of a body is defined as the total radiation emitted per unit time per unit area of its surface. From both experimental and theoretical considerations, Kirchhoff was led to the general law of radiation connecting these quantities and stated in the next section.

9. Kirchhoff's Radiation Law.—The relation between absorptivity (A) and emissive power (E) is given by Kirchhoff's law, which may be stated as

$$\frac{E}{A} = \text{constant} \tag{14-4}$$

at a given temperature, for all bodies. Since $A = 1$ for a so-called perfect black-body radiator, it follows that the law may be stated, in words: *at a given temperature, the ratio of the emissive power to the absorptivity of any body is the same for all bodies and is equal to the emissive power of a black body at the same temperature.*

---

[1] For a more detailed discussion of these developments, as well as of the quantum theory of spectra, the reader is referred to Richtmyer, "Introduction to Modern Physics," McGraw-Hill, and Reiche, "Quantum Theory," Dutton.

10. Stefan-Boltzmann Law.—In 1879, Stefan proposed the relationship

$$E = \sigma T^4, \tag{14-5}$$

where E is the total emissive power of a black body at an absolute temperature T, and σ* is a constant. Subsequently, the same law was deduced theoretically by Boltzmann, who applied the reasoning of the *Carnot cycle* of energy exchange in heat engines to a hypothetical engine in which radiation was the working substance. The Stefan-Boltzmann law has been verified experimentally. It should be emphasized that the radiation dealt with has a continuous spectrum.

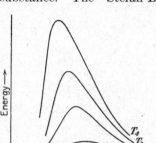

Fig. 14-2.—Showing the displacement toward the violet, with increasing temperature, of the wave-length (λ_{max}) of the energy maximum.

11. Wien's Displacement Laws.—In 1893, on the basis of classical thermodynamics, Wien announced his famous *wavelength-temperature displacement law*, which may be put in the form

$$\lambda_{max} \cdot T = \text{constant}, \tag{14-6}$$

in which λ_{max} is the wave-length for which there is the maximum energy of radiation at absolute temperature T. The value of the constant product is found to be 0.2884 cm.-deg. By the particular nature of the theoretical considerations upon which the law is based, Wien was enabled to obtain another relation, namely, the *energy-temperature displacement law*, which may be written

$$E_{max} = \text{constant} \times T^5, \tag{14-7}$$

where E_{max} is the energy of radiation at the maximum for T. These laws have been verified by experiment. Equation 14-6 is illustrated graphically in Fig. 14-2. Further comprehension of the significance of the displacement laws may be gained by consideration of Fig. 14-3, in which are plotted as ordinates experimental values of E_λ/T^5 against values of λT as abscissae for three temperatures. E_λ is an expression for the energy

---

* The experimental value of σ is usually given as 5.735×10^{-5} erg cm.$^{-2}$ deg.$^{-4}$ sec.$^{-1}$.

corresponding to a given wave-length, and may be called the monochromatic emissive power. As predicted by theory, the

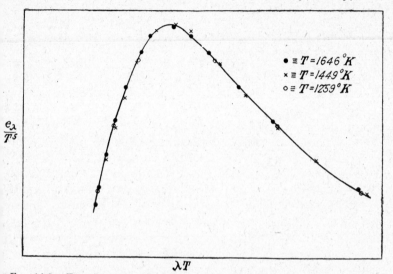

FIG. 14-3.—Experimental verification of the displacement laws of black-body radiation. (*From Richtmyer, Introduction to Modern Physics.*)

curve is the same for all temperatures. From this it may be concluded that E_λ/T^5 is some unknown function of λT, or

$$\frac{E_\lambda}{T^5} = f(\lambda T).$$

Combining this with eq. 14-6, it follows that

$$E_\lambda = C\lambda^{-5} \cdot f(\lambda T). \tag{14-8}$$

12. Distribution Laws.—From considerations based on classical theory Wien derived a formula which gave an evaluation of $f(\lambda T)$, of the form

$$E_\lambda = C_1\lambda^{-5}e^{-C_2/\lambda T}, \tag{14-9}$$

where C_1 and C_2 are constants and e is the natural logarithmic base. It is evident that eq. 14-9 gives for a black-body radiator the *distribution of energy as a function of wave-length*. While it gives calculated values of E_λ which agree with experimentally determined values quite well for wave-lengths in the visible region, the values for longer wave-lengths are too low. Slightly different distribution formulas, obtained by various processes of deduction based on classical theory, were obtained by others, notably the Rayleigh formula

$$E_\lambda = C_1\lambda^{-4} \cdot T \cdot e^{-C_2/\lambda T} \qquad (14\text{-}10)$$

in which C_1 and C_2 are not necessarily the same constants as in Wien's formula. Rayleigh's theoretical treatment was later extended by Jeans, who proposed the formula

$$E_\lambda = CkT\lambda^{-4}, \qquad (14\text{-}11)$$

in which C is a constant and kT is the total energy associated with each degree of freedom of the medium in which the radiation is supposed to exist.[1] The formulas of Rayleigh and Rayleigh-Jeans agree with experiment for very long waves, but they give values which are too high in the visible spectrum.

13. Planck's Quantum Hypothesis.—Experimental tests carried out by Lummer and Pringsheim proved conclusively that none of the distribution laws completely agreed with observations. Numerous attempts to modify the formulas derived from classical theory so as to bring complete agreement with experiment failed. Finally, in 1900, Planck decided to alter his method of deducing the distribution law by introducing a new and radical concept. In all previous deductions, the energy of radiation had been supposed to be divided among a great many hypothetical "oscillators" in the black body. In arriving at the mean energy it had been customary to suppose that an individual oscillator might possess any possible quantity of energy. Planck's radical departure consisted in postulating that the energy of the radiator was divided into a *finite number of discrete units of energy* of magnitude ϵ, these energy units or "quanta" being distributed at random among the individual oscillators. The number of different ways in which this distribution of energy may be divided among the oscillators was called by Planck the *thermodynamic probability* of a particular arrangement or distribution. Making use of well-established rules of mathematical

---

[1] It should be kept in mind that no attempt is made here to give the student a complete understanding of the *theoretical bases* of these formulas. Fascinating as the development of the subject is, it is intended here only to *introduce* the formulas so as to contrast them with the more successful formula of Planck, whose work was part of the prelude to the *quantum theory of spectra*.

procedure, with the aid of this novel concept Planck arrived at an expression for the mean energy $\bar{U}$ of an oscillator:

$$\bar{U} = \frac{\epsilon}{e^{\epsilon/kT} - 1},\tag{14-12}$$

in which k is a constant. But from classical considerations alone, Planck had deduced that

$$E_\lambda = \frac{\bar{U}}{\lambda^2}\tag{14-13}$$

while it is evident from eq. 14-8 that the *displacement laws*, which are in rigorous agreement with experiment, hold that E_λ is proportional to some function $f(\lambda T)$. Hence it follows that $\bar{U}$ is proportional to some function of (λT). Planck concluded that in view of the form of eq. 14-12, and the necessity for keeping in agreement with the displacement laws, it followed that

$$\epsilon = h\nu,$$

where ν is the frequency of the radiation and h is a constant. The symbol h stands for *Planck's quantum of action* and has the value 6.547×10^{-27} erg sec. Planck's distribution formula is

$$E_\lambda = c_1\lambda^{-5}\frac{1}{e^{c_2/\lambda T} - 1},\tag{14-14}$$

where c_1 and $c_2{}^*$ are constants. For short waves this is the same as Wien's formula, and for long waves is the same as the Rayleigh-Jeans formula.

14. The Rutherford Atom Model.—During the time when the laws of radiation were engaging the attention of many research workers, and in the decade following, older concepts of the nature of matter were being subjected to rigorous scrutiny. The discovery of radioactivity and the development of the concept of a fundamental unit of electrical charge, *the electron*, stimulated experiments which showed conclusively that the older ideas concerning the structure of atoms must be modified. Finally, in 1911, on the basis of experimental results obtained in a lengthy investigation of the manner in which α-particles were scattered

---

* c_2 is equal to hc/k, where c is the velocity of light, and k is Boltzmann's constant, the gas constant R_0 divided by the Avogadro number N_0. k has the value 1.3708×10^{-16} erg deg.$^{-1}$. The value of c_2 is 1.432 cm.-deg.

by thin metallic foil, Rutherford postulated that an atom consisted of a positively charged nucleus of extremely small dimensions, surrounded by planetary negatively charged electrons, the distances between the electrons and the nucleus being very great compared to the dimensions of the charged particles themselves.

15. The Bohr Theory of Spectra.—At first it seemed as if the Rutherford atom model would lead the way on classical grounds to a solution of the riddle of emission (bright line) spectra, for it can be shown that the frequency of revolution of the planetary electrons depends upon the energy of the atom. On the other hand, the radiation of any part of the energy would necessarily lead to a gradual change of that frequency, and hence to the emission of a *continuous spectrum*, and not the separate line spectra which are observed. The problem, for the hydrogen atom at least, was finally solved by Bohr, who assumed the Rutherford atom model, and in addition made three hypotheses concerning the manner in which the radiation takes place.

Bohr assumed, first, that the planetary electrons revolve about the nucleus, not in all possible paths but only in certain discrete orbits. He assumed that the orbits are circular and are limited to those for which the angular momentum is an integral multiple of $h/2\pi$, where h is Planck's quantum constant. He assumed, second, that no radiation takes place while an electron remains in one of these orbits, but only when it passes from a given orbit to one of lesser energy, *i.e.*, to one of smaller radius. He assumed, third, that when the electron passes from one of these quantum orbits of energy W_2 to one of lesser energy W_1, radiation is emitted whose frequency, ν, is given by[1]

$$\nu = \frac{c}{\lambda} = \frac{W_2 - W_1}{h}. \tag{14-15}$$

The calculation of the values of W_2 and W_1 for hydrogen is simple. If a is the radius of a given orbit, e the charge on the electron, and E the charge on the nucleus, then the force of attraction is eE/a^2. For equilibrium this must be equal to the

---

[1] In making this assumption, Bohr was adopting not only Planck's hypothesis, but a far more drastic one proposed by Einstein to explain the photoelectric effect (see Sec. **15-20**).

centrifugal force on the electron, which is $ma\omega^2$, where m is the mass of the electron and ω the angular velocity, or

$$ma^3\omega^2 = eE. \qquad (14\text{-}16)$$

If Z is the atomic number, then $E = eZ$. Also, by Bohr's first hypothesis, the angular momentum is a multiple of $h/2\pi$, or

$$ma^2\omega = \frac{nh}{2\pi}, \qquad (14\text{-}17)$$

where n is an integer. From eqs. 14-16 and 14-17 it is possible to obtain values of a_n and ω_n, the radius and angular velocity corresponding to orbit n.

and
$$\left.\begin{aligned} a_n &= \frac{n^2h^2}{4\pi^2e^2Zm}, \\[2mm] \omega_n &= \frac{8\pi^3e^4Z^2m}{n^3h^3}. \end{aligned}\right\} \qquad (14\text{-}18)$$

The total energy W in an orbit is the sum of the kinetic and potential energies, or

$$W = \frac{1}{2}ma^2\omega^2 - \frac{e^2Z}{a},$$

which by the use of eq. 14-16 becomes

$$W = -\frac{e^2Z}{2a}.$$

Combining this expression with the first of eqs. 14-18, it follows that

$$W_n = -\frac{2\pi^2e^4Z^2m}{h^2n^2}.$$

Combining this expression with eq. 14-15, we obtain finally

$$\nu = \frac{c}{\lambda} = \frac{2\pi^2e^4Z^2m}{h^3}\left(\frac{1}{n_1^2} - \frac{1}{n_2^2}\right). \qquad (14\text{-}19)$$

This may now be compared with the Rydberg formula, eq. 14-3. While $\bar{\nu}$ is the *wave number*, ν is the frequency, so that $\bar{\nu}c = \nu$.

Hence it follows from eqs. 14-3 and 14-19 that the Rydberg number is

$$R = \frac{2\pi^2 e^4 m}{h^3 c},$$

a result which may be verified by calculation, given

$$e = 4.770 \times 10^{-10} \text{ e.s.u.}$$
$$m = 9. \times 10^{-28} \text{ gr.}$$
$$h = 6.547 \times 10^{-27} \text{ erg sec.}$$
$$c = 2.998 \times 10^{10} \text{ cm. sec.}^{-1}.$$

Although the Bohr formula gives values of the wave-lengths agreeing well with experiment for hydrogen, much more extensive hypotheses have been necessary to formulate a quantum theory of spectra which holds for all atomic and molecular radiation. It is found, for instance, that the concept of *circular orbits* fails. The existence of *discrete energy states*, however, is completely verified, as is also the concept, expressed in eq. 14-15, that the frequency of a given spectrum line is proportional to the differences of energies of the beginning and end energy states involved in a transition of an electron from a higher to a lower energy state.

It was pointed out in Sec. **14-4** that the Rydberg number is nearly the same for all elements. The slight variation is because of the effect of the mass of the nucleus, which has been neglected in the preceding discussion. From elementary mechanics it follows that instead of m, the mass of the electron, the quantity $mM/(m + M)$, where M is the mass of the nucleus, should be used in eq. 14-19. Then the value of R conforms more closely to the experimental values. The value of M may be calculated from

$$M = \frac{\text{atomic wt. of element} \times \text{mass of oxygen atom}}{16}.$$

The quantity $mM/(m + M)$ is known as the *reduced mass*. It approaches m as M approaches ∞.

16. Energy-level Diagrams.—In the foregoing sections an explanation has been presented of the manner in which the simple Bohr formula in terms of physical quantities such as the charge on and mass of the electron, Planck's constant, and the atomic number, may be applied to give the wave-lengths of atomic spectral lines. These wave-lengths, or, more precisely, wave numbers, are expressed in terms of the differences between energy states of the atom, and the energy states, in turn, are identified with circular orbits in which satellite electrons move. In the preceding section it was indicated that certain concepts of this picture as, for instance, the concept of circular orbits, have been found to be not in agreement with observation. Nevertheless, the essence of Bohr's assumption remains—that radiation of a particular frequency corresponds to a transition of the electron from a higher to a lower energy state. The energy associated

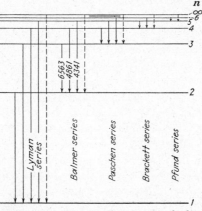

Fig. 14-4.—Simplified energy-level diagram for hydrogen. Each arrow pointing downward indicates a possible transition in which radiant energy is given out by the atom. In a diagram to correct scale, the length of each vertical line corresponds to the frequency of a spectrum line.

with each state is no longer considered necessarily as the motion of the electron in a circular orbit, but is energy of a certain special mode of motion of a satellite electron. It is possible to plot the energy states, and the transitions corresponding to spectral lines, graphically in what is called an *energy-level diagram.*

Energy level diagrams representing the energy states and transitions for heavy atoms are sometimes complicated. That for the hydrogen atom is simpler, and is shown in Fig. 14-4. The horizontal lines represent on an arbitrary scale the different quantities of energy possible to the hydrogen atom. Radiation of a particular frequency ν is represented by a vertical line drawn from an upper to a lower energy level. This is in agreement with Bohr's third postulate, which is that $h\nu = W_n - W_m$, where W_n and W_m are the higher and lower energy states, respectively.

17. Band Spectra of Molecules.—In addition to the so-called *line spectra* due to emission of radiation by atoms, there is another type of spectrum due to radiation by molecules. The former consist in the main of spectral lines which for any particular series are far apart, while the latter, called *band spectra*, appear with sufficient dispersion to be bands of closely grouped lines having a definite regularity in their spacing and, in many cases, with insufficient dispersion, to be continuous. A *band* is characterized by a *head*, either on the violet or red side, the lines there being usually so close as to be indistinguishable, and becoming gradually more widely spaced and fainter toward the *tail* (see Fig. 14-6). Bands having the head on the violet side are said to be degraded toward the red, while those having the head on the red side are degraded toward the violet. For heavy molecules such as MnO_2, S_4, etc., the bands are more closely spaced than for light molecules such as CO, N_2, etc., while the series of bands belonging to H_2 are so widely spaced and overlap to such an extent that the system resembles an atomic spectrum.

As in the simple Bohr theory of atomic spectra, the energy states in the molecule are limited to those for which the angular momentum due to its rotation is an integral multiple of $h/2\pi$. Using j for the running number indicating different states (*i.e.*, $j = 0, 1, 2$, etc.), and deriving from mechanics the expression for the angular momentum of the molecule, it may be shown that the energy W_r due to the rotation in any state is given by

$$W_r = \frac{h^2 j^2}{8\pi^2 I},$$

where I is the moment of inertia. The difference between values of W_r for different values of j will represent a change in rotational energy. But changes may also take place in what might be called the *internal energy*, W_{int} of the molecule, owing to changes of the electronic orbits in the atoms, and to vibrations of the atoms within the molecule. For this reason, the total energy W is given as

$$W = \frac{h^2 j^2}{8\pi^2 I} + W_{int}. \tag{14-20}$$

One of the problems in the analysis of band spectra is to establish the relationship between the frequencies of the spectral lines in a band and the transitions between energy states in the molecule.   According to quantum theory, the frequency of the line is given by ν in

$$h\nu = W' - W'', \tag{14-21}$$

where W' is the higher, and W'' the lower energy state.   Thus the frequency may be found by substituting values of W from eq. 14-20 into eq. 14-21.   Before doing this, however, it should be stated (a) that modern quantum theory substitutes $j(j + 1)$ for j^2, and (b) that the value of I may also change during a transition, because of a change in the size of the molecule.   With these details in mind, we obtain

$$\tilde{\nu} = \frac{W' - W''}{hc} = \frac{h}{8\pi^2 c}\left[\frac{j'(j' + 1)}{I'} - \frac{j''(j'' + 1)}{I''}\right] + \frac{1}{hc}[W_{int}' - W_{int}'']. \tag{14-22}$$

It should also be stated that changes in rotational and internal energy are independent.   The change in the internal energy accounts for the location of the band in a particular region of the spectrum; the change in rotational energy, for the *line* in the band.   The quantities j' and j'' are quantum integers which according to certain *selection principles* have a difference $\Delta j(= j' - j'')$ which can have only the values -1, 0, or $+1$. A further condition holds that neither j' nor j'' can be less than zero.

Putting $j'' = j$, and

$$\frac{1}{hc}[W_{int}' - W_{int}''] = A,$$

$$\frac{h}{8\pi^2 c}\left[\frac{1}{I'} + \frac{1}{I''}\right] = B,$$

$$\frac{h}{8\pi^2 c}\left[\frac{1}{I'} - \frac{1}{I''}\right] = C,$$

the three possible values of Δj give three series of wave numbers conventionally designated as

$$R(j) = A + B(j + 1) + C(j + 1)^2 \qquad j = 0, 1, 2, \cdots ,$$
$$Q(j) = A + Cj + Cj^2 \qquad j = 0, 1, 2, \cdots ,$$
$$P(j) = A - Bj + Cj^2 \qquad j = 1, 2, 3, \cdots .$$

These three equations therefore describe three *branches*, P, Q, and R, which exist in any electronic band for which the conditions given above hold. Figure 14-5 is a diagram in which the values of wave numbers are shown as plotted as abscissas against the quantum numbers j as ordinates. In the case illustrated $I' > I''$,

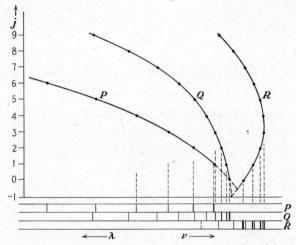

Fig. 14-5.—At the bottom are shown the wave numbers and intensities of individual lines in the branches of a band system, while above they are plotted against quantum number j. The band represented is degraded toward the red.

and the band degrades toward the red. This diagram shows that the *head* is simply the position of the turning point of one of the branches. The greater intensity of the head is usually because of the close grouping of the lines at that point, although sometimes the lines in that part of the branch are also more intense.

In Fig. 14-6 are shown several typical band spectra with dispersion permitting illustration of the structure described above.

18. Continuous Absorption and Emission by Atoms.—Ordinarily the absorption of white light by atoms of a given element results only in line absorption such as that found in solar and stellar spectra, but under proper conditions it is possible to produce continuous absorption also. If the frequency ν of the light incident upon the absorbing gas is sufficiently great, the energy communicated to some of the atoms will be sufficient to eject an electron completely, causing ionization. The absorption will take place at a wave-length shorter than that corresponding to $n_2 = \infty$ in eq. 14-3. This is the same as saying that when the

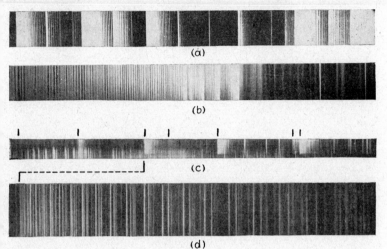

FIG. 14-6.—Photographs of band spectra. (a) Some bands of the NO molecule (Mulliken); (b) the CN band at 3883 angstroms (Mark Fred); (c) bands of F_2 molecule (Gale and Monk) with low dispersion and an iron comparison spectrum; (d) one of the F_2 bands with high dispersion.

n in the first of eqs. 14-18 becomes infinite, the value of a_n becomes infinite, and the Bohr theory ceases to apply, so that all energies are possible. Since all such high frequencies will thus eject the electron, there will be a continuous absorption band to the violet of the convergence frequency of the line series.

FIG. 14-7.—Line absorption and continuous absorption by the sodium atom. Decreasing wave-length toward the right. On the left of the arrow indicating the convergence limit are several members of the spectrum of sodium; on the right is the continuous absorption. (*Photograph by G. R. Harrison.*)

It should be stated that, while the discussion strictly applies to the hydrogen atom, it applies to the general case with some changes of quantum details. Continuous absorption is illustrated by the photograph of the sodium spectrum in Fig. 14-7.

In a similar manner, a continuous *emission* spectrum may be produced, by the radiation of energy by atoms to whose finite energy levels an ejected electron has returned from orbits other than those represented by a series of finite integers n_2.

The energy level diagram representing these cases is shown in Fig. 14-8, the shaded portion at the top representing the continuum of energy levels greater than $n_2 = \infty$. A continuous absorption by *atoms in a gas* is represented by arrows from discrete levels and ending in the shaded area; and continuous emission by arrows starting in the shaded area and ending at the discrete levels.

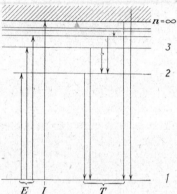

Fig. 14-8.—Energy level diagram for emission and absorption. Vertical lines E represent absorption by *excitation; I*, ionization; T, types of emission; the line downward from the continuum to level 1, continuous emission.

19. The Structure of Spectral Lines. General.

A spectral line owes its characteristics mainly to three things: (*a*) It is an image of the source, which is usually a very narrow slit; (*b*) it depends upon the character of the diffraction or interference pattern produced by the dispersive instrument; (*c*) it depends upon causes inherent in the source. It is the third of these which is to be discussed here. The conditions in the source may result in a broadening of the line, either symmetrical or asymmetrical, or it may split up the line into a complex of lines.

20. The Broadening of Lines. *a. The Natural Breadth of a Line.*

In quantum mechanics, the discrete energy levels postulated by the Bohr theory are considered rather as the locations of *maxima* in a probability distribution of energy changes in the atom. This may best be visualized by considering the horizontal lines representing levels in such a diagram as Fig. 14-4, not as infinitely thin lines but having width and a density distribution. A spectrum line due to like transitions in many atoms will, therefore, have a width and shape depending on the characteristics of the two levels involved in the transition.

b. The Doppler Broadening.—This is due to the random motions of the radiating atoms and hence is often subject to experimental control. It can be shown that the "half width" of a line, as shown by Fig. 14-9, is given by $1.67\frac{\nu}{c}\sqrt{\frac{2RT}{u}}$, where ν is the frequency for no motion of the atom, c is the velocity of light, R is the universal gas constant, T is the absolute temperature, and u the molecular weight.

c. Breadth Due to Collision.—It is assumed that while an atom which is absorbing or radiating energy collides with another atom, the *phase* and *amplitude* of the radiation may change. This leads to a half width equal to $4Nr^2d\sqrt{\frac{RT}{u^3\pi}}$, where N is the Avogadro number, d the density of the gas, r the average distance between nuclear centers when closest, and R, T, and u have the same significance as before.

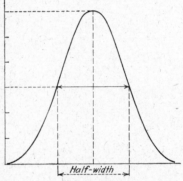

Fig. 14-9.—Illustrating the half-width of a spectrum line.

d. Broadening and Asymmetry Due to Pressure.—It is found that increasing the pressure on a radiating gas causes an unsymmetrical widening of the line and a shift of its maximum toward longer wave-lengths. This may also be considered as due to the interaction of the electric fields of the atoms and ions in a discharge, and thus, as a broadening due to the Stark effect (see Sec. **21**d below).

21. The Complex Structure of Lines. *a. Fine Structure (Multiplet Structure).*—An electron in a given energy state has *orbital motion* and *spin motion*. The angular momenta of these may be coupled in different ways, giving rise to a splitting of the energy levels postulated in the simple Bohr theory into sublevels. For instance, if a given level, $n = 2$, is divided into two, rather close together, there will be two spectral lines instead of one, as in the case of the sodium doublet 5890 and 5896. The spacing of these *multiplets*, *i.e.*, doublets, triplets, etc., in the spectrum increases with atomic weight, being so small for the lighter elements that the lines appear single except with the highest resolution. The fine structure separation for the two components of the red hydrogen line 6563 angstroms is only 0.14 angstrom. On the other hand, the multiplets of heavier elements may be separated by over 100 angstroms.

b. Hyperfine Structure.—As the name suggests, this is a complex structure of much less separation than fine structure.

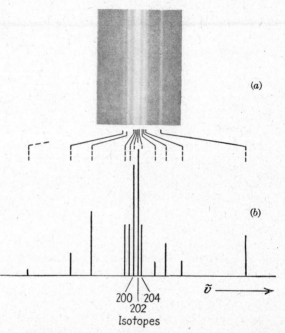

Fig. 14-10.—Hyperfine structure of the green mercury line, 5461 angstroms. Above, photograph with the second order of a concave grating, 30-ft. radius of curvature, and 30,000 lines per inch, ruled by Gale at Ryerson Laboratory. Below, the theoretical hyperfine spin and isotope structure. The displacements in wave number from left to right are −0.765, −0.468, −0.315, −0.093, −0.064, −0.037, 0, +0.020, +0.121, +0.195, +0.305, +0.753 cm.$^{-1}$. Visually, all but the strong central five components are easily resolved with the grating used.

Hyperfine structure is due to two causes. One of these is the presence in a source of more than one isotope of an element, giving rise to a line for each nuclear mass; the other is the spin of the atomic nucleus. Figure 14-10a is a photograph of the mercury green line, 5461 angstroms, while b shows the theoretical structure. In this case both causes of hyperfine structure are present.

c. The Zeeman Effect.—In a strong magnetic field, a single line is split up into many components whose separation depends on the strength of the field. This effect is to be discussed in detail in Chap. XVI.

d. The Stark Effect.—An effect similar to that discovered by Zeeman is produced if the source is in a strong electric field. This effect will also be discussed in Chap. XVI.

Problems

1. Using the simple Bohr formula, calculate the wave numbers of the first five members of the spectrum emitted by ionized helium, *i.e.*, helium atoms which have lost one satellite electron by ionization and are radiating with the second. Make a chart of the energy levels and transitions for these five lines.

2. Taking R to be 109,677.7, and using eq. 14-2, calculate the values of $\bar{\nu}$ and λ for the *convergence* of the Balmer series, *i.e.*, the value of λ for which $n = \infty$. From the relationship $h\nu = eV$, where e is the charge on the electron, calculate the value of V in volts required to excite this line.

3. Considering the sun as a black-body radiator with a surface temperature of 6000° abs., compute the total energy in ergs radiated by it in one year. How much of this is intercepted by the earth?

4. Calculate the radius of the normal orbit $(n = 1)$ of an electron in a hydrogen atom. Calculate also its velocity along the orbit, and its total energy.

5. The atomic weight of hydrogen is 1.0082, and of deuterium, (heavy hydrogen) 2.01445. Compute the separation in wave number and wave-length of the first two lines of the hydrogen and deuterium Balmer series.

6. If the value of λ_{max} for a black body is 5000 angstroms, what is its absolute temperature? At this temperature, what energy in ergs does it radiate in an hour for each square centimeter of surface?

7. The *reduced mass* may be represented by

$$\frac{m}{1 + \dfrac{m}{A M_h}}$$

where A is the atomic weight and M_h is the mass of the oxygen atom divided by 16. Calculate the values of R for hydrogen, deuterium, helium, oxygen, copper, and silver. Plot them against the atomic weights. To what value of R (called R_∞) is the curve through the plotted points asymptotic?

8. When an electric-arc light between terminals of, say, iron is enclosed in a chamber and subjected to an atmospheric pressure of several atmospheres, many of the spectrum lines are widened and show self-reversal (by self-reversal is meant the appearance of a sharp dark center to the bright emission line). Explain these two effects (see Sec. **14-1c**).

CHAPTER XV

LIGHT AND MATERIAL MEDIA

In all the preceding chapters except Chap. XIV, which traced the rise of the quantum theory of spectra, the principles dealt with have been those which concern only the light itself, no account being taken of its interaction with material media through which it passes. This is true even in the case of the treatment of prismatic dispersion and chromatism, for there was no further discussion of the nature of the media, except that the refraction of the light took place in accordance with Snell's law. In the present and following chapters, the nature of the media will be taken into account. The subject is far too extensive for an exhaustive discussion, which would, indeed, be out of place in an intermediate text. It is the intention, however, to present it fully enough to give the student an introduction to modern theories of the interaction of light with media through which it is transmitted.

1. Absorption.—Light energy incident upon the surface of a medium undergoes absorption, refraction, reflection, or scattering. A large part of the energy absorbed is changed to heat or chemical energy. Some substances absorb light of one wavelength group and afterward emit light of another, almost invariably greater, this phenomenon being known as fluorescence. For some substances the absorption is *general*, *i.e.*, it is the same or nearly so for all wave-lengths. Others exhibit *selective* absorption which is more or less complete for certain spectral regions while for others the transmission is very high. Among substances showing general absorption are thin metallic films, lampblack, and metallic blacks which are composed of finely divided particles of pure metal. These "blacks" will be discussed later.

The absorption by a gas of energy corresponding to those frequencies which atoms may emit has been discussed in Chap. XIV.

2. Laws of Absorption.—If a beam of light of intensity I_0 is incident upon absorbing material, it may be said that each element of thickness, or each layer, absorbs the same fraction of the light passing through it. Then the intensity I of the light after passing through a total thickness d is given by

$$I = I_0 e^{-\mu d},$$

where μ is the coefficient of absorption of the material and e is the Napierian logarithmic base. This is known as Lambert's law. The value of μ depends upon the wave-length of the light.

A similar relation has been proposed for absorption by solutions. Here the absorption depends not only upon the thickness d traversed but also upon the total number of absorbing molecules and hence upon the concentration, whereupon we have

$$I = I_0 e^{-Acd},$$

in which A is the absorption coefficient for unit concentration, or the *molecular-absorption coefficient*, and c the concentration. This is known as Beer's law. While Lambert's law is upheld by observations, Beer's law does not always hold, since in some cases A varies with the concentration.

3. Surface Color of Substances.—Most substances owe their surface color to selective absorption. Internal reflections and refractions take place beneath the surface between the particles as well as absorption by them, the light which is finally returned from the substance being that which is least absorbed. Therefore an object which is red because of selective absorption of shorter wave-lengths will appear almost black if illuminated only with blue light. A small amount of color is, of course, reflected from the particles in the outermost layer.

The internal reflections and refractions which thus account for color would not take place if the medium were homogeneous. It is evident therefore that a mixture of two colored pigments does not produce the same color that results when two light beams of the same two colors are combined. While in the latter case the eye receives the actual wave-lengths in the combination, in the former the absorption of the mixed pigments is not necessarily the sum of the separate absorptions.

A substance which appears white has that property because it is composed of finely divided transparent particles which are either not in optical contact, as in the case of powdered glass or crystal, or are embedded in a transparent medium of different index of refraction, as in the case of white paint. If either the finely divided powder or the surrounding medium have selective absorption, the paint will appear not white but colored.

4. Color Transmission.—The color transmitted by an absorbing medium depends mainly upon the selective absorption. If the medium is homogeneous, so that the same fraction is absorbed by each unit layer, the intensity of the transmitted light is given by Ia^t, where I is the intensity of the light refracted into the first surface of the medium, t is the thickness, and a is the *transmission coefficient*.

Certain aniline dyes exhibit a characteristic of transmission called *dichroism* (or dichromatism). For instance, while the

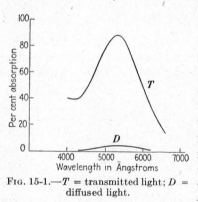

Fig. 15-1.—T = transmitted light; D = diffused light.

light transmitted by a concentrated solution of cyanine appears red, that by a dilute solution is blue. Also, with greater concentration there is an increase in the purity[1] of the color. This is so because the coefficient of transmission for the blue is smaller than that for the red, while at the same time the visual sensation due to the blue is greater than that for the red. Because of the latter factor, with small concentration blue will predominate, in spite of the small transmission coefficient, while great concentration will practically absorb all the blue, leaving only red with increased purity.

Similar results are obtained with thick and thin layers of substances exhibiting dichroism, provided the concentrations are equal.

Scattering is also partly responsible for color of transmission, especially in colloids, although even there it plays a minor role. In Fig. 15-1 are shown the relations, for a colloidal solution of gold, between the coefficient of absorption, the transmission, and the scattering of light.

---

[1] Purity is the ratio of the luminosity of the dominant monochromatic radiation to the total luminosity.

5. Absorbing Blacks.—In Sec. **15-1** was mentioned the property of general absorption possessed by certain metallic blacks, such as lampblack, platinum black, chemically precipitated silver, and other metals in a finely divided state. These substances which when in solid blocks exhibit high reflection, either specular if polished or diffuse if rough, owe their peculiar blackness to the finely divided state. In this state the lampblack or metal is really a mass having great porosity. The light is reflected mostly *into* the open spaces between the particles, with a partial absorption at each reflection. The ideal arrangement of particles for this effect would be an array of needle-shaped highly absorbing particles all on end to the surface, as in the case of black velvet.

6. Early Theories of Dispersion.—Reference has already been made to Cauchy's dispersion formula, which is simply an empirical relation of the form

$$n = n_0 + \frac{B}{\lambda^2} + \frac{C}{\lambda^4} + \cdots \qquad (15\text{-}1)$$

in which n_0, B, C, etc., are constants depending on the substance. This formula tells us nothing of the nature of that substance, nor of its interaction with the light passing through it. Moreover, it is not in agreement with the facts in all cases. For substances which are not transparent for all wave-lengths but show selective absorption, the index of refraction, n, does not increase continuously as the wave-length decreases, as required by Cauchy's formula. Instead, for wave-lengths slightly shorter than those in the region of absorption, the index is less than for wave-lengths slightly greater than those of light absorbed. The effect, known as *anomalous dispersion*, can be examined by means of successive dispersion by two prisms whose refracting edges are at right angles.[1]

A formula, due to Sellmeier representing the situation, is

$$n^2 = 1 + \frac{D\lambda^2}{\lambda^2 - \lambda_s^2}. \qquad (15\text{-}2)$$

The particles of the substance are supposed to possess a natural period of vibration whose frequency corresponds to λ_s. D is a

[1] For detailed descriptions of such experiments the reader is referred to Wood, "Physical Optics," Editions of 1911 and 1934, Macmillan.

constant.   In the case of a substance which shows more than one absorption band, the formula may be written

$$n^2 = 1 + \sum \frac{D\lambda^2}{\lambda^2 - \lambda_s^2}. \tag{15-3}$$

A graphical description of the results for two absorption bands is given in Fig. 15-2.

Sellmeier's formula is an improvement on that of Cauchy because it gives more accurate values for n as the region of an absorption band is approached.   In regions very close to the

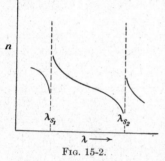

FIG. 15-2.

absorption band, however, it cannot be applied, since n becomes infinite. In other regions it represents the experimental results very well. Helmholtz proposed a mechanical formula based upon the supposition that the atoms, being capable of vibration about fixed positions within the molecule, were subject to vibrations due to the oscillatory motion of the light wave transmitted

through the medium.   In order to overcome the difficulty inherent in Sellmeier's formula, and to account for *absorption*, he supposed also that the vibration of the atom was attended by a damping force of a frictional character.   The theory of Helmholtz was extended by Ketteler, who produced a modified formula containing a term for the index of refraction for very long waves. Both the Helmholtz and the Helmholtz-Ketteler dispersion formulas are found to agree within limits with experimental results.   Although the latter formula is not unlike that obtained on the basis of the electromagnetic theory, and involves a term for the dielectric constant of the medium, for purposes of comparison with eq. 15-3 it will be given in the simplified form

$$n^2 = 1 + \sum \frac{D'\lambda^2}{\lambda^2 - \lambda_s^2 + G\lambda^2}, \tag{15-4}$$

where D' is a constant, and $G\lambda^2$ the term representing the frictional force.[1]

---

[1] For a good summary of the earlier theories of dispersion see Preston, "The Theory of Light," Macmillan.

7. The Electromagnetic Theory of Dispersion.—The formulas given in the preceding section were either empirical or based upon the assumption of material particles possessing natural vibration periods, and set into oscillation mechanically by the light wave While the generality of the Helmholtz-Ketteler formula was greater than that of any which preceded it, particularly because of the inclusion of the damping term, its fundamental assumptions were not in harmony with the electromagnetic theory and the electron theory of matter. The basis of a more rigorous electromagnetic theory of dispersion was laid down by Drude and Voigt,[1] and later was brought into harmony with modern theory.

In this theory a concept of a damping factor was introduced as in that of Helmholtz. According to the modern electron theory of matter, atoms consist of positively charged nuclei and negatively charged electrons. In the electric field of the light wave these are set into oscillation. The idea may be illustrated by considering a body carrying positive and negative charges to exist in the electric field of a condenser. Owing to the field, the negative charges will be displaced toward the positive plate of the condenser and the positive charges toward the negative side resulting in an induced *dipole moment* in the body. If the condenser is discharged, the dipole will be set into oscillation. A similar picture holds for the effect of the electromagnetic light wave upon the atoms of the substance through which the light passes. An equation of motion, which includes also a damping term to account for the absorption of light energy, may be set up. This equation leads to a solution which may be expressed in terms of the dielectric constant of the medium. The manner in which this may be related to the index of refraction is as follows.

According to the electromagnetic theory, for frequencies of vibration as great as those of light, the index of refraction of a material medium is given by $n = \sqrt{\epsilon}$, where ϵ is the *dielectric constant*, or specific inductive capacity, of the medium. If the

[1] See Drude, "Optics," Longmans, and Houstoun, "A Treatise on Light." For more modern presentations see Lorentz, "Problems of Modern Physics," Ginn; also Slater and Frank, "Introduction to Theoretical Physics," McGraw-Hill. A summary of theories of dispersion and a review of the quantum theory of dispersion is presented by Korff and Breit in Reviews of *Modern Physics*, **4**, 471, 1932.

medium is absorbing, its index of refraction n is best given as a complex quantity, and may be written $\bar{n} = n(1 - i\kappa)$ where κ is the *absorption index*.[1] The resulting dispersion formula is

$$\bar{n}^2 = n^2(1 - i\kappa)^2 = 1 + \sum \frac{N\dfrac{e^2}{m}}{\nu_s{}^2 - \nu^2 + iG\nu}, \quad (15\text{-}5)$$

in which N is the number of electrons per unit volume, e the charge on the electron, m its mass, ν the frequency of the light, and ν_s the natural frequency of vibration of an electron.

When ν is not near ν_s, the frictional term G may be neglected, the right-hand side of the equation is real, and eq. 15-5 becomes

$$n^2 = 1 + \sum \frac{N\dfrac{e^2}{m}}{\nu_s{}^2 - \nu^2}. \quad (15\text{-}6)$$

Upon using the relation $c = \nu\lambda$ to change from frequency to wave-length, eq. 15-6 takes the form

$$n^2 = 1 + \sum \frac{Ne^2\lambda_s{}^2}{mc^2} \cdot \frac{\lambda^2}{\lambda^2 - \lambda_s{}^2}, \quad (15\text{-}7)$$

which has the same form as Sellmeier's formula, eq. 15-3.

On the other hand, for values of ν very close to ν_s, the frictional term is important and cannot be neglected. Considering the case for absorption by gases, for which n is very close to unity,

---

[1] Sometimes called the *extinction coefficient*, and sometimes the *coefficient of absorption*. The two are related, but not the same. In traversing perpendicularly a thin layer of absorbing material of thickness d, the amplitude of vibration of light of wave-length λ decreases in the ratio $1 : e^{-2\pi\kappa\frac{d}{\lambda}}$, where κ is the *extinction coefficient*. In consequence, the ratio of the intensities of the emerging and incident light is given by $I_1/I_0 = e^{-4\pi\kappa\frac{d}{\lambda}}$. For an absorbing layer of thickness λ, this ratio is given by $I_1/I_0 = e^{-4\kappa\pi}$, from which it follows that $\kappa = \dfrac{1}{4\pi} \log \dfrac{I_0}{I_1}$. The *coefficient of absorption*, which may be called μ, is related to the extinction coefficient by $\mu = 4\pi\kappa/\lambda$, since $I = I_0 e^{-\mu d}$. The term *absorption index* is preferred, because the word *extinction* implies *complete* dissipation of the light energy.

and assuming only one natural frequency ν_s, eq. **15-5** may be written

$$n^2(1 - i\kappa)^2 = 1 + \frac{Ne^2}{2m} \cdot \frac{1}{\nu_s{}^2 - \nu^2 + iG\nu}.$$

Separating this into real and imaginary parts, we obtain

$$n^2(1 + \kappa)^2 = \frac{Ne^2}{2m} \cdot \frac{\nu_s{}^2 - \nu^2}{(\nu_s{}^2 - \nu^2)^2 + G^2\nu^2} \qquad (15\text{-}8)$$

and

$$2n^2\kappa = \frac{Ne^2}{2m} \cdot \frac{G\nu}{(\nu_s{}^2 - \nu^2)^2 + G^2\nu^2}. \qquad (15\text{-}9)$$

The values of n and κ are plotted in Fig. 15-3.

The results given above are for gases, in which each molecule is considered to be entirely free from the influence of others. In liquids and solids this influence must be taken into account. The result is a dispersion formula of the same form as eq. 15-5, except that the natural frequencies are different by a factor depending upon the effects of the molecules upon each other.

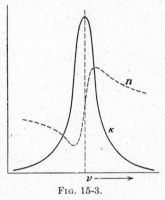

Fig. 15-3.

8. The Quantum Theory of Dispersion.—From the preceding sections on dispersion it is evident that on the basis of any classical model the index of refraction of a medium is given by a formula containing a term proportional to

$$\frac{1}{\nu_s{}^2 - \nu^2},$$

where ν is the frequency of the incident radiation and ν_s is the frequency of an oscillator whose character depends upon the particular assumptions involved. According to the quantum theory of spectra, however, this oscillation frequency is not that of the radiation, yet experiments show that there must be some intimate connection between the refraction, dispersion, and absorption of a medium. In terms of the quantum concept of the origin of spectra, there should, then, be some relation between the change of energy $h\nu_a$ in absorption (and hence the frequency corresponding to an absorption region of the spectrum) and the dispersion of the light. Experimentally it is shown conclusively that there are absorption bands in spectral regions of so-called "anomalous" dispersion.

This discrepancy between the meaning of ν_s in dispersion formulas and the significance of ν_a for absorption in spectral theory was one of the indications that the quantum theory in its earlier form was not sufficiently comprehensive to account for a wide range of associated phenomena. Owing to the efforts of many investigators in the past decade, there has grown out of this difficulty a more satisfactory theory known as *quantum mechanics*. So far as spectra are concerned, the older concepts of energy states and much of the complex mechanism of the older quantum theory are retained. With regard to dispersion, the concept outlined in Sec. **15-7,** that the index of refraction depends upon the electric dipole moment acquired by the particles under the influence of radiation, holds as in the electromagnetic theory. The quantum mechanics dispersion formula is the same in form as eq. 15-6, except that (a) the term ν_s no longer relates to the natural frequencies of vibration of the particles, but to frequencies associated with the *transitions between energy states*, and (b) the numerator comprises terms which depend upon the *probabilities of the transitions*. In addition, the more general quantum theory of dispersion[1] accounts also for the existence in scattered radiation of the *Raman effect*, which is to be discussed in Sec. **15-19.**

9. Residual Rays.—In 1896 E. F. Nichols, working in Rubens' laboratory, discovered that in the regions of wave-length 8.5 microns (= 85,000 angstroms) and 20 microns, crystal quartz possesses metallic reflecting power; i.e., for those wave-lengths it is as good a reflector as is a polished metal surface for visible light. Nichols' work was quickly followed by investigations of other crystalline solids. The discovery of this property of *selective reflection* was of great importance, for in these same wavelength regions crystal quartz has pronounced absorption bands. Consequently the absorptive characteristics of solid transparent

[1] Originally developed by Kramers and Heisenberg, *Zeitschrift für Physik*, **31,** 681, 1925, and later derived from the general considerations of quantum mechanics. The mathematical theory involved is beyond the scope of this text, but may be found in any comprehensive treatise on quantum mechanics.

substances may be determined by finding its *residual rays* (reststrahlen). Also, substances with this characteristic, used as reflectors, serve to isolate rather narrow bands of wave-length in the infrared, thus taking the place of filters for isolating such regions.

Of considerable importance theoretically is the fact that observations on residual rays permit determinations of the characteristic frequencies of the absorbing substances, since these frequencies are evidently associated with the mechanism of absorption.

In spectral regions at which ordinary transmitting substances exhibit high selective absorption the value of the absorption index κ (eq. 15-5) may be sufficiently large compared to $(n - 1)$ so that the reflectivity[1] is considerably higher than for other wave-lengths. This correspondence between *selective reflection* and *selective absorption* of transparent substances has been verified by numerous experiments on residual rays. The table shows the wave-lengths of residual rays of maximum intensity and absorption maxima for a number of solid substances.

Residual rays of substances	Residual rays, microns	Absorption maximum, microns
Lithium fluoride, LiF............	17.0	32.6
Sodium fluoride, NaF............	35.8	40.6
Sodium chloride, NaCl (rock salt).	52.0	61.1
Potassium chloride, KCl (sylvite).	63.4	70.7
Rubidium chloride, RbCl........	73.8	84.8
Potassium bromide, KBr.........	81.5	88.3
Potassium iodide, KI............	94.1	102.0
Silver chloride, AgCl............	81.5	
Silver bromide, AgBr............	112.7	
Thallium chloride, TlCl..........	91.9	117.0
Thallium bromide, TlBr.........	117.0	
Thallium iodide, TlI............	151.8	
Zincblende, ZnS	30.9	
Fluorspar, CaF$_2$	2.4, 31.6	
Quartz, SiO$_2$	8.5, 20.0	
Calcite, CaCO$_3$	6.76, 28.0, 90.0	

[1] This quantity is defined in the next section.

It is evident that the region of maximum absorption does not coincide exactly with the region of strongest intensity of the residual rays, the former being displaced toward longer wave-lengths.[1]

10. Metallic Reflection.—In the preceding paragraphs dealing with the characteristics of ordinary transparent and semi-transparent substances, it has been stated that there is apparent a relation between ordinary selective absorption and the possession by the substance of characteristic electronic frequencies of vibration. In the discussion of residual rays, it appears, further, that so-called transparent media often have the property of metallic reflection for certain wave-lengths in the infrared, and at the same time have strong absorption for those wave-lengths. Turning to a consideration of ordinary metallic substances, it is found, conversely, that for certain wave-length regions these may also act like transparent media.

Transparent substances and metals are also at opposite extremes with regard to electrical conductivity. Most transparent substances are good dielectrics, *i.e.*, they are poor conductors. The property of electrical conductivity has been found to be associated with the presence of so-called free electrons, which are not bound in fixed relation to the molecules or atoms as are the electrons, mentioned above, responsible for absorption bands, but which may migrate more or less freely through the metal in response to an electromotive force. The peculiar optical properties of metals, namely, their reflectivity, absorption, and transmission, are therefore dependent not only upon the bound electrons, but also upon these free electrons. For certain wave-length regions, therefore, a knowledge of the optical constants of metals may be obtained from a knowledge of the electrical conductivity. Theoretically also, it is possible to study the manner in which these free electrons act under the influence of electromagnetic waves of light.

The reflectivity R of a metal is defined as the ratio for normal incidence of the intensity of the reflected to that of the incident light. This may be obtained for metals from Fresnel's equations. In eq. **13-12** the amplitude of the reflected light for normal

---

[1] For a discussion of the theory of residual rays the reader is referred to Max Born, "Optik."

ncidence for vibrations *perpendicular* to the plane of incidence
s given as

$$a_1 = -a\frac{n-1}{n+1},$$

and in eq. 13-13, for vibrations *in* the plane of incidence, as

$$b_1 = b\frac{n-1}{n+1}.$$

These equations are for transparent media.   For metals, which
absorb strongly, n must be replaced by $n(1 - i\kappa)$, as indicated
in Sec. **15-7**.   Making the substitution in eq. 13-12 we obtain

$$\frac{a_1}{a} = \frac{1 - n + in\kappa}{1 + n - in\kappa},$$

which, multiplied by its conjugate, gives the *reflectivity*

$$R = \frac{(n-1)^2 + n^2\kappa^2}{(n+1)^2 + n^2\kappa^2}, \qquad (15\text{-}10)$$

and for transparent media becomes simply

$$R = \frac{(n-1)^2}{(n+1)^2}.$$

From the electromagnetic theory of light it can be shown that

$$n^2\kappa = \frac{\sigma}{\nu}, \qquad (15\text{-}11)$$

where σ is the electrical conductivity and ν is the frequency of
the light.   From eqs. 15-10 and 15-11 and making use of assumptions based on experimental results, it is possible to obtain R in
terms of σ.   Equation 15-10 may be put in the form

$$R = 1 - \frac{4n}{(n+1)^2 + \kappa^2 n^2}. \qquad (15\text{-}12)$$

Also, we may make the assumption that for metals the absorption
is very nearly unity.   Putting $\kappa = 1$, there results

$$R = 1 - \frac{4n}{2n^2 + 2n + 1}. \qquad (15\text{-}13)$$

For very long wave-lengths it is found that n for metals is very
much greater than unity, so that we may ignore all terms in the

denominator of eq. 15-13 smaller than $2n^2$. Also, in eq. 15-11, putting $\kappa = 1$, we have $n^2 = \sigma/\nu$. Making these approximations and substitutions in eq. 15-13, we have

$$R = 1 - \frac{2}{\sqrt{\sigma/\nu}}. \tag{15-14}$$

This simplified and only approximate relationship between the reflectivity and the conductivity of a metal does not apply below 5 microns. For copper, using infrared radiation of wavelength 12 microns, Hagen and Rubens found experimentally the value $1 - R = 1.6 \times 10^{-2}$, while from the conductivity the calculated value is 1.4×10^{-2}.

11. Optical Constants of Metals.—It has been shown that the value of the index of refraction n and the absorption index κ may be found in terms of the electrical conductivity of a metal. These quantities may also be found by direct optical experiment. It may be shown by the electromagnetic theory that incident plane-polarized light becomes, on reflection from the surface of a metal, elliptically polarized. The extent of this polarization depends upon the azimuth of the plane of vibration of the beam and its angle of incidence. It may be shown that the following equations[1] hold with a fair degree of precision:

$$\left. \begin{array}{l} \kappa = \sin \Delta \tan 2\psi, \\[2mm] n = \sin \varphi \tan \varphi \dfrac{\cos 2\psi}{1 + \cos \Delta \sin 2\psi}, \\[2mm] n^2(1 + \kappa^2) = \sin^2 \varphi \tan^2 \varphi \dfrac{1 - \cos \Delta \sin 2\psi}{1 + \cos \Delta \sin 2\psi}, \end{array} \right\} \tag{15-15}$$

where Δ is the difference of phase introduced by reflection between the component of the vibration parallel, and that perpendicular, to the plane of incidence, and φ is the angle of incidence. The angle ψ is called the angle of the restored plane of polarization[2] measured from the plane of incidence. Thus, when incident plane-polarized light is changed by reflection to elliptically polarized light, it may be changed to plane-polarized light once more by a $\lambda/4$-plate or Babinet compensator, and

[1] The derivation of these equations may be found in Drude's "Theory of Optics."

[2] It will be recalled that the plane of polarization is perpendicular to the plane of vibration.

an ψ is given by the ratio of the component (of the reflected light) parallel, to that perpendicular, to the plane of incidence. Methods of determining φ and ψ are described in Experiment 21, for the case where $\Delta = \pi/2$.

A value of the reflectivity R is found by substituting n and κ obtained from eqs. 15-15 in eq. 15-10.[1]

12. The Scattering of Light by Gases.—If a strong beam of white light is passed through a cloud of small particles of dust or condensed water vapor, the cloud takes on a color which depends upon the size of the particles. With the smallest particles the color will be blue, while with increasing size the light scattered will contain longer and longer wave-lengths until finally it is gray, or even white. At the same time, the light of the direct beam transmitted through the cloud will appear more and more red, until it cannot be seen at all. The same general effect may be observed with particles in suspension in a liquid. A simple experiment may be performed by mixing a weak solution of hyposulphite of soda (hypo) with a little dilute acid, causing a precipitation of sulphur. The aggregations of sulphur particles increase in size as the chemical action proceeds. Although the best method for demonstrating the effect of size on scattering is to project a beam of light from a strong source through the liquid, a simpler way is instructive. The mixture may be made in a large beaker or battery jar, and a 25- or 40-watt lamp plunged beneath its surface, taking care, of course, not to bring about a short circuit in the socket. After a minute or so, the image of the lamp takes on an orange hue which becomes more pronounced until it can no longer be seen through the side of the jar. At the same time the *scattered* light seen by looking at the side of the jar changes from a blue white to a yellowish white.

The selective scattering of light by particles can also be seen in the smoke from a freshly lighted cigar, which is blue from the tip while that drawn through the cigar and exhaled, being made up of coagulations of carbon particles, is gray. The colors of sunsets in a cloudy sky are also due to the scattering of light by water drops and sometimes dust particles. Often the most lurid sunset reds may be seen in the neighborhood of a smoky industrial district.

[1] A good summary of formulas, data, and bibliography is given by J. Valasek in the International Critical Tables, Vol. V, p. 248.

Because of these common observations it was originally supposed that the blue color of a clear sky was due to minute dust particles in suspension in the upper atmosphere. It was shown by Lord Rayleigh that this is not the case, and that the sky owes its blue color to the scattering of light by the molecules of the atmosphere. An overcast sky is, then, gray or dull white because the light is scattered by water drops of larger size. Also if there were no atmosphere, the sky would be absolutely black at all times except for those points where celestial objects would appear.

That ordinary skylight contains very little red is shown by landscape photographs taken through yellow or red color filters with plates specially sensitized to the red. With even a pale yellow filter a clear sky appears dark in a photographic print paling to a lighter shade at the horizon. For aerial surveys of landscapes photographic plates specially sensitized to the infrared are used, since details ordinarily obscured by scattered light of shorter wave-lengths are thus brought out distinctly. In this manner, landscapes many miles distant have been photographed from aeroplanes.

The scattering of light by small particles was studied experimentally by Tyndall. He showed that the larger the scattering particles, the larger proportion of longer wave-lengths the scattered light contained, *i.e.*, the less blue it became. His experiments led him to the conviction that gas particles were not responsible for any of the scattering. The principles on which the scattering may be explained were first stated by Rayleigh. He showed that the sky owes its blue color to scattering of light by the molecules of the atmosphere, the intensity of scattering being proportional to the inverse fourth power of the wave-length. Rayleigh's published papers on this topic appeared through a period of almost half a century, and treat the problem in all details. His conclusions may be summarized briefly as follows:[1]

The molecules of a gas traversed by the incident light may be considered as sources of secondary waves. Each molecule acts on the light individually, *i.e.*, as if unaffected by the presence of other molecules. Between the primary wave incident upon a molecule and the secondary wave given off from it there exists a definite phase relation. Because the molecules are distributed

[1] See Schuster, "Theory of Optics," 2d ed., p. 325.

at random, the phases of the individual scattered waves have no fixed relation to each other, except in the direction of propagation, where they will have the same phase.   Hence, in order to express the intensity of the scattered light, the sum of the intensities of the individual scattered waves is taken instead of the sum of the amplitudes.   The effect of all the molecules in a layer is arrived at by summing up the effects of Fresnel zones into which the layer is divided.   The resultant vibration thus obtained is combined with the vibration of the incident wave, the result being a change of phase which may be considered as due to a change in velocity like that which occurs when light enters a refracting medium. This accounts for the entry of the index of refraction into the final formula.   The expression thus obtained for the intensity of the scattered light is

$$I = A^2 \frac{2n^2(n-1)^2}{N\lambda^4}(1 + \cos^2 \beta), \qquad (15\text{-}16)$$

in which A^2 is the intensity of the incident light, n the index of refraction of the scattering gas, N the number of molecules per unit volume, and β the angle at the molecule between the direction of observation and the direction of propagation of the incident light.   Equation 15-16 holds only if the incident light is unpolarized.   It appears that the intensity of the scattered light is inversely proportional to the fourth power of the wave-length, a relation which holds for liquids and solids as well as for gases.

13. Polarization of Scattered Light.—While Rayleigh's law for the intensity of scattering given in eq. 15-16 is essentially correct, it was shown by Cabannes[1] that it is necessary to take into account a factor depending upon the state of polarization of the light.   Experiment shows that if the incident light is unpolarized, the light scattered at right angles to the direction of propagation of the incident light is almost entirely plane-polarized, with the plane of vibration perpendicular to the common plane of the incident and scattered beams.   This may be explained in the following way: Consider unpolarized radiation proceeding from source S to molecule m (Fig. 15-4).   We choose a direction

---

[1] A comprehensive discussion of the scattering of light is given by Cabannes: "La diffusion moléculaire de la lumière."   A very readable survey of the subject is contained in a small volume by Raman, "The Molecular Diffraction of Light," published by Calcutta University, 1922.

S' perpendicular to Sm in which the scattered light is to be observed. In accordance with the usual treatment of problems in polarization, the unpolarized beam is considered to be resolved into two components of vibration, one perpendicular to the plane SmS', the other in that plane. The direction of vibration of the second of these components is the same as the direction of propagation mS' of the scattered beam under observation and thus will contribute nothing to the light at S'. The light at S' should therefore be completely plane polarized with its direction of vibration perpendicular to the plane SmS'. The argument holds for any point of observation on a plane, containing mS', to which Sm is normal. At points of observation as S'' not in this plane,

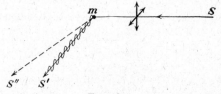

FIG. 15-4.

the light should be partially polarized. Actual experiments show that the light scattered in directions perpendicular to the direction of propagation of the incident light is *not* completely polarized, for reasons which will be discussed later. The use of a double image prism such as a Wollaston reveals a strong component of vibration perpendicular to the plane of S and S' and a weak component parallel to it.[1] Cabannes finds that the intensity of scattering is represented more closely if the right-hand side of eq. 15-16 is multiplied by a factor

$$\frac{6 + 6\rho}{6 - 7\rho},$$

where ρ is the ratio of the weak (parallel) to the strong (perpendicular) component of polarization.

The existence of some unpolarized scattered radiation in a direction at right-angles to the direction of propagation of the incident beam is believed to be because some of the molecules are

---

[1] It should not be assumed that this means the presence of two plane-polarized beams, one perpendicular and one parallel to the mutual plane of propagation, but rather that the scattered light is a mixture of plane-polarized and ordinary light.

anisotropic. This term may be explained in the following manner. Suppose a molecule to consist of three atoms, one with a positive charge and two with negative charges, as in the case of carbon dioxide. As long as the geometrical center of the double negative charge coincides with the position of the positive, the molecule has no electric moment, but if this coincidence does not exist, the molecule is said to have an electric *dipole* moment. Also, if the centers of electrical charge do coincide, the imposition of an external electric field will cause a relative displacement of the charges, resulting in an *induced dipole*. We may consider the vibration of these induced dipoles to be the origin of the scattered radiation. Since the molecules are oriented at random, the vibrations of many of them will be at angles with the direction of vibration of the light incident upon them. Such molecules are said to be *optically anisotropic*, and their contribution to the scattering is responsible for that part of the light which is unpolarized.

Accurate measurements of the intensity and state of polarization of the light scattered by gases are extremely difficult. Not only is its intensity a minute fraction of the incident light, but it is often completely masked by the greater scattering from dust particles. It is also difficult to get rid of multiple reflections in the apparatus.[1] In much of the earlier work it is probable that improper collimation of the incident light gave spurious results. In accounting for the phenomenon of scattering in the atmosphere still other disturbing factors enter, such as the presence of a certain amount of light scattered by the earth's surface, and *secondary scattering* by the atmosphere. At the same time, scattering is of considerable importance, since in some details it depends upon molecular structure, and thus offers a means of investigating that structure. Also, as is evident from eq. 15-16, it provides a method of determining N, the number of molecules per unit volume, and, from it, calculating the Avogadro number.

14. Fluorescence.—While irradiated with light, many substances emit in all directions some of the energy of radiation which they absorb, the color of the light emitted by these sub-

---

[1] See an article by R. J. Strutt (Rayleigh the Younger), *Proceedings of the Royal Soc. (London)*, **95**, 155, 1918.

stances, which are said to exhibit the property of *fluorescence* depending upon the substance and not upon the wave-length of the incident light. Radiation of short wave-length, such as ultraviolet light or x-rays, is particularly effective in producing fluorescence. The term owes its origin to the fact that the effect was first noticed in fluorspar, which emits a blue light when irradiated with sunlight.

Among other common substances which fluoresce with a blue light are: paraffine wax, kerosene, benzene, some lubricating oils, an aqueous solution of aesculin, and an aqueous solution of quinine sulphate with a few drops of sulphuric acid added. A solution of chlorophyll in alcohol shows red fluorescence. Fluorescene in solution shows yellow green, as does also uranium glass. When irradiated with x-rays or cathode rays, most glasses fluoresce, the color depending on the kind of glass. Ultraviolet light causes the cornea and lens of the eye and the teeth to fluoresce strongly, and, in smaller amount, the hair and nails also, the strength of the effect appearing to depend on personal characteristics, such as pigmentation. It has been observed that after passing through a solution which fluoresces, the light exhibits reduced power of exciting the same fluorescence, because of absorption of the exciting light. Thus a weak light falling upon a solution excites marked fluorescence only in the layer it first strikes.

The fluorescent light is not of a single wave-length but a band with a pronounced maximum of intensity. It was formerly believed that the wave-lengths emitted were always longer than those of the radiation effective in producing the fluorescence, a conclusion reached by Stokes and known as *Stokes' law*. More recent investigations have shown that while Stokes' law is generally obeyed, the wave-length of maximum intensity of fluorescence is independent of the wave-length of the exciting light. The intensity of the fluorescence of any solution also depends upon the character of the solvent.

15. Polarization of Fluorescence.—It has been found that fluorescence of solutions is polarized. The degree of polarization in some cases depends upon the concentration and the temperature. In general, the more viscous the solvent, the more strongly is the fluorescence polarized, probably because of the tendency of the solvent to hold the molecules in a fixed orientation.

In the case of isotropic substances, the polarization also depends upon the obliquity of emission. Some fluorescent crystals also exhibit peculiarities of polarization. No such degree of polarization exists in fluorescence, however, as in scattering of light, where almost complete plane polarization exists, the vibrations being at right angles to the incident beam.

16. Phosphorescence.—The term fluorescence is used when the process of emission goes on while the substance is being irradiated. Substances which continue to emit light for some time *after* the exciting light is removed are termed *phosphorescent*. The emission continues for different periods of time, depending on the substance and sometimes on temperature changes. Calcium sulphide continues its phosphorescence for many hours after the exciting radiation is removed, and is for this reason used as an ingredient in phosphorescent paint.

Phosphorescence and fluorescence are difficult to distinguish, since the former persists in some cases only for an extremely small fraction of a second after the exciting light is removed. Actually, all solid fluorescent substances are phosphorescent. It is customary to limit the use of the term phosphorescence to the property exhibited by certain crystalline substances which contain impurities in the form of metallic particles. It is these particles which are responsible for the phosphorescence. In all other cases of so-called phosphorescence a better term is *delayed*, or *persistent, fluorescence*.

Little is known of what is actually going on in a solid which absorbs light and fluoresces. It is believed that a photochemical process takes place owing to the absorption of light energy, the process later reversing with the accompaniment of light emission.

17. Fluorescence in Gases.—Rayleigh the younger has observed that the *D*-lines of sodium (5890 and 5896 angstroms) are emitted from a glass container of sodium vapor when it is irradiated by the light of the zinc line at 3303 angstroms. This is a case of true fluorescence, and is explained by the quantum theory of spectra in the following manner.

The *D*-lines of sodium constitute the first member of the principal series, of which the second member is the doublet 3302.3 and 3302.9. Upon being irradiated by light of that wave-length (of the zinc spectrum in the case quoted) the atoms of the sodium vapor absorb energy of radiation, thereupon undergoing a corresponding change of energy. According to spectral theory, this change of energy consists of an electron passing from the lowest, or ground, level to an upper level, as shown in Fig. 15-5 by the arrow pointing upward. The atom then passes to the lowest level of energy in two steps, the first corresponding

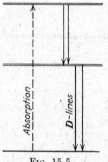

Fig. 15-5.

to the emission of a red line, the second to the emission of the *D*-lines. While the *D*-lines were observed, the red line was not. It has been shown that the difference of energy corresponding to the missing red line is transformed into energy of motion, *i.e.*, heat energy, by collision between atoms.[1] Many other cases of *fluorescence of atoms* have been observed. While the fluorescent spectrum of liquids and solids is a continuous band of some width, that of a monatomic gas or vapor is composed of lines. The character of the fluorescence of atoms varies greatly with the presence of inert gases, because of the energy changes due to atomic collisions with the molecules of the inert gas.[2]

Under certain conditions, an increase of density of a gas causes a decrease in the intensity of the fluorescent light. The explanation is that at the higher density the molecules or atoms have more opportunities for collisions with each other. The result is an increased proportion of the energy of the incident beam being changed into heat energy and a smaller amount being scattered as fluorescent light.

18. Resonance Radiation.—In the course of some experiments on the fluorescence of sodium vapor with white light, R. W. Wood limited the wave-length of the exciting light by means of a monochromator to a very narrow band at the region of the sodium *D*-lines. He found that the spectrum of the fluorescent light thus excited consisted of a number of single lines distributed

[1] Collisions of this sort, in which the potential energy possessed by excited atoms or molecules is given up to other atoms and thus changed to kinetic energy of agitation, are called *collisions of the second kind.* If a collision occurs between atoms or molecules by which one of them is raised to an excited state (*i.e.*, an electron moved to a higher energy level), it is called a *collision of the first kind.*

[2] For an extensive discussion of fluorescence the reader is referred to Wood, "Physical Optics," 2d ed., Chaps. XVIII, XIX, XX, Macmillan.

throughout the spectrum. The wave-length distribution changed with slight alterations in the exact wave-length range allowed to pass from the incident light by the monochromator. The fluorescence obtained in this manner he called *resonance radiation*, and the spectra, *resonance spectra*. Resonance radiation may be obtained by the use of an irradiating source consisting of a single line of a metallic spectrum, and also with other vapors than that of sodium.

19. Raman Effect.—In 1928, Raman, after several years of investigation of light scattering, discovered that when a trans-

FIG. 15-6.—Raman effect in carbon tetrachloride.   Above, the spectrum of the incident light.   Below, the spectrum of the scattered light, showing the Raman lines on either side of the stronger lines due to ordinary scattering.   (*From Raman and Krishnan, Proceedings of the Royal Society of London,* **122,** 23, 1929.)

parent liquid is irradiated with monochromatic light from a strong source the spectrum of the scattered light contains, in addition to the exciting line of frequency ν, several weaker lines on either side, whose frequencies are given by $\nu \pm \Delta\nu$. Later, the same effect was discovered in solids and gases. The differences $\Delta\nu$ are independent of the frequency of the original radiation and depend only on the nature of the scattering medium. The appearance of the displaced lines, known as the *Raman effect*, is illustrated in Fig. 15-6. As is evident, it is not necessary to use strictly monochromatic light provided the spectrum of the source contains only relatively few lines.

The lines displaced to the red are often referred to as *Stokes lines* and those to the violet as *anti-Stokes* lines. This custom arose from the hypothesis proposed by Stokes many years earlier, and referred to in Sec. **15-14,** that secondary radiation such as fluorescence was always of longer wave-length than the incident light. In the Raman effect the anti-Stokes lines are invariably fainter than the Stokes lines.

The displaced lines are so much fainter than the lines of the exciting radiation that very long exposures are necessary to photograph them. A simple type of apparatus is shown in Fig. 15-7. The source M is usually a quartz mercury arc of great intensity. The liquid to be examined is contained in a horn-shaped tube R, shielded from extraneous light and surrounded by a water cooler W, the small end of the horn being blackened and curved so that light reflected internally will be directed away from the larger end at which the observations are made.

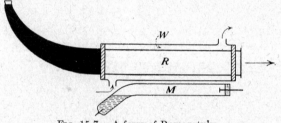

FIG. 15-7.—A form of Raman tube.

The discovery of Raman was not entirely unexpected. In 1923, A. H. Compton, while examining the spectra of x-rays scattered by a solid, discovered in the spectrum of the scattered radiation a line of smaller frequency than that of the incident x-rays. Also, in the same year, it had been predicted by Smekal[1] that in addition to light of the same frequency as the incident radiation there should be present in the spectrum of ordinary scattered radiation lines with combination frequencies $\nu \pm \nu_m$, where ν_m is a characteristic frequency of absorption of the molecule, to be observed in the absorption spectrum in the infra-red. Smekal's suggestion was that when a photon of energy $h\nu$ is incident on a molecule there will take place an exchange of energy in which the photon will either be augmented by, or have subtracted from it, an amount of energy $h\nu_m$. In 1924, a similar prediction was made by Kramers[2] upon the basis of a new quantum theory of dispersion (Sec. **15-8**), which was pub-

[1] *Naturwissenschaft*, **11**, 873, 1923.
[2] *Nature*, **113**, 673, 1924.

lished in more complete form by Kramers and Heisenberg the following year.

Raman's discovery seemed at first to be a complete confirmation of Smekal's prediction. Further observations soon disclosed that, although for many Raman lines the frequency differences $\Delta\nu$ (of the first paragraph of this section) agreed approximately with the frequencies in infra-red absorption bands, actually Raman lines are often observed for which there exist no corresponding observed absorption frequencies. Moreover, some substances having strong absorption bands show no Raman lines with corresponding values of $\Delta\nu$. It was further

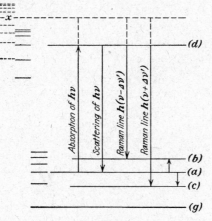

Fig. 15-8.

discovered that, even in those cases where a rough agreement existed between the values of $\Delta\nu$ and the frequencies ν_m of absorption bands, there was no agreement between the intensities.

Classical theories offer no satisfactory explanation of these observations. Those theories would require that the molecules of the irradiated substance have natural vibration frequencies ν_m which, combined with the frequency of the incident light, give rise to radiation of combination frequencies $\nu \pm \nu_m$. On the other hand, the Bohr theory postulates definitely that radiation is a mechanism in which the frequencies of the orbital motions of radiating electrons are *not* the frequencies of the spectral lines. These latter are, instead, proportional to the energy differences between the so-called stationary states in the molecule. Moreover, in the Raman effect the intensities of the lines displaced toward the red are greater than those displaced toward the violet, as shown in Fig. 15-6, an effect also not in accordance with the classical concept of combination frequencies. The explanation of the Raman effect is really to be found as an integral part of the quantum theory of dispersion and may be reduced to the following simple terms.

Consider a molecule in the energy state indicated by a vibrational energy level a, Fig. 15-8, to be struck by a photon of energy $h\nu$, and raised to an energy state represented by level d, for which the transitions $d \to b$ or $d \to c$ are not possible according to the selection rules of theory. Then Raman radiation is possible only if there exist in the molecule higher energy levels, represented by the group of horizontal dotted lines x, between which and the two levels b and c transitions are possible: It is to be understood that b and c likewise each represents a family of levels, so that *groups* of Raman lines will be observed. Also, the incident quantum may be that corresponding to any line emitted by the irradiating source.

There are three possible ways in which radiation may take place. Either the molecule, upon being struck by a photon of energy $h\nu$, may scatter the same quantum, contributing to the intensity of a spectral line of the same wave-length as that of the incident photon (ordinary scattered light); it may reradiate a quantum $h\nu_1 = h\nu - (E_a - E_b)$ where $E_a - E_b$ is the difference of energy $h\Delta\nu$ between levels a and b, contributing thereby to the intensity of a Raman line displaced toward the red; or it may reradiate a quantum $h\nu_2 = h\nu + (E_c - E_a)$, contributing thereby to the intensity of a Raman line displaced toward the violet. The level a represents only one of a number of possible energy states in which the molecule may be at the time it is struck by the photon. This bears upon the question of the intensities of the Stokes and anti-Stokes lines, and the dependence of these intensities upon the transition probabilities. If, as usually happens, the molecule is in a low energy state, representing a relatively small total energy of the molecule, then the probability is enhanced that it will reradiate with energy

$$h(\nu - \Delta\nu).$$

If, on the other hand, the original level a is relatively high (a more unusual circumstance for substances under ordinary temperature conditions), the probability is enhanced that it will reradiate with energy $h(\nu + \Delta\nu)$. Hence it is apparent that there is no dependence of the Raman line intensities upon the probability of transitions between levels a and b or a and c, but only on the probability of the transitions $a \rightarrow x$ and $x \rightarrow b$ or $x \rightarrow c$.

In the complete theory of the Raman effect, of which the foregoing is only a condensed and oversimplified account, it is supposed that the transitions to and from the level represented by the dotted lines x are not real but *virtual*. This means that the initial photon of energy $h\nu$ does not actually raise the molecular energy to the level x. If scattering takes place, the upper level is one such as d from which an actual transition $d \rightarrow a$ may occur. If Raman lines appear, the dual energy change $a \rightarrow x$ and $x \rightarrow b$ theoretically represented as responsible for each Stokes line really consists of *only a single transition*,[1] the same being true for the anti-Stokes lines. This theoretical interpretation agrees with the fact mentioned earlier, that in some cases no infrared absorption bands are found at frequencies corresponding to the values of $\Delta\nu$. Not only do the differences of frequency $\Delta\nu$ appear in the Raman spectrum, but theory holds that the Raman lines *cannot occur* unless energy levels such as a and b actually exist. In this manner the Raman effect offers an experimental method of finding those characteristic energy states of the molecule, even though there can be found no absorption bands in the spectrum to correspond to them.

A superficial comparison of the Raman effect with fluorescence may leave the reader in doubt as to the difference between them, since in both cases the substance radiates energy corresponding to frequencies other than those of the irradiating light. In the case of fluorescence the reradiated energy is of a frequency which the fluorescing substance is able to absorb, with no dependence upon the frequency of the incident light, while in the Raman effect there is a fixed frequency difference $\Delta\nu$ between the displaced radiation and the incident radiation, no matter what the frequency of the latter may be.[2]

[1] There will, accordingly, be a modification of the usual selection rules, given in Sec. **14-17**.

[2] A full discussion of experimental work in the Raman effect will be found in R. W. Wood, "Physical Optics," Macmillan, 1934.

One important difference between ordinary and modified scattered radiation, *i.e.*, between that which gives rise to the undisplaced spectrum line and that which causes the Raman lines, is in the phase relationship which the two bear to the incident light. In ordinary scattering there is a definite phase relation between the incident and scattered radiation. In the Raman effect the radiations from different molecules have phase differences which vary from one molecule to the next, and also different states of polarization. For this reason, ordinary scattering is called *coherent*, and the Raman, *incoherent* scattering.

20. The Photoelectric Effect.—For the most part the phenomena described in this chapter illustrate the importance of the quantum theory of radiation whenever the interaction of that radiation with matter is involved. The usefulness of that theory will be still more fully brought out in the following chapter. Historically, however, its first great success in explaining the interaction of light and matter was in connection with a phenomenon which is not strictly optical, but which involves the effect of light, called the *photoelectric effect*. It is that whenever a metallic surface is irradiated by visible or ultraviolet light, x-rays, or γ-rays from radioactive substances, electrons are ejected from the surface. The effect is much greater for some metals, such as sodium, potassium, and cesium, than for others, these metals being largely used, accordingly, in the construction of the modern photoelectric cell. It is found that the velocity possessed by an ejected electron depends, not upon the *intensity* of the radiation, but upon its *frequency*. This result cannot be explained on the basis of classical theory, since, if we call the kinetic energy of the electron $\frac{1}{2}mv^2$, there is every reason to believe that more intense radiation, possessing greater energy, might communicate more energy to the electron and thus give it a greater velocity than does weaker radiation.

The true explanation was given by Einstein in 1905, by an extension of Planck's hypothesis, that the energy of the "oscillators" in a black-body radiation consists of integral amounts of some indivisible unit of energy ϵ (see Sec. **14-13**), proportional to $h\nu$. It follows inescapably from that theory that the energy of radiation must itself be quantized.

Einstein carried this result still farther by the hypothesis that the energy of each quantum of radiation is not, as required by classical theory, distributed equally over the wave front which spreads out from the source, but retains its individuality and proceeds as a "directed" unit of energy. These units of energy are now known as *photons*. The energy of a photon is equal to $h\nu$, where h is Planck's quantum constant and ν is the frequency of the radiation.

The kinetic energy, $\frac{1}{2}mv^2$, of the electron after emission is not quite as large as that of the photon which ejects it, since some energy w is required to remove the electron from the surface of the metal. Einstein's photoelectric equation

$$\frac{1}{2}mv^2 = h\nu - w$$

has been found to be in complete agreement with experiment.[1]

From the standpoint of the present discussion, there remains an apparent conflict between the classical wave picture so well substantiated by older light phenomena and the photon theory so essential to the explanation of many phenomena such as the photoelectric effect. At present this conflict is not resolved in simple terms.[2]

[1] For a more detailed discussion of the photoelectric effect see Richtmyer, "Introduction to Modern Physics," McGraw-Hill.

[2] The student may profit by reading sections bearing upon this question in Compton and Allison, "X-rays in Theory and Experiment," Van Nostrand.

CHAPTER XVI

THE EFFECTS OF MAGNETIC AND ELECTRIC FIELDS

That division of physical optics in which are grouped the phenomena due to the effect of an *external magnetic field* upon such characteristics of light as the frequency or state of polarization is called *magneto-optics*. Similarly, that division in which are grouped phenomena due to the effect of an *external electric field* is called *electro-optics*. In general, there are two ways in which either sort of external field may be imposed upon the light, (*a*) the source itself may be placed in the field, (*b*) the light beam after leaving the source may be made to pass through the field. Yet in this broad division into two classes there is involved an oversimplification of ideas, which might lead one to believe that only the light and the field are concerned. This is not so. The phenomena of magneto- and electro-optics concern also (*a*) the matter in which the light has its origin, or (*b*) that through which it passes. A more complete though unwieldy title to this chapter might therefore be, the effects of magnetic and electric fields upon the interaction of light and matter.

When the external field is imposed upon the source, there are modifications of both the *frequency* and *state of polarization* of the emitted light. When it is imposed upon matter through which the light is passing, or from which it is reflected, there are modifications of both the *state of polarization* and *refraction* of the light. These statements apply both to magnetic and electric fields. The effects of fields upon the source will be described first.

1. The Zeeman Effect.—Comprehending that an external field causes changes in the state of material substances which could be detected by the effect of those changes on light, Faraday tried in 1862 to discover what effect a magnetic field has upon a light source, by examining the spectrum of a sodium flame placed between the poles of a strong electromagnet. He failed to discover any difference in the spectrum lines when the field was on. His belief that some change should occur in the lines was justified, for in 1896, with much more powerful apparatus and improved technique, Zeeman found that placing a source in a magnetic field resulted in a broadening of its spectrum lines. Lorentz predicted from theory that the edges of the lines should be polarized. Later, Zeeman found this to be true, and, concluding that stronger fields would resolve the lines into several components, verified this by experiment. The splitting of spectral lines into components by placing the source in a strong magnetic field is known as the *Zeeman effect*.

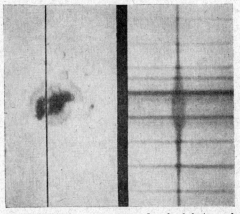

Fig. 16-1.—Zeeman effect in a sunspot. On the left is a photograph of a region on the sun's disk, showing a spot on the slit of the spectrograph. On the right is shown an absorption line in the sun's spectrum, exhibiting Zeeman tripling in the region of the spot. The horizontal lines crossing the spectrum are divisions in the polarizing equipment over the slit, and should be ignored.

The splitting of absorption lines into components when the absorbing medium is in a strong magnetic field is known as the *inverse Zeeman effect*. In 1908, G. E. Hale at the Mount Wilson Observatory showed that the spectroscope revealed the presence of strong magnetic fields in sunspots, as illustrated in Fig. 16-1. This discovery confirmed the inference which had been made from other spectroscopic solar observations that the sunspots are really enormous vortices on the surface of the sun. Later, Hale instituted and directed a lengthy series of experiments on spectra from different latitudes along the meridian of the sun, in an attempt to find the possible effect of a general magnetic field of the sun upon the spectral lines. The results were in agreement with theory and showed that the sun has a general magnetic field similar to that of the earth. The observations and measurements of the absorption lines in this experiment were of the most exacting character and constituted a triumph of technical spectroscopy.

2. Classical Theory of the Zeeman Effect.—According to the theory of Lorentz, an electron moving in its orbit about an atomic nucleus should suffer, when in an external magnetic field, a change $\pm \Delta\nu$ in its frequency of orbital motion ν. This change in frequency is given as

$$\Delta\nu = \frac{eH}{4\pi mc},\tag{16-1}$$

where e is the charge on the electron in e.s.u., H the field strength in gauss, m the mass of the electron, and c the velocity of light.[1]

The classical picture may be explained as follows: Consider a large number of atoms, each contributing radiation to a given spectrum line. The orbital electrons of these are moving in planes possessing all possible orientations in space. The motions

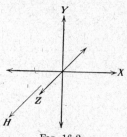

Fig. 16-2.

of any electron may be resolved into components in X-, Y-, and Z-directions as in Fig. 16-2. On the average, the projections of these motions on a particular coordinate plane, say the XZ-plane, will be of the same amplitude as the projections upon the XY- and YZ-planes. Looking along the Z-direction, only the transverse vibrations which take place in the XY-plane will be observed. Also, since for all the atoms the amplitude is on the average the same in all directions in that plane, no polarization will be observed. The same reasoning holds for light observed in any direction.

The foregoing holds in the absence of an external field. To aid in an understanding of the effect of an external magnetic field, consider the case of only one atom. Suppose the electron is moving with a motion which may be resolved into component linear simple harmonic motions. Consider one of these simple harmonic motion components before and after the field is

---

[1] For a derivation of eq. 16-1 see Houstoun, "A Treatise on Light," Longmans.

applied. Before, it will continue unchanged. After, it will still be simple harmonic, but along a line which is rotating with a frequency $\Delta\nu$, about an axis parallel to the direction of the field, and passing through the center of force. This combination of simple harmonic motion and rotation of the line along which it is executed results in a rosettelike orbit illustrated in Fig. 16-3, if the line and the field are perpendicular. If they are parallel, there is no modification of the motion. Thus this alteration takes place for all electronic motions which have components in the XY-plane.

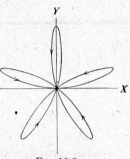

FIG. 16-3.

Another way of illustrating the effect of a field is to make use of the device described in Sec. **13-21** in the discussion of the rotation of the plane of vibration in optically active media. A plane vibration, as, for instance, in the Y-direction, such as has

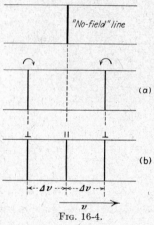

FIG. 16-4.

just been described, may be thought of as the resultant of two circular motions in the XY-plane, one clockwise, the other counterclockwise. In the absence of an external field these will have the same frequency, but when the field is imposed, an increase of one frequency and a decrease of the other will give a resultant vibration which slowly rotates in the XY-plane. The resultant motion will be that shown in Fig. 16-3.

If the light is observed in the Z-direction, *i.e.*, parallel to the field, in place of one spectrum line two will be seen, displaced equal distances from the position of the no-field line, and oppositely circularly polarized, as indicated in Fig. 16-4a. These will be of equal intensity since there are as many components of motion in one as in the other.

If, instead, the light is viewed perpendicularly to the field, say in the X-direction, the circular vibrations, projected on the

YZ-plane, will be alternately parallel and perpendicular to the direction of propagation of the light. In the former case, no light will be seen; in the latter two spectral lines will appear, one, displaced to the violet, corresponding to the increased frequency, one, to the red, corresponding to the decreased frequency. But components of vibration in the *Z*-direction will now also be transverse to the line of sight, and, since they are unaffected by a field in the *Z*-direction, will give rise to an undisplaced line. The three components shown in Fig. 16-4*b* constitute a *normal triplet*.

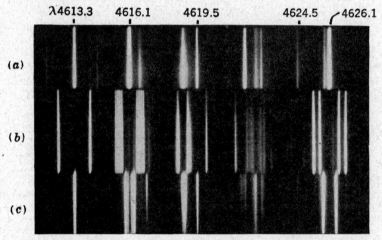

Fig. 16-5.—Zeeman effect for some lines of *chromium*. (*a*) Spectrum without magnetic field; (*b*) σ-components, and (*c*) π-components, both photographed simultaneously with light emitted at right angles to a magnetic field of about 30,000 gauss. (*Courtesy of H. D. Babcock, Mount Wilson Observatory.*)

3. The Anomalous Zeeman Effect.—Observations soon showed that most of the Zeeman patterns are not triplets but more complex. Photographs of typical patterns obtained with high resolving power are shown in Fig. 16-5. The classical theory just described failed to account for these more complex patterns, but it served a purpose in furnishing a means of measuring the value of e/m, the ratio of the charge on the electron to its mass, which agreed with the value obtained by other experimental methods. This gave strong support to the theory which attributed the emission of light to the motion of electrons, and so helped to confirm the existence of the electron. It should be emphasized, however, that in the quantum theory of the Zeeman effect which supplanted the inadequate classical theory, eq. 16-1 still holds.

If, instead of the frequency change $\Delta\nu$, the change in *wave number* $\Delta\bar{\nu}$ is desired, it will be given by

$$\Delta\bar{\nu} = \frac{eH}{4\pi mc^2}. \tag{16-2}$$

Triplet patterns in which the ratio $\Delta\bar{\nu}/H$ is given by eq. 16-2 are said to exhibit the *normal Zeeman effect;* triplets with other separations and patterns of greater complexity than the triplet are said to exhibit the *anomalous Zeeman effect.* The term

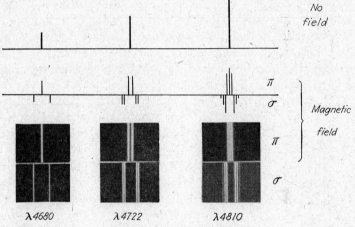

FIG. 16-6.—The anomalous Zeeman effect for a multiplet in the spectrum of zinc. (*Photograph by Mark Fred.*)

"anomalous" had its origin in the failure of these more complicated patterns to agree with the predictions of classical theory.

It was discovered by Runge that displacements in *all* patterns can be expressed as rational multiples of the normal triplet separation. The Runge rule is illustrated in Fig. 16-6, a diagram of the components of three sharp lines constituting a multiplet[1] in the spectrum of zinc. The vertical lines indicate by their positions the displacements from the no-field line position and by their lengths, the intensities. Those above the horizontal line are the components polarized with their direction of vibration

---

[1] The term *multiplet* should not be confused with the Zeeman structure. For its meaning see Sec. 14-21.

parallel to the field and those below, perpendicular to the field. These are conventionally called the π (parallel) and σ (perpendicular) components, respectively. The case illustrated is, of course, when the source is observed at right angles to the field. If D is the value of the displacement in wave number for the normal triplet, then the displacements of the components in the anomalous pattern are given by the table following:

Line	π-components	σ-components
$\lambda4680$	0	$\pm\frac{4}{2}D$
$\lambda4722$	$\pm\frac{1}{2}D$	$\pm\frac{3}{2}D,\ \pm\frac{4}{2}D$
$\lambda4810$	$0,\ \pm\frac{1}{2}D$	$\pm\frac{2}{2}D,\ \pm\frac{3}{2}D,\ \pm\frac{4}{2}D.$

An inspection of these data will make it plain that the patterns of the anomalous Zeeman effect yield as good values of e/m as normal triplets, since from them may be obtained many semi-independent values of D, the value of $\Delta\bar{\nu}$ in eq. 16-2.[1]

4. Quantum Theory of the Anomalous Zeeman Effect.—It will be recalled that the quantum theory accounts for radiation of a

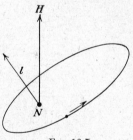

FIG. 16-7.

given frequency by postulating that $h\nu = E_2 - E_1$, the difference between two energy states in the atom. In order to understand the reason for the complex patterns of the anomalous Zeeman effect, let us consider an electron moving in an elliptic orbit about an atomic nucleus N (Fig. 16-7). In general, the normal to the plane of the orbit will not be parallel to the direction NH of the field and will, in consequence, precess about that direction. The angular momentum due to the orbital motion is limited to integral values of $h/2\pi$, and it is customary to use the letter l in this case to indicate the value of the integer. The angular momentum, measured in units of $h/2\pi$ is then indicated in the figure by a vector l perpendicular to the plane of the orbit at N. If, in the presence of a magnetic field, all possible orienta-

[1] The best value of e/m based on the anomalous Zeeman effect has been obtained by H. D. Babcock at the Mount Wilson Observatory; *Astrophysical Journal*, **58**, 149, 1923, and **69**, 43, 1929.

tions of l could exist, the frequency of radiation ν obtained from $h\nu = E_2 - E_1$ would have all possible values over a range $2\Delta\nu$, and the effect of the field would be simply to broaden the spectrum lines, since in practice there are many atoms contributing to a spectrum line.   The presence of separate sharp components in the *normal* Zeeman effect is accounted for by the introduction of the hypothesis of *space quantization*.   This concept is that the plane of the electron's orbit cannot, upon the imposition of an external field, take on all possible angles, but only certain ones which are determined by theory.   In other words, the angle between l and NH is limited to certain discrete values. In terms of an *energy-level diagram*, each no-field level is split

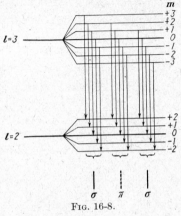

FIG. 16-8.

up into a number of equally spaced components, as shown in Fig. 16-8.   The transitions between these so-called m levels are governed by selection principles[1] in such a manner that several energy differences are the same, and give rise to a single Zeeman component.

Thus far we have applied *space quantization* only to the *normal* effect.   The *anomalous* effect is explained by the introduction into the calculations of the energy due to the *spin* of the electron on its axis.   In some cases the axis of spin is so oriented with respect to the plane of the orbital motion of the electron that it makes no difference, whereupon we have the normal effect.   In all other cases the spin vector must be taken into account.   The space quantization is then no longer that of the electron orbit only, *i.e.*, the orientation of l to NH, but of the orientation of a vector j to NH, where j is the resultant of the vector l and the spin vector.   In terms of an energy-level diagram, equal spacing of the levels is no longer the same for the initial and final states as is represented in Fig. 16-8.   The anomalous case is represented for the sodium doublet at 5890 and

[1] The selection principle applying in the case of the Zeeman effect is that Δm may have only the values 0 or ± 1.

5896 angstroms in Fig. 16-9. As before, the selection principle $\Delta m = 0$ or ± 1 applies. Because of certain results of the quantum theory of spin, the values of m are half integers instead of whole numbers.

The *relative intensities* of the components are also explained on the basis of rules which are in agreement with the quantum theory of spectra, but which are too complicated for discussion in this brief introduction to the subject.

One point which requires emphasis is that the component separations described thus far are of a magnitude obtainable with what is known as a *weak field*. For most elements the

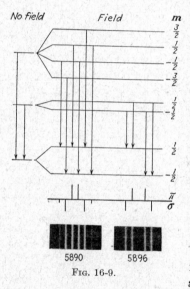

FIG. 16-9.

strongest field obtainable in practice is a weak field. By a *strong field*, in the parlance of spectroscopists, is meant one for which the Zeeman separation is greater than, or of the order of magnitude of, the separation of the multiplet components. As an illustration, consider the field H which would be required to produce a separation of 6 angstroms between the center and displaced component of the Zeeman pattern of a line in the neighborhood of 6000 angstroms. This would be approximately a strong field for the sodium doublet at 5890 and 5896 angstroms. From eq.

16-2 it follows that a field of about 350,000 gauss would be required. Fields of this order of magnitude or larger are strong fields for the sodium lines. Any field much less would be weak for the sodium spectrum, but it might be strong for multiplets having a much smaller separation.

In strong fields, defined according to these terms, the anomalous Zeeman effect is replaced by one which closely approaches the normal triplet in appearance. This is called the *Paschen-Back effect*, after the investigators who first used a strong field to produce a normal triplet in a multiplet which, with weaker fields, shows only the anomalous effect. Using a field of 43,000 gauss, they observed the lithium doublet at 6708 angstroms as a magnetic triplet. In this case the value of $\Delta\bar{\nu}$ is about six times the value of the doublet separation, which is 0.34 wave number.

The continuous transition, with increasing field strengths, from the anomalous effect with weak fields to the normal effect with strong fields is known as the *partial Paschen-Back effect*. The production of the normal triplet with the strongest field is known as the *complete Paschen-Back effect*. Obviously, neither effect can be produced for many spectra, since with present equipment fields much over 50,000 to 100,000 gauss cannot be produced for a sufficient length of time to permit the observation with high resolution of the faint sources which in many cases must be employed.

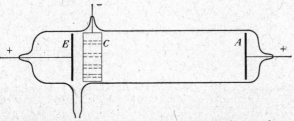

FIG. 16-10.—Diagram illustrating Stark's discharge tube.

5. The Stark Effect.—For years after the discovery of the Zeeman effect, an analogous effect due to an *electric* field was sought for. Finally, in 1913, Stark found that the Balmer lines of the hydrogen spectrum are split up into components if the source is in a strong electric field. The effect was observed about the same time by Lo Surdo in a different type of discharge, but its significance was first pointed out by Stark. The Stark effect has not been so useful to spectroscopists as the Zeeman effect because the manner in which it depends upon the energy states in the atom is much more complex. That its discovery was delayed so long is probably due to the fact that it is difficult to maintain strong electric fields in a discharge. Also, Stark was the first to examine the spectrum of hydrogen, in which the effect is most noticeable.

The apparatus used by Stark is illustrated in Fig. 16-10. Close to the cathode C of a discharge tube containing hydrogen at very low pressure there is a third electrode, E. C is perforated so that ions may pass through it and traverse the space CE. The potential drop between C and E must be over 20,000 volts. Since the space between C and E is very small, the potential drop will be of the order of 100,000 volts per cm.   Positive ions proceed from A to C, some of which will become neutralized, so that passing through the perforated cathode there are fast-moving atoms and positive ions constituting a *canal ray* beam moving

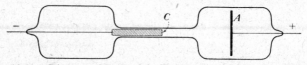

Fig. 16-11.—Diagram of Lo Surdo's discharge tube for the Stark effect.

in the direction of the field.   Since, owing to the low pressure, E is in the cathode dark space, there is practically no light of the ordinary discharge such as is emitted from the region between C and A.   Thus the light between E and C is due to the canal rays.   The *transverse* Stark effect is observed in the spectrum of the light emitted in a direction perpendicular to the tube.   In

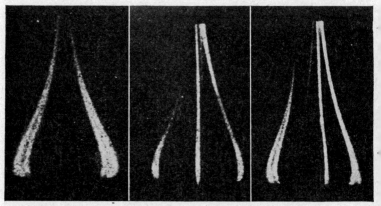

Fig. 16-12.—Stark effect patterns obtained by Foster.

order to observe the effect *parallel* to the field, it is necessary to arrange the electrodes somewhat differently.

Lo Surdo observed the Stark effect in a capillary discharge tube like that shown in Fig. 16-11, in which C, the cathode, is a wire fitted into the capillary, and A is the anode.   A field of about 50,000 volts across the tube will produce patterns like those shown in Fig. 16-12.   It will be noticed that at the cathode the separation of the lines is much greater than that obtained in the Zeeman effect.

The Lo Surdo method has been improved by J. Stuart Foster,[1] who used a cathode which could be rotated so as to present a fresh surface from time to time, the effect of pitting of the surface by the action of ions thus being minimized. A modification of the Lo Surdo method has also been made by J. A. Anderson,[2] permitting the study of the Stark effect for metals.

The Stark effect cannot be explained by classical theory. It is generally considered that the Bohr theory received its first triumphant corroboration in the quantum theory of the Stark effect.[3] The details of the derivation are too complex for presentation here, the main points being as follows: For a hydrogenlike atom the energy of interaction between an atom and an external electric field is given by

$$W = W_0 + AF + BF^2 + \cdots , \qquad (16\text{-}3)$$

where W_0 is the energy of the atom in the absence of the field, and F is the field strength. The linear term AF is known as the energy of the *first-order Stark effect*, the quadratic term BF^2, the energy of the *second-order Stark* effect, and so on. It can also be shown that for hydrogenlike atoms

$$AF = \frac{3hF}{8\pi^2 mecZ} n(n_2 - n_1), \qquad (16\text{-}4)$$

where h is Planck's constant, m the mass and e the charge in e.s.u. of the electron, c the velocity of light, and Z the atomic number. The numbers n_2 and n_1 are two new quantum numbers which depend upon the effect of the field, while n is the total quantum number corresponding to the n used in simple spectral theory (Chap. XIV). By the principles of quantum mechanics it follows that for a hydrogen atom,

$$(n - 1) - n_1 - n_2 = n_3, \qquad (16\text{-}5)$$

where n_3 is a quantum number relating to the total angular momentum about the direction of the electric field, and hence

[1] *Physical Review*, **23**, 669, 1924.

[2] *Astrophysical Journal*, **46**, 153, 1917.

[3] See Ruark and Urey, "Atoms, Molecules, and Quanta," McGraw-Hill; also White, "An Introduction to Line Spectra," McGraw-Hill.

having sets of values associated with the energy levels into which any no-field level is split. With the aid of selection rules which are somewhat complicated the values of these new energy levels may be calculated and an energy-level diagram prepared.

It should be pointed out that the patterns of components indicated in such a diagram and in those illustrating the Zeeman effect are only those due to the imposition of the external fields. Actually, superposed upon a complex line structure due to an external field are complex structures due to other causes, such as the presence of more than one isotope of an element in the source, the effect of the spin of the atomic nucleus on some axis, and in the case of very light atoms, the multiplets themselves. The disentanglement of the fine structure in the spectral lines due to these various causes calls for apparatus of the highest resolving power and technical skill of the highest order.

6. The Faraday Effect.—Faraday discovered in 1845 that when a transparent isotropic medium is in a strong magnetic field, there is a rotation of the plane of vibration of light which is transmitted through the medium in the direction of the field. Unlike the rotatory effect in quartz and other *optically active* substances, the direction of rotation depends on whether the light traverses the medium in the direction of the lines of force, *i.e.*, from N to S pole, or oppositely. Hence on reflection back through a medium in a strong magnetic field, the effect is doubled, while the rotation due to optically active substances is canceled upon reflection of the light back on its path.

The effect may be produced with a solenoid of sufficient strength, the substance being placed along its axis as shown in Fig. 16-13. When the nicols are crossed without a field, no light will be seen, but the light will reappear when the field is on. Turning of the analyzer to the new point of extinction gives the angle through which the plane of vibration has been rotated. The direction of rotation does not depend upon whether the substance is paramagnetic or diamagnetic. A rotation is known as *positive* if it is in the same direction as the flow of current[1] producing the field, and *negative* if in the opposite direction. That is, it is positive if it appears clockwise to an observer looking in the direction of the lines of force.

[1] *Flow of current* is here used in the older Amperian sense, and not in the sense of direction of electron flow.

The rotatory effect in naturally optically active substances such as quartz may be explained by considering the transmitted plane vibration to be the resultant of two opposite circular vibrations, one propagated through the medium faster than the other (see Sec. **13-20**). In order to apply this explanation to the Faraday effect it is necessary to assume (*a*) that the same sort of resolution of the plane vibration exists for an isotropic medium in a magnetic field, and (*b*) that the velocity of propagation of a circular vibration depends on the *direction* of the vibration, *i.e.*, whether it is clockwise or counterclockwise, as well as upon the index of refraction of the medium. The second of these assumptions was shown to be true by Righi and Becquerel working independently. The first was proved correct by Brace.[1] In 1904, the velocities of the two circularly polarized components were measured by Mills,[2] who found that the ray traveling faster was the one for

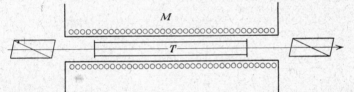

Fig. 16-13.—*T* is the tube, containing the liquid, on the axis of a solenoid magnet *M*.

which the direction of the circular vibration was the same as that of the current producing the field.

For a given temperature and wave-length the angle of rotation by a field is given in minutes of arc by

$$\theta = RlH,$$

where *l* is the light path in centimeters in the medium and *H* is the magnetic field strength in gauss. The constant *R* is known as Verdet's constant. If its value is known accurately for specified conditions, the Faraday effect may be used to calibrate a magnetic field in terms of current strength.

The magnitude of the Faraday effect for different substances is shown in Table 16-1, the values being given for the sodium lines and for room temperature. The dependence upon temperature is slight, being given for carbon disulphide as

$$R = 0.04347(1 - 1.69 \times 10^{-3} \cdot t).$$

[1] *Philosophical Magazine*, **1**, 464, 1901.
[2] *Physical Review*, **18**, 65, 1904.

Table 16-1

Substance	Verdet's Constant, Minutes of Arc for the D-lines
Crown glass	0.0203
Heavy flint glass	0.0647
Ethyl alcohol	0.0107
Benzene	0.0297
Carbon disulphide (liquid)	0.0441
Water	0.0130
Atmosphere	6.83×10^{-6}
Carbon dioxide	13.00×10^{-6}

Kundt[1] found that very large rotations were produced by thin semitransparent films of ferrous metals deposited on glass. These films, only a fraction of a wave-length of light in thickness, were deposited electrolytically on platinized glass plates. Kundt found that the rotation in an iron film 5.5×10^{-6} cm. thick was as much as $1° 48'$, over 30,000 times that for an equal thickness of glass.

The Faraday effect in solutions is not proportional to the concentration, since the interactions of the molecules must be taken into account.

The rotation due to a magnetic field may be expressed in terms of e/m, the ratio of the charge on the electron to its mass, in a relationship originally deduced empirically by Becquerel. The existence of two velocities, and hence of two indices of refraction, for the oppositely rotating circular components is thought of as being due to the addition or subtraction of a small precession angular velocity ω_p to the large angular velocity ω of the components. This precession is due to the field's effect on the orbital motion of the electrons. Since $\omega = 2\pi\nu$, it follows from eq. 16-1 that

$$\omega_p = \frac{e}{2mc} \cdot H \qquad \text{(radians per sec.)} \qquad (16\text{-}6)$$

where e is in e.s.u.   Also

$$\omega = \frac{2\pi c}{\lambda}. \qquad (16\text{-}7)$$

The time required for the faster component of velocity v_+ to traverse a centimeter of the medium is $1/v_+$, while that for the

[1] *Philosophical Magazine*, **18**, 308, 1884.

slower component is $1/v_-$. Hence the angle in radians through which the plane of vibration is turned is

$$\theta = \frac{1}{2}\omega\left(\frac{1}{v_+} - \frac{1}{v_-}\right).$$

But

$$v_+ = v + \omega_p\frac{dv}{d\omega} \quad \text{and} \quad v_- = v - \omega_p\frac{dv}{d\omega}$$

so that

$$\theta = \frac{1}{2}\omega\left(\frac{1}{v + \omega_p\dfrac{dv}{d\omega}} - \frac{1}{v - \omega_p\dfrac{dv}{d\omega}}\right),$$

which reduces to

$$\theta = \frac{1}{2}\omega\left(\frac{-2\omega_p\dfrac{dv}{d\omega}}{v^2 - \omega_p{}^2(dv/d\omega)^2}\right).$$

Since both ω and $dv/d\omega$ are very small compared to v, very approximately

$$\theta = -\frac{\omega\omega_p}{v^2}\frac{dv}{d\omega}. \tag{16-8}$$

Substituting in this the values of ω, ω_p, and $d\omega$ obtained from eqs. 16-6 and 16-7, and the values of v and dv from $n = c/v$, where n is the index of refraction, it follows that

$$\theta = -\frac{e}{2mc^2} \cdot H \cdot \frac{\lambda dn}{d\lambda} \tag{16-9}$$

radians per centimeter of thickness.[1]

7. The Kerr Magneto-optical Effect.—In Sec. **13-14** it was stated that in ordinary metallic reflection incident plane-polarized light becomes elliptically polarized, except (a) at normal incidence, and (b) when the plane of vibration of the incident light is in or perpendicular to the plane of incidence. Kerr[2] found that if the reflection takes place at the polished pole face of a strong electromagnet, elliptical polarization results even

[1] For this derivation see Larmor, "Aether and Matter," Cambridge University Press; also Campbell, "Modern Electrical Theory," Cambridge Physical Series.

[2] *Philosophical Magazine*, **3**, 321, 1877; **5**, 161, 1878.

in cases (*a*) and (*b*) above.   He found no effect when the wave front of the incident light is parallel to the direction of the magnetic field.   The ellipticity is small, so that the effect may be considered for simplicity merely as a rotation of the plane of vibration.   The amount of this rotation is found to be proportional to the intensity of magnetization ϑ, that is,

$$\theta = K\vartheta,$$

where K is the *magnetic Kerr constant*.

A method, due to duBois, combining the Faraday and Kerr effects, makes possible an accurate measurement of strong mag-

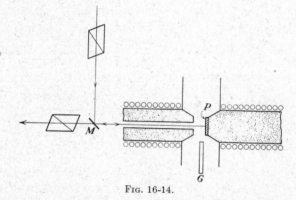

Fig. 16-14.

netic fields and great magnetizations.   The arrangement of the apparatus is shown in Fig. 16-14, in which P is the polished pole piece at which the Kerr effect is measured, giving the magnetization ϑ.   To obtain the field strength, a plate G of glass for which the Verdet constant is known is then inserted.   This plate is silvered on the side farthest from the source so that the light is reflected back, doubling the rotation of the plane of vibration. The angle of rotation is measured, and H is calculated.

8. The Kerr Electro-optical Effect.—Faraday long sought for an electrical rotatory effect corresponding to the Faraday effect due to magnetic fields, but with no success.   It was first observed by Kerr,[1] who discovered that an isotropic dielectric medium placed in a strong electric field acquires the properties of double refraction of a uniaxial crystal with its optic axis in the direction of the lines of force.   Some substances behave like positive and

---

[1] *Philosophical Magazine*, **1**, 337, 1875, also papers in subsequent issues.

others like negative crystals. Kerr first obtained results with a block of glass into which two holes were drilled from opposite sides, ending about $\frac{1}{4}$ in. apart. The terminals of a powerful induction coil were placed in these. Before the coil was put in action, the light transmitted at right angles through the gap between the terminals was extinguished with a pair of crossed nicols, one on either side of the block. After the switch was closed, the light reappeared. It could not be entirely extinguished by rotating the analyzer and hence was elliptically polarized.

In this experiment the light does not appear as soon as the exciting electrical field is turned on, but takes about 30 sec. to reach its maximum intensity; similarly, it takes about the same time to fade when the field is removed. The effect is greatest when the principal section of the polarizer makes an angle of 45 deg. with the direction of the field, and zero when it is parallel or perpendicular. Care must be taken in drilling the holes and fitting the terminals to avoid any mechanical strains in the glass, as these restrict the region in which the effect is observed, and may even mask it altogether.

It is not clear from this experiment alone that the effect is the production of an anisotropic condition by the electrical stress, since the lag in the appearance of the light might also indicate a temperature effect because of the slight conductivity of the glass. Kerr believed that it was really due to a rearrangement of the molecules by the electrical stress, the delay being because of opposing frictional force. That the effect may be compensated by placing in the light path between block and analyzer a thin strip of glass, compressed or stretched in the direction of the field, is taken as an indication that the glass truly takes on the characteristics of a uniaxial crystal. The double refraction exhibited by glass is like that of a *negative* crystal and is the same whether alternating or direct current is used, the effect being proportional to the *square* of the field strength.

In liquids the rearrangement of the molecules is more rapid, permitting the use of the Kerr effect for many important experiments, some of which will be discussed later. The liquid is placed in a glass vessel with flat ends and a pair of metal plates, arranged like parallel condenser plates, as shown in Fig. 16-15. It is extremely important that the windows, or ends, through which the light passes should be of optical glass free from strains and with flat surfaces.   The vessel with liquid and plates installed is called a *Kerr cell*.   When an electric field is applied to the plates, the liquid becomes double-refracting.   Since the light transmitted is elliptically polarized, it may be analyzed by means of a Babinet compensator (see Sec. **13-12**), placed between the cell and the analyzer.   Or instead, a Wollaston prism may be used (see Sec. **13-10**), in which case the analyzer should be oriented so that the two images are of equal intensity.

Oils in general show negative, while carbon disulphide, molten sulphur, bromine, and many other substances show positive

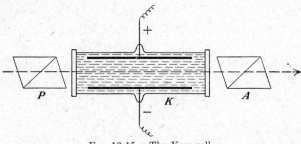

Fig. 16-15.—The Kerr cell.

double refraction.   The strength of the effect in any substance is given by its *electrical Kerr constant* C_e.   This is expressed in terms of the relative retardation in optical path produced between the components of the elliptical vibration parallel and perpendicular to the field, for unit thickness of the dielectric. Let δ be this retardation, then

$$\frac{\delta}{\lambda} = \frac{l(n_e - n_o)}{\lambda} = C_e l E^2, \qquad (16\text{-}10)$$

where l is the thickness in centimeters and E is the field strength in e.s.u.   The effect also depends upon the temperature of the substance.   The value of C_e for carbon bisulphide at 20°C. for $\lambda = 5.893 \times 10^{-5}$ cm. is 3.22×10^{-7}.   Values for several other substances are given in Table 16-2 at the end of the following section.

As the table shows, gases exhibit a Kerr electric effect which is about $\frac{1}{1000}$ that for ordinary liquids.   In gases the value of C_e, which depends upon the temperature and pressure, can be represented as the sum of a number of terms

$$C_e = k_1 + k_2 + k_3 \cdots ,$$

in which k_1 is proportional to $1/RT$, k_2 to $1/R^2T^2$, etc., where R is the gas constant and T is the absolute temperature. The values of k are positive or negative for different gases, as in the case of liquids, but the sign is sometimes a function of the temperature.

9. The Cotton-Mouton Effect.—Cotton and Mouton found that the same type of double refraction observed in the Kerr electro-optical effect could be produced in a dielectric when it was placed in a *magnetic* field. By an equation analogous to eq. 16-10, the retardation in path, δ, is given by

$$\frac{\delta}{\lambda} = \frac{l(n_e - n_0)}{\lambda} = C_m l H^2, \qquad (16\text{-}11)$$

in which C_m is the Cotton-Mouton magnetic birefringence constant, and H is the magnetic field strength in gauss. This effect should be distinguished from the magnetic Kerr effect discussed in Sec. **16-7,** which is a rotation of the plane of polarization analogous to the Faraday effect. The Cotton-Mouton

The electric birefringence $\gamma_e = 100(C/C_{CS_2})_e$.   (5893A)
The magnetic birefringence $\gamma_m = 100(C/C_{C_6H_5NO_2})_m$.   (5780A)

Substance	Symbol	γ_e	γ_m
Liquids:			
Carbon disulphide	CS_2	+ 100.0	− 19.6
Carbon tetrachloride	CCl_4	+ 2.3	
Chloroform	$CHCl_3$	− 100.2	− 2.8
Benzene	C_6H_6	+ 12.0	+ 23.3
Ethyl alcohol	C_2H_5OH	+ 23.8	0
Acetone	C_3H_5OH	+ 505.0	+ 1.6
Nitrobenzene	$C_6H_5NO_2$	+10,070.0	+100.0
Nitrotoluene	$C_7H_7NO_2$	+ 5,500.0	+ 77.0
Nitric acid	HNO_3		+ 2.5
Water	H_2O	+ 123.0	
Gases:			
Sulphur dioxide	SO_2	+ 0.051	
Ammonia	NH_3	+ 0.018	
Carbon dioxide	CO_2	+ 0.007	

effect is analogous to the Kerr electro-optical effect in the sense that both are the production of artificial double refraction in media. The former is sometimes called *magnetic birefringence* and the latter *electric birefringence*. In Table 16-2 are given the values of the electric and magnetic birefringences for several substances. In accordance with custom, the electric effect is given in terms of carbon disulphide (CS_2) and the magnetic effect in terms of nitrobenzene ($C_6H_5NO_2$). The value of C_m for nitrobenzene at 20°C. for $\lambda = 5.780 \times 10^{-5}$ cm. is 2.46×10^{-12}.

10. Measurement of Time Intervals with Kerr Cells.—Abraham and Lemoine devised a method for measuring very short time intervals, of the order of magnitude of 10^{-9} sec., with Kerr cells. This is done by using as the source of the trans-

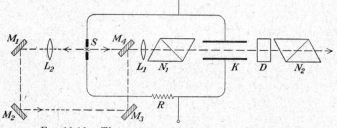

Fig. 16-16.—The apparatus of Abraham and Lemoine.

mitted light a spark discharge which is in series in the same circuit which actuates the cell. A diagram of the apparatus is shown in Fig. 16-16. The light from the spark can be passed directly into the cell through the lens L_1, or it may be passed over a longer path by reflection at mirrors M_1, M_2, M_3, and M_4. In the latter case, one or more auxiliary lenses are used, these being indicated in the figure by L_2, in order to procure a beam of the proper intensity and divergence at the Kerr cell K. The polarizing nicol N_1 and the analyzing nicol N_2 are at 90 deg. with each other and at 45 deg. to the field of the Kerr cell. A double-image prism D is so oriented that the two images may be made of equal intensity with their vibrations in perpendicular planes. The analyzer may be set for extinction, or, with D in place, for equality of intensity, by means of an auxiliary source placed before N_1. This source is then removed, and the spark discharge S started. The discharge is oscillatory, giving rise to an intermittent spark. If the light from a single flash of the spark passes through the Kerr cell while the latter is still actuated, it will be necessary to turn the analyzer through an appreciable angle to bring about equality in the intensities of the two images. If, however, the light is delayed in its passage to the cell, the field will have diminished and the angle through which the analyzer is turned will be smaller. If very long light paths are introduced, the cell will be completely restored to the isotropic state before the light reaches it, and no change in angle will be required.

It is possible to dispense with the double-image prism, and measure simply the angle through which N_2 must be rotated in order to reduce the intensity of the transmitted elliptically

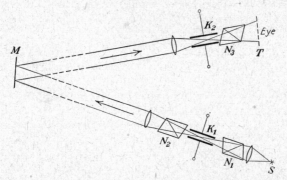

FIG. 16-17.—A schematic outline of the apparatus of Karolus and Mittelstaedt. The letter M represents a *system* of mirrors.

polarized light to a minimum. This is not as exact a method as matching the intensities of the two images given by the double-image prism.

One of the factors which must be considered in experiments with Kerr cells is the delay in the establishment of the anisotropic state after the cell is charged, and the delay in the decay of the field after the charge is removed. In liquids, these times are very small, of the order of about 10^{-9} sec. The lag in the Kerr effect has been measured with considerable precision in recent years.[1]

11. Velocity of Light with Kerr Cells.—It is possible to obtain light flashes of extremely short duration by the use of two Kerr cells in series. Such an apparatus has been used by Karolus

[1] See, for instance, an article by Beams and Lawrence, *Proceedings National Academy of Sciences*, **13**, 505, 1927.

and Mittelstaedt for measuring the velocity of light.[1] The arrangement of the apparatus is shown in Fig. 16-17. The light from S was polarized by a nicol N_1, in a plane of vibration at 45 deg. to the field of K_1. When K_1 was actuated, the elliptically polarized light passed through a second nicol N_2, whose plane of transmission was at 90 deg to N_1. After reflection back and forth from several mirrors, the light then passed to a second Kerr cell K_2, and a third nicol N_3. The total path was 332 m. The two Kerr cells cut off the beam at intervals which could be varied. As the result of 755 measurements, a value of the velocity of light of 299,778 km./sec. ± 20 km./sec. was reported, in good agreement with the most recent values obtained by Michelson and his associates.[2]

Problems

1. If the illustration of the Zeeman effect given in Fig. 16-6 has been magnified eight times from the original photograph of the spectrum, on which the dispersion was 1.1 angstrom per millimeter, what was the strength of the magnetic field used?

2. Will the normal longitudinal Zeeman effect, produced in a field of 10,000 gauss, be observable as a distinct separation of components with a spectrometer using a grating 7.5 cm. long and having 6,000 rulings per centimeter? The perpendicular effect? Assume actual resolving power about 60 per cent of theoretical, and specify the order used.

3. Other things being equal, should lines in the violet or in the red be examined in order to observe the Zeeman effect? Explain your answer.

4. The indices of refraction of a certain block of glass 10 cm. long are, for the D-lines, 1.5688; for the C-line, 1.5657; and for Hg-5461, 1.57125. When placed in a magnetic field, the plane of vibration of a beam of plane-polarized light of the sodium lines is rotated through 10 deg. What is the strength of the field? What is the Verdet constant for the glass?

[1] *Physikalische Zeitschrift*, **29,** 698, 1928.

[2] Since this book went to press, an article by W. C. Anderson has appeared (*Review of Scientific Instruments*, **8,** 239, 1937) describing a modified apparatus for measuring *c*, using a relatively short base line, a single Kerr cell, and a photoelectric cell for the detection of the light beam modified by the Kerr cell.

CHAPTER XVII

THE EYE AND COLOR VISION

The beginner or casual worker in the field of light is likely to overlook the importance of the eye in visual observations It is important (*a*) because of considerations of purely geometrical optics, including defects of image formation; (*b*) because it has certain characteristics which may be classified as psychophysiological, such as susceptibility to illusions, color vision, and

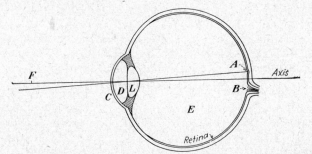

Fig. 17-1.—The schematic eye. *A*, fovea; *B*, blind spot; *C*, cornea; *D*, aqueous humor, index = 1.3365; *L*, crystalline lens, index = 1.4371; *E*, vitreous humor, index = 1.3365; *F*, principal focal point. Radius of curvature of cornea, 7.829 mm.; of front of lens, 10.000 mm.; of rear of lens, −6.000 mm.; distance between cornea and lens = 3.6 mm.; distance between surfaces of lens = 3.6 mm.

difference in degree of "normality." Because of these, modification of observed phenomena is possible, and ignorance of this modification may lead the observer to false conclusions. Optical experiments, especially those involving visual photometry and color, should not be undertaken without some understanding of the functions of the human eye.

1. The Optical System of the Eye.—The essential optical features are illustrated in Fig. 17-1. The meanings of the letters are given in the legend. The surfaces here represented are not such definite boundaries between media as in ordinary optical systems. Neither are the media themselves entirely homogeneous, the crystalline lens especially being composed of "shells" which vary in density and structure. For these reasons it is customary in describing the optics of the eye to give the radii of curvature, indices of refraction, and other details of a "schematic eye" which in operation most closely duplicates the human eye. The diagram in Fig. 17-1 is that of a schematic eye.

The portion of the retina where vision is most distinct is the *fovea*. The diameter of the fovea is about 0.25 mm. and subtends an angle somewhat less than one degree in the object space. The sensitivity of the retina diminishes with increasing distance from the fovea and the field of distinct vision is quite small. When one "looks at" an object, its image falls on the fovea. At the point where the optic nerve enters the eye, the retina is insensitive to light and is called the *blind spot*. The blind spot

●
A

●
B

Fig. 17-2.

is a short distance from the fovea toward the nasal side, so that with either eye an object to one side of that on which attention is fixed may be unseen, provided it is the proper distance away. If the reader closes the right eye while Fig. 17-2 is held an appropriate distance away (about 6 in.), spot *A* will disappear when the attention is fixed on *B*, while with the left eye closed spot *B* will disappear when the attention is fixed on *A*. It may be necessary to experiment a little to find the proper distance of the book before this effect is obtained.

2. Defects in the Optics of the Eye.—*Accommodation* of the eye for objects at different distances is brought about by changes in the tension of the ciliary muscles which control the shape of the crystalline lens.

The nearest position to the eye at which a small object can be distinctly seen is called the *near point;* that on which the eye is focused when relaxed, the *far point* of the eye. For nearby objects the lens is permitted to become more spherical in form, so that the focal length of the system is reduced. The power of accommodation decreases with age, so that it becomes difficult to distinguish small objects within the range of normal reading distance without the aid of glasses. There are also defects of the eye, not necessarily associated with age, which may be partly overcome with glasses. The three most common are *myopia*.

hyperopia, and *astigmatism*. The first two are the result of abnormalities in the distance from the front of the eye to the retina, while the last is caused by lack of sphericity of the refracting surfaces, principally the cornea. An eye in which light from a distant object is focused exactly at the retina when accommodation is entirely relaxed is said to be *emmetropic*. Eyes which are myopic or hyperopic are said to be *ametropic*. These conditions are illustrated in Fig. 17-3. That the eye also suffers from barrel-shaped distortion can be shown by looking at a grid of perpendicular lines. The pattern will appear convex if held close to the eye.

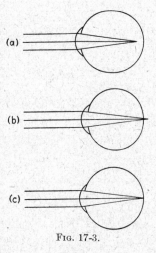

Fig. 17-3.

3. Binocular Vision.—Ability to bring the image of an object simultaneously on the fovea of each eye is called *binocular* vision. The pupils of the eyes in humans are separated by a distance of a few inches, so that with one eye the superposition of objects along the line of sight is not quite the same as it is with the other. The resulting slight difference in the images formed on the fovea of each eye enables one to determine *depth* in the object, or, in other words, to perceive space in three dimensions. Other factors enter into the situation, especially when illumination is poor, the distance great, or the scene unfamiliar. A person having only one eye capable of seeing may make use of other criteria of distance, such as the relative size of objects, their relative displacement in the case of motion, or a recollection of past experiences.

4. The Stereoscope.—In an ordinary photograph, objects at different distances are all projected on a single plane, so that the picture itself gives no effect of depth or relative distance and dependence must be made upon experience and judgment in forming a mental picture of the depth of the scene. To enhance the effect of depth, the *stereoscope* is used. Two photographs are taken, with a slight lateral displacement of the camera, or with a stereoscopic camera which takes two pictures at the same time with twin lens systems separated by a few inches. The prints are then mounted side by side and looked at through a

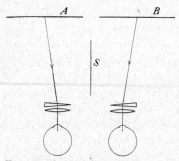

stereoscope, one form of which is illustrated in Fig. 17-4. With a little practice some persons are able to achieve stereoscopic vision of a pair of photographs without aid, the process consisting of seeing each photograph separately, the left-hand picture with the left eye and the right-hand picture with the right eye, and bringing the two into coincidence.

Fig. 17-4.—A form of stereoscope.

The principles of binocular vision are made use of in the construction of microscopes and telescopes, duplex optical systems being set side by side in the instrument. Some so-called binocular microscopes are not stereoscopic in the true sense, having merely two oculars both of which receive the image formed by the objective, through a mirror or prism system. The purpose in this case is to enable the observer to use both eyes and relieve eyestrain.

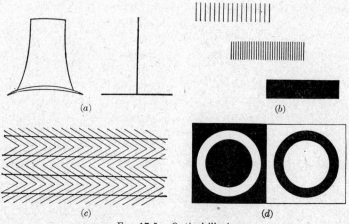

Fig. 17-5.—Optical illusions.

5. Optical Illusions.—Ocular experience with the commonplace often leads one astray in viewing the uncommon. Ordinary optical illusions are illustrated in Fig. 17-5, in which *a, b,* and c are geometrical-optical, and d is due to irradiation. In d the white center circle looks larger than the black, although it is exactly the same size. Irradiation is sometimes a source of error in the measurement of spectral line positions, especially in absorption spectra. When the background between the lines is more dense than that on either side there is a tendency to estimate the lines to be farther apart than their positions shown by a purely objective microphotometric measurement.

6. The Contrast Sensitivity of the Eye.—While an extensive treatment of the limitations and capabilities of the human eye would carry us beyond the field of physics and into those of psychology and physiology,[1] certain characteristics of vision which are important in experimental optics will be discussed briefly in this and the following sections.

The eye is designed to afford satisfactory vision over as wide a range of conditions as possible, and for this reason it is not a good judge of differences of brightness or intensity except under the most restricted conditions. The ability to distinguish between areas of different brightness is made use of in photometry. Most photometers are arranged so that the two fields to be compared are seen at the same time, one, the standard, being capable of fairly rapid variation of brightness. It is important that the two areas be arranged so that the effect of contour on relative brightness is reduced to a minimum. Ordinarily one of the areas is a small square or circle at the center of a like figure of considerably greater area. The *contrast sensitivity* may be measured by adjusting the brightness of the center spot so that it is barely different from that of the larger area. If the difference of brightness is ΔB, and the brightness of the larger area B, then $\Delta B/B$ is the contrast sensitivity. It is practically constant for brightness above about 1 candle per square meter, but it increases very rapidly as the brightness decreases.

7. Flicker Sensitivity. Persistence of Vision.—The sensation in the retina does not cease at once when the stimulus is removed, and in consequence the intermittency of a flickering light will not be detected, provided the flicker is rapid enough. With a

[1] See, for instance, Helmholtz, "Physiological Optics," English translation by J. P. C. Southall, published by the Optical Society of America; also Troland, "Psycho-physiology," Van Nostrand; Parsons, "Introduction to the Study of Colour Vision," Cambridge University Press; and Collins, "Colour Blindness," Harcourt, Brace.

field brightness of about 1 candle per square meter the critical frequency beyond which no flicker may be detected is about 30 times per second. The critical frequency is a function of the alternation in brightness.

A flicker method is often used for the comparison of photographs in which slight changes are to be sought, as in photographs of areas of the sky, taken at different times. In order to detect the presence of stellar objects whose proper motion (motion across the line of sight) is great compared to those of the general background of stars, the two photographs are arranged so that by shifting a mirror back and forth, first one and then the other may be seen in the field of a microscope. If any stellar object is in different positions in the two photographs, its displacement relative to the general background may be detected and, with a micrometer eyepiece, measured.

The *flicker photometer* may be used for the comparison of the intensities of two sources between which there is a considerable difference of color. The light of one source is reflected to the eye from a stationary white screen S_1. The light of the other source is reflected from the surface of a rotating disk S_2, with white vanes. This disk is so placed that S_1 may be seen through its open spaces, which have the same total area as the vanes. The disk may be rotated at a speed such that while the colors blend, the illuminations do not. The sense of flicker which is experienced when the two sources are not of the same intensity disappears when their distances are adjusted so as to equalize the illuminations. The flicker photometer should be used under carefully controlled conditions, and only when the intensities are sufficiently high so that there is no Purkinje effect (see Sec. **17-8**).

Flicker methods are also used to reduce the intensity of a source, the light usually being passed through a disk from which sectors have been cut. In this case the rate at which the light is alternated by reason of the interposition of the opaque parts of the disk must be greater than the critical frequency mentioned above. It has been proved that the apparent brightness of an object viewed through such a rotating disk is proportional to the ratio of the angular aperture of the open to the opaque sectors. This is known as *Talbot's law*.

8. Spectral Sensitivity.—The sensitivity of the normal eye as a function of wave-length is shown by the solid curve in Fig. 17-6 for ordinary illumination.   For illumination at the threshold of vision the maximum of visibility shows a marked shift to the violet as given by the dotted curve.   Both curves are plotted with relative visibility as ordinate in arbitrary units.   This shift of the wave-length region of maximum visibility is called the *Purkinje effect,* after its discoverer.   It is generally attributed to the character of the adaptation which the eye undergoes at low intensities of illumination.   This "darkness adaptation" is an increase of acuity of vision for *brightness* but not for color.[1]

9. Color.—In the field of physics an object is said to have a given surface color when it exhibits a certain selective absorption.

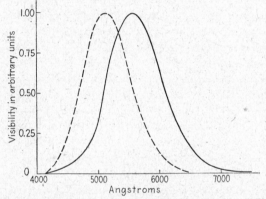

Fig. 17-6.—The Purkinje Effect.   Solid curve shows relative visibility for ordinary brightnesses; dotted curve, at threshold of vision, on an arbitrary scale.

There is a household usage of the term color characterized by its association with the words *tint,* a mixture of a color with white, and *shade,* a mixture with black.   In the field of color vision still a third meaning is introduced, that used by the psychologist and physiologist in referring to a given sensation transmitted by the eye as a result of an external physical stimulus.   Moreover, the term *spectrum* has a different significance in different fields.   The physicist thinks of the spectrum of visible light as a wave-length band terminating in long waves associated with deep red fading into invisible infrared at one end, and in violet fading into invisible ultraviolet at the other.   On the other hand, to the psychologist the colors form a continuous circle, the violet being a blend of red and blue in which blue predominates, and,

[1] "In the dark all cats are gray."—Old proverb.

beyond the violet, purple, a "nonspectral" blend of blue and red in which red predominates once more.[1]

The psychological definition of color is perhaps best given in the following words:[2] "Color is the general name for all sensations arising from the activity of the retina of the eye and its attached nervous mechanisms, this activity being, in nearly every case in the normal individual, a specific response to radiant energy of certain wave-lengths and intensities."

10. Hue.—The spectrum is said to be made up of hues. Four of these, red, yellow, green, and blue, are unique in that they are not composed of mixtures of others. Orange is considered as a mixture of red and yellow. Two other blends of contiguous hues are blue-green and yellow-green. Violet is a mixture of red and blue with blue predominating; purple, a nonspectral mixture of red and blue with red predominating. With the addition of black and white, from these nine hues all colors may be produced. "Hue is that attribute of certain colors in respect of which they differ characteristically from the gray of the same brilliance and which permits them to be classed as reddish, yellowish, greenish, or bluish."

The sensation of white is produced by any color if sufficiently intense. Hence yellow, which produces relatively the largest stimulus, is said to contain the greatest amount of white.

11. Saturation.—A color is said to be saturated when it is mixed with the smallest possible quantity of white or black. According to the preceding section, yellow is less saturated than the red obtained from the same white-light spectrum. However, if the entire spectrum is reduced in luminosity, the red is said to become *desaturated* by mixture with black, while at the same time the yellow approaches saturation by a reduction of its

[1] As a result of the combined planning and research of those whose chief interest is in the field of colorimetry, the subject of color has been lifted from the realm of vague concept and discordant terminology to the position of a well-developed technology with precise techniques. This has come about largely through the exchange of ideas and deliberations of international commissions meeting at intervals of several years, and dealing with the subjects of illumination, color, and spectrophotometry. Several of the references in the following sections are to reports of these commissions.

[2] This definition, as well as those of *hue*, *saturation*, and *brilliance* quoted in following sections, are from the Report of the Committee on Colorimetry for 1920–1921, *Jour. Opt. Soc. Amer.*, **6**, 527.

luminosity. "Saturation is that attribute of all colors possessing a hue which determines their degree of difference from a gray of the same brilliance."

12. Brilliance.—The term closest to this in meaning in physics is brightness or luminosity, but since these have already been used with objective meaning, the term brilliance will be used to indicate the relative excitability of the retina for different parts of the spectrum. Thus, the yellow is the most brilliant color in the spectrum of a white-light source of ordinary intensity.[1] "Brilliance is that attribute of any color in respect of which it may be classed as equivalent to some member of a series of grays ranging between black and white."

13. Color and the Retina.—The retina of the human eye is a complicated structure composed of many layers, each of a composite structure. The parts most directly associated in theory with color vision are the *rods* and *cones*. That the rods and cones play an important part in the mechanism is shown by the following observed relations.[2]

a. In case of congenital absence of both rods and cones, blindness exists.

b. If the fovea has no rods, that part of the retina suffers from *night blindness*, a term describing various degrees of inability to see with low illumination.

c. Color blindness accompanies a congenital absence of cones.

d. Animals having a predominance of rods (bats, owls, etc.) have good night vision and poor day vision, while birds, with a predominance of cones, have the opposite characteristics.

e. Rapidity of adaptation to dark is associated with the extent of changes which take place in the rods.

The relationships just given support the theory that the rods are important in brightness vision and the cones in color vision.

All parts of the retina do not have the same degree of sensitivity to color, which is probably due to the cones becoming relatively infrequent as the periphery is reached. In normal eyes the retina is sensitive to yellow over the largest area and to blue

[1] It is perhaps worth while to warn against confusion of this distribution of brilliance with the distribution of radiant energy associated with a source at a given temperature, as described by Wien's distribution law.

[2] These relations have been adapted from Bills, "General Experimental Psychology," Longmans.

over one almost as large, to red over a still smaller area, and to green over the smallest.

14. Complementary Colors.—If two colored lights are mixed, the resulting stimulus matches that of a third, the exact color of which depends upon the proportions of the mixture. Often in such cases the match is not perfect, the mixture being less saturated than the third color. As the spectral separation (difference of wave-length) of the two colors mixed is increased, the saturation becomes less. Two colors sufficiently far apart in the spectrum give, when mixed, the sensation of white. Such colors are called *complementary*. Table 17-1, of complementary colors, is due to Helmholtz.[1]

Color		Complementary color	
Red.................	6562A	Green blue.........	4921A
Orange.............	6077A	Blue..............	4897A
Yellow.............	5853A	Blue..............	4851A
Yellow.............	5739A	Blue..............	4821A
Yellow.............	5671A	Indigo blue........	4645A
Yellow.............	5644A	Indigo blue........	4618A
Yellow green........	5636A	Violet.............	4330A and beyond

15. Theories of Color Vision.[2]—It is found by experiment that a color stimulus may be accurately matched by a mixture of correct amounts of three color stimuli. The first person to make use of this as the basis of a mechanistic theory of color vision seems to have been the versatile genius, Thomas Young. His postulation of the existence in the human eye of three independent mechanisms of color perception, each correlated with one of the three primaries, red, green, and blue, is the basis of what is now universally known as the Young-Helmholtz theory of color vision. Equal stimulation of all three mechanisms results

[1] A more extended table of complementaries, based on the standard source for colorimetry, used in place of the so-called white-light source of earlier research (see Sec. **17-18**), is to be found on p. 31 of the "Handbook of Colorimetry," by A. C. Hardy, The Technological Press, 1936. The values of complementaries listed in this table are those of the dominant wave-lengths of complementary colors (see item *b*, Sec. **17-19**).

[2] For a more extensive treatment see Parsons, "An Introduction to the Study of Colour Vision," Cambridge University Press.

in gray.   Black is the absence of any stimulus.   The relative
sensitivity of the different mechanisms is illustrated by Fig. 17-7.
The Young-Helmholtz theory accounts for after-images as due
to retinal fatigue, but does not account for the gray after-image
of black nor the black after-image of gray.   It does not account
for contrast, nor for the existence of color-sensitive zones in the
retina.   It accounts only partly for color blindness, not providing
for the gray vision of the color blind.   On the other hand, the
correspondence between the fundamental postulate of Young and
the experimental facts of the science of colorimetry make the
theory a suitable conveyance for the concepts and nomenclature
of the purely metrical phases of that science.

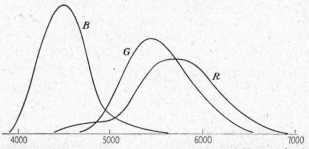

FIG. 17-7.—Relative sensitivity of the red, green, and blue mechanisms of
color perception.   The shape of the curves is illustrative only, and conforms
to no particular set of data.

The theory of Hering claims the existence in the retina of two
mutually exclusive processes: (a) anabolism, the process by
which matter is transformed into tissues; and (b) catabolism, the
process by which substance is broken down in the tissue.   This
theory recognizes the presence in the retina of three mechanisms
which can be excited in either of these processes.   Anabolic
excitation yields the sensations of green, blue, and black; cata-
bolic, red, yellow, and white.   This theory explains the phenomena of complementary colors, but not the mixture of black
and white to form gray.   It accounts only partly for color
blindness.

The theory of Ladd-Franklin assumes that in the rods and
cones of the retina exist types of molecules which are affected
and modified by the action of the light.   This bold hypothesis
goes far to bring the *trichromatic* theory of Young-Helmholtz
and that of Hering into accord.   It does not account for binoc-

ular effects. Also, the possibility of molecular changes and motions occurring with the rapidity required by visual phenomena has been gravely questioned. It is a theory which concerns chiefly the psychologist and physiologist. Those interested only in the physical aspects of color vision and colorimetric measurements find the trichromatic theory of Young a suitable conveyance for the concepts and definitions involved in their work.

16. Color Mixing versus Pigment Mixing.—Colored lights may be mixed in a variety of ways, some of which will be described in the next section. A simple method, however, is to paint on a disk a red sector and a green one. With a suitable choice of angle of the two sectors, on rotating the disk the visual sensation will be yellow. If some of the same pigments are mixed, the mixture will not appear yellow, but dull brown. The difference is that while in the first case there is a true mixture of the two stimuli, both occurring at the retina, in the second case the light received by the eye is that which is not absorbed. With the red and green pigments mixed, the light which is not entirely absorbed contains not only yellow, but some red and some green.

17. Colorimeters.—A colorimeter is an instrument for measuring the character and intensity of a stimulus due to a color or a mixture of colors. One of the earliest precision colorimeters is the color-patch colorimeter of Abney. This is a spectrometric device equipped with two or more slits at the plane where the spectrum is focused, by means of which varying relative amounts of different spectral regions can be isolated. These are then brought into superposition in a field of some area and compared with the original white light. Another instrument, designed by H. E. Ives, makes use of filters instead of slits to isolate the spectral primaries. There are many difficulties to be overcome in the construction and use of a colorimeter, in part because of the dual character of vision, *i.e.*, sensitivity to color and to brilliance. While the subject is too extensive for complete treatment here, certain developments of the past decade which have transformed colorimetry into a precise quantitative science will be discussed.

18. Color Matching.—It is found by experiment that a color stimulus may be accurately matched by a mixture of correct amounts of three color stimuli. Three colors thus used are called *primaries*. No three primaries will combine to match all colors, but, as will be seen later, this is not as severe a limitation as might at first appear. We may express this additive character of color stimuli by the equation

$$S = P_1 + P_2 + P_3, \qquad (17\text{-}1)$$

where S is the color stimulus to be matched and P_1, P_2, and P_3, are the three primaries. Sometimes the color stimulus produced by the mixture is unsaturated, and to compensate for this a suitable amount of white must be added to S.

In the earlier work done in color mixture, the different regions of the spectrum were matched with combinations of three given primaries, and the amounts of the primaries recorded by the observer. But observers differ slightly among themselves, even though they have normal color vision. Consequently, in more recent compilations of colorimetric data it has been the practice to average the results obtained by numbers of carefully selected observers. Those data have been standardized by international commissions. The negative values of the primary stimuli which occur in matching certain spectral colors with any given set of primaries are eliminated by a simple mathematical transformation. Let r, g, and b be three values in energy units of the three original primaries which, an observer finds, will mix to match a certain wave-length from a given source, and r', g', and b' the translated values in terms of a new set of primaries. Then

$$\left.\begin{aligned}
r' &= k_1 r + k_2 g + k_3 b, \\
g' &= k_4 r + k_5 g + k_6 b, \\
b' &= k_7 r + k_8 g + k_9 b,
\end{aligned}\right\} \qquad (17\text{-}2)$$

where the k's are the values of the original primaries in terms of the new primaries. Thus the values obtained with any set of primaries may be translated in terms of any other set, and hence in terms of a set so chosen that it contains no negative values. It follows, however, that the set so chosen by international agreement is based on primaries which are not real colors, an expedient which, because of the linear transformation given above, causes no unsurmountable difficulty.

The values of the primaries corresponding to wave-lengths at intervals of 50 angstroms throughout the visible spectrum are given in energy units in the report of the Committee on

Colorimetry[1] for 1928–1931, and also in the "Handbook of Colorimetry."[2]   These values are called *tristimulus values* and are designated by $\bar{x}$, $\bar{y}$, $\bar{z}$ for luminous sources and X, Y, Z for

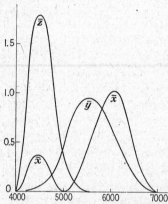

FIG. 17-8.—Tristimulus values for standard illuminant C. (*Adapted from A. C. Hardy, "Handbook of Colorimetry."*)

diffuse reflection from colored surfaces.   In Fig. 17-8 the values are plotted as ordinates against wave-length as abscissas.   For instance, the tristimulus values of the recommended standard source (illuminant C, Appendix VII) for wave-length 4800 angstroms are given by the ordinates at that wave-length of the three curves.

Thus it is now possible to obtain the *chromaticity*, or color value, of a source in terms of an internationally adopted set of specifications by comparing it spectrophotometrically with the adopted standard.   The chromaticity is given in terms of three so-called *trichromatic coefficients:*

$$x = \frac{\bar{x}}{\bar{x} + \bar{y} + \bar{z}},$$
$$y = \frac{\bar{y}}{\bar{x} + \bar{y} + \bar{z}}, \qquad (17\text{-}3)$$
$$z = \frac{\bar{z}}{\bar{x} + \bar{y} + \bar{z}}.$$

The chromaticity is by this means evaluated as a quantity independent of the total brightness (brilliance).

19. Graphical Representations of Chromaticity.   *a. The Color Triangle.*—The experimental results of color mixture give support to the construction of a geometrical figure which will express graphically all the known results and concepts associated with the science of colorimetry.   If the concept of *brilliance* is omitted, this can be done on a plane figure called the *color triangle*, shown

[1] *Transactions of the Optical Society (London)*, **33**, 73, 1931–1932.

[2] Compiled by A. C. Hardy and associates; published by the Technology Press, 1936.

in Fig. 17-9. The color triangle proper is shown by the heavy inscribed line along which the respective spectral positions are given by the Fraunhofer letters.

In order to express also the concept of brilliance, the color diagram must have a third dimension. The resulting figure is generally called a color pyramid. No single three-dimensional diagram has been proposed which embodies all the experimental facts and the concepts of color vision. Perhaps the best figure is one which indicates only the dimensions as in Fig. 17-10.[1] In what follows, however, it will be seen that in reality only two dimensions are required, provided the tristimulus values are evaluated in terms of trichromatic coefficients.

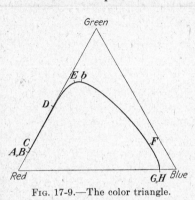

FIG. 17-9.—The color triangle.

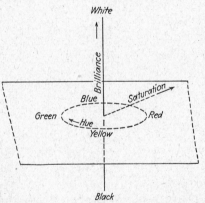

FIG. 17-10.—A three-dimensional color diagram.

b. The Chromaticity Diagram.—For purposes of colorimetric evaluation, the color triangle has been standardized, and by international commission has been referred, not to the indefinite quantity known as white light, but to standard illuminant *C* (see Appendix VII). The resulting figure is called a *chromaticity*

[1] Adapted from the report of the Committee on Colorimetry, *Journal of the Optical Society of America,* **6,** 527, 1922.

diagram, shown in Fig. 17-11.[1]   The dotted line joining the ends
is the region in which the nonspectral color mixtures (purple) are
located.   The saturation of each color is given by its distance
from the center point, which represents white.   A straight line
drawn through the white point terminates in two colors which
are complementary.   The coordinates of each point on the
curved line are the trichromatic coefficients of a wave-length

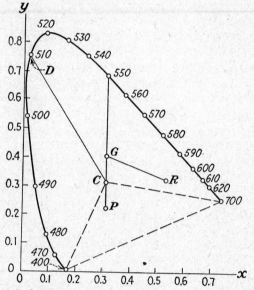

Fig. 17-11.—A chromaticity diagram. The numbers on the curve indicate
the wave-lengths in millimicrons (1 millimicron = 10 angstroms). (*Adapted
from A. C. Hardy, "Handbook of Colorimetry."*)

in the spectrum between 4000 and 7000 angstroms, calculated
from the tristimulus values for the standard illuminant.   The
chromaticity of any source of light or colored surface is given
by a point in the diagram.   For instance the chromaticity of the
standard illuminant C is given by the point C at the approximate
coordinate values $x = 0.310$, $y = 0.316$.   Several interesting
properties are given by the chromaticity diagram:

a. The color resulting from a mixture of two colors, say, red and green,
will lie on the straight line joining their chromaticity points, R and G.

[1] Adapted from A. C. Hardy, "Handbook of Colorimetry," The Technology
Press, 1936.

b. Hence, if a straight line is drawn from C to a point D on the curve (see Fig. 17-11), the color corresponding to any point on that straight line will result from a mixture of illuminant C and the spectrum color corresponding to D.   The point D then gives the *dominant* wave-length of the color in question.

c. The purples are all represented by points lying within the dotted triangle.

d. As in the case of the earlier color triangles, complementaries as, for instance, G and P lie on a straight line drawn through C, which is analogous to the white point.

Problems

1. An object is 30 cm. from the eye.   What is the numerical aperture when the entrance pupil of the eye is 5 mm.?

2. A person whose vision is hypermetropic possesses a range of accommodation permitting him to see clearly objects closer than 150 cm. If he is fitted with glasses which are convergent lenses of 20 cm. focal length, how near may he bring a printed page and still see the print clearly?

3. A farsighted person can see objects clearly if they are more than 50 cm. away.   If he uses a reading glass of 15 cm. focal length, what lateral magnification does he obtain?

4. A person with normal vision adjusts a telescope for his own use. It is then used by a person who has no power of accomodation for nearby objects.   What adjustments should the second person make?   If it is to be used instead by a person who is very shortsighted, what adjustments should he make?

5. Can objects be seen distinctly when the eye and object are under water?   Explain your answer.

EXPERIMENTS IN LIGHT

EXPERIMENT 1

FOCAL LENGTHS OF SIMPLE LENSES

Apparatus.—An optical bench about 2 m. long; an assortment of convergent and divergent lenses; a source of light; a glass mirror which can be rotated about horizontal and vertical axes; a ground glass or white screen; a spherometer; calipers; meter sticks, steel tape. The source of light may be a frosted electric light bulb enclosed in a metal box which has one side plane and painted white, with an opening in the white area crossed by wires. If the lenses are thick, it is desirable that they should be mounted in metal cells on which are marked rings to indicate the principal planes. The distance which ordinarily would be measured to a thin lens should then be measured to the appropriate principal plane of the lens.

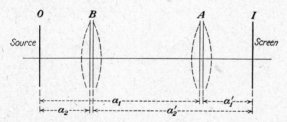

FIG. 1.—If $a + a'$ is greater than $4f$, there will be two positions of the lens for which a focus is obtained.

Part A. The Focal Length of a Simple Lens.—Set up the source at one end of the optical bench and the white screen at the other. Select a double-convex lens whose focal length, roughly determined by obtaining the image of a distant object, is between 20 and 30 cm. It may be as much as 40 to 45 cm., but a shorter length is desirable. A plano-convex lens may be used, in which case the convex side should be toward the source, since in this position the spherical aberration of such a lens is a minimum. Set the lens with its axis parallel to the bench, and slide it along until an image is formed on the screen. If the image distance from the lens is smaller than the object distance, as for position A (Fig. 1), there will be another lens position at B for which there

343

will be an image on the screen. Then, referring to Fig. 1, $a_2' = a_1$ and $a_2 = a_1'$. Measure the distances as accurately as possible and calculate the focal length f of the lens from the equation $\frac{1}{a} + \frac{1}{a'} = \frac{1}{f}$. Keep in mind that unless the lens is thin, the values of a and a' should be measured from the object and image planes to the principal planes P and P', respectively.

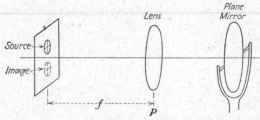

Fig. 2.—Auto-collimating method for determining f.

Part B. Focal Length by the Autocollimation Method.—Set up the source, lens, and plane mirror as shown in Fig. 2, using the same lens as in Part A. Adjust the mirror and lens so that an image of the cross wires falls on the white surface of the lamp enclosure. The distance from the lens (or its nearer principal plane if this is known) to the cross wires is the principal focal length f.

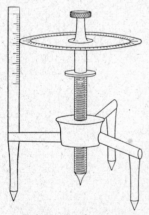

Fig. 3.—A spherometer.

Part C. Index of Refraction with a Spherometer.—First set the spherometer (Fig. 3) on a plane glass surface or metal plate and screw the center point up or down until it is just in contact with the plate. If it is too far down, the spherometer will rock on its legs. Holding the center knob firmly in this position, twist the micrometer dial on its shaft until its zero mark comes into coincidence with the vertical scale. The reading on the vertical scale is the zero mark for the measurement which is to be made, and should be on one of the divisions. If it is not, it is probable that the micrometer either is not flat or its plane is not perpendicular to the screw of the spherometer, in which case a record of the variation should be made.   Place the spherometer on the lens surface to be measured and turn the center knob until the center point just makes contact with the lens with no rocking. Record the amount the center point has been elevated (or depressed for a concave surface) from the zero point previously determined.   Press the leg points on a piece of paper and measure the three distances d between each pair of legs, and obtain an average value for d.   In case the points are flattened by wear, be sure that the distances measured are not to the centers of the depressions in the paper but to the edges corresponding to the points of the legs which were in contact with the lens surface. Calculate the radius of curvature by means of the equation

$$r = \frac{d^2}{6s} + \frac{s}{2},\tag{1}$$

where s is the distance measured with the spherometer.   Repeat for the second surface.   Calculate the index of refraction by means of the equation

$$\frac{1}{f} = (n - 1)\left(\frac{1}{r_1} - \frac{1}{r_2}\right).\tag{2}$$

Part D.   The Focal Length of a Divergent Lens.—Choose a convergent lens of somewhat longer focal length than the divergent lens to be measured and set it up on the optical bench as in

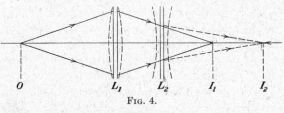

Fig. 4.

Fig. 4.   There will be a real image at I_1.   Place the divergent lens L_2 between this image and L_1.   Then I_1 will serve as a virtual source for which L_2 will form an image at I_2.   The distances I_1L_2 and I_2L_2 are a and a', respectively, in the equation

$$\frac{1}{a} + \frac{1}{a'} = \frac{1}{f}.$$

Part E.   Index of Refraction of a Divergent Lens.—Repeat Part C for the divergent lens whose focal length has been found in Part D.

Part E'.   Curvature of a Concave Surface.   Second Method.—
The curvature of the concave surface may be found by the spherometer and also by another method which serves as a check on
the spherometer measurement.   In a suitable clamp set up a
polished strip or small rod of metal, as for instance, a large
needle.   Illuminate it with a lamp held near by, and set it at a
position in front of the concave surface where the inverted
image of its point will coincide exactly with it as shown in Fig. 5.
The point of coincidence may be determined by eliminating the
parallactic displacement as the eye is moved from side to side
and up and down.   If the other lens surface also reflects enough
light to interfere, smear it with a little vaseline which can be

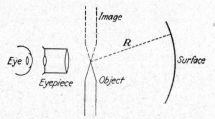

Fig. 5.—A point and its image coincide at the center of curvature of a spherical
mirror.

wiped off later with a soft cloth or lens paper.   Some observers
will find it desirable to use an eyepiece of moderate power in
eliminating the parallax.   The distance from the object point
to the lens surface is the radius of curvature of the surface.

In addition to the details of measuring technique and manipula-
tive skill in this experiment, there are some important lessons
to be learned regarding the effect of inaccuracies in the different
observations.   For the divergent lens, calculate the error introduced into the measurement of radius of curvature by an error
of 1 per cent in the measurement of the distance between the
spherometer legs.   How does this compare with the mean error
of three successive observations of r by method E'?   Conclude
your report of the experiment with a discussion of the relative
accuracy of measurement of f by the methods outlined, the
probable percentage of error in the measurement of the index
of refraction, and the sources of all errors.

If the principal planes of the lenses are known, what additional
accuracy is gained by measuring all distances from them rather

than from the vertices of the lens surfaces or the mean positions of the surfaces?

Verify eq. 1.

EXPERIMENT 2

CARDINAL POINTS OF LENS SYSTEMS

The theory of lens systems will be found in Chap. III.

Apparatus.—A source of light and a collimating lens for the projection of a parallel beam; a nodal slide; a small screen on which to focus images; an assortment of lenses.

The source of light may be a concentrated point, or a tungsten lamp filament which lies nearly in a single plane. The collimator should be a fairly good lens of 10 to 15 cm. diameter and of about 1 m. focal length. It may be placed in one end of a tube or box, with the lamp at the other end, capable of adjustment for focal distance. The beam may be collimated with a laboratory telescope, previously focused for parallel light, set up in the beam, with a smoked-glass filter between the eyepiece and the eye to prevent injury to the eye.

A nodal slide is essentially an optical bench which may be turned about a vertical axis. It is possible to obtain such apparatus possessing many refinements, but a satisfactory arrangement is that shown in Fig. 1. A rigid bar of metal or wood is made in the shape of a trough in which may be placed the cylinders containing the lenses. The bar is mounted with one end clamped on a spectrometer table, or on an

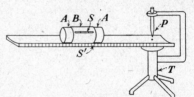

FIG. 1.—A nodal slide. AA, two lenses in cylindrical cells; B, a cylinder with a slot S to hold the lenses; S', a scale; T, a tripod support; P, a pointer at the axis of the slide.

improvised vertical axis, and is equipped with a pointer P, as shown, by which the axis of rotation may be determined. A scale or meter stick should be fastened to the side of the bar.

The screen may be a ground-glass disk about 1 in. in diameter, mounted on an arm which can slide along a bar parallel to the direction of the beam of light.

The lenses need not be of the same diameter, but should be mounted in brass cylinders of the same size, on which are marked rings indicating the positions of the principal planes. A tube about 8 in. long, with a $\frac{1}{4}$-in. slot cut nearly its whole length should be provided, into which the lens cylinders can be fitted, thus holding them a fixed distance apart for each set of measurements.

The experiment is to determine the manner in which the cardinal points of a combination of two equal lenses vary in position as the distance d between them is changed. The theory and equations for the positions of the cardinal points will be found in Chap. III.

Select two biconvex lenses of equal focal length, say, about 15 to 20 cm. Place one of them on the nodal slide and measure its focal length, which will be the distance from an image of a distant source to the emergent principal plane P'. Repeat for the other lens. Put the two lenses together in the holding tube, with the distance d between their inner principal planes as small as possible. Lay the combination on the nodal slide, obtain a good focus of the source on the screen, and rotate the slide back and forth about its vertical axis. If the image also moves from side to side, move the lens combination and the screen together along the nodal slide, until a position is reached where rotation of the slide causes no shift of the image from side to side. It is essential to keep the image well focused as these maneuvers are carried out. When the position of no lateral shift is reached, the axis of rotation of the slide passes through the emergent nodal point of the combination. Since the system has the same medium on both sides, this is also the emergent principal point.

Record the distances f', p', and d for about eight different separations of the lenses. The value of d should be varied from the smallest to the largest obtainable experimentally. Make a comparative table of these values and those calculated from equations.

Discuss the reasons for the differences between the calculated and observed values.

EXPERIMENT 3
A STUDY OF ABERRATIONS

For the theory of Aberrations see Chap. VI.

Apparatus.—An optical bench, a mounting for lenses with a turntable graduated to degrees, a concentrated source of light, lenses, diaphragms, and red, blue, and green filters.

Spherical Aberration.—The source of light should preferably be monochromatic. This may be obtained by focusing the light of a mercury arc on a hole about 1 mm. in diameter through a color filter which transmits only the green line of mercury, 5461 angstroms. If this is too faint, use a concentrated filament lamp or a Point-o-lite. Mount the turn-table so that it may slide along the bench. The screen may be a large sheet of bristol board, or white celluloid.

For a lens, an ordinary projection lantern condenser is suitable. It should be mounted in a brass cylinder on which grooves are cut coinciding with the principal planes. A diaphragm like that shown in Fig. 1 is then mounted over the lens. Notice that the holes are arranged,

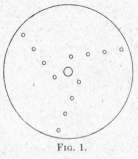

Fig. 1.

not radially, but so that the images will not fall on each other as the focal position is changed.

The purpose of the experiment is to obtain a set of measurements of the longitudinal spherical aberration (L.S.A.) for different focal distances. Adjust the lens in its holder with the convex side toward the source, and with its axis passing through the source. For several object positions, each obtained by moving the lens, find the focal distance for rays through the center opening, and also for rays through the openings at distances h_1, h_2, and h_3 from the center. The maximum range of difference of the focal distance between the focus for the center opening and that for the outermost zone should give the L. S. A. Calculate the values of the L. S. A. from the following equation:

$$\text{L.S.A.} = \frac{a'^2(n-1)}{n^2} \cdot \frac{h^2}{2}\left[\left(\frac{1}{r_1} + \frac{1}{a}\right)^2 \cdot \left(\frac{n+1}{a} + \frac{1}{r_1}\right) + \left(\frac{1}{r_2} - \frac{1}{a'}\right)^2 \cdot \left(\frac{n+1}{a'} - \frac{1}{r_2}\right)\right].$$

If a plano-convex lens is used, with the plane surface away from the source, $r_2 = \infty$, and h is the appropriate distance of a given circle of holes from the center of the diaphragm.

Plot on a graph the image distances against the corresponding values of h, the distances of holes from the axis. Write a brief statement regarding the use of a front stop to reduce aberration in the lens used.

Astigmatism.—To obtain astigmatic focal distances it is preferable to select a double-convex lens of about 10 cm. diameter and 30 to 40 cm. focal length. Prepare a diaphragm having

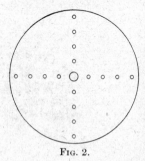

Fig. 2.

two rows of holes, as shown in Fig. 2, and place it over the lens so that one row of holes coincides with the axis of the turntable. Rotate the turntable and lens so that the optic axis makes an angle of about 20 deg. with the direction to the source. Move the screen so that the horizontal row of holes comes approximately to a point or area of confusion. The distance from the lens to the screen is the primary focal distance s_1. The distance s_2 will be found by placing the screen similarly at the position where the vertical row of holes comes to a focus. Calculate the values of s_1 and s_2 from the equations

$$\frac{1}{s} + \frac{1}{s_1} = \frac{2(n-1)}{r \cos i},$$

$$\frac{1}{s} + \frac{1}{s_2} = \frac{2(n-1) \cos i}{r},$$

and the value of the astigmatic difference, $s_2 - s_1$, from

$$\frac{1}{s_1} - \frac{1}{s_2} = \frac{2(n-1) \sin i \cdot \tan i}{r}.$$

Coma.—Select a plano-convex lens, a double-convex lens, an ordinary achromatic doublet, and a spherical mirror. If possible, they should have about the same relative aperture. Each lens should be divided into alternate transmitting and opaque concentric zones. It is easy to render the nontransmitting zones opaque by pasting on the lens rings cut out of black paper, but, if the lenses are needed for other purposes, these rings may be pasted on a thin disk of glass the size of the lens. A transmitting center disk and three transmitting zones are recommended.

The source should be a small point of high intensity. This can be a Point-o-lite lamp or an illuminated pinhole about 1 mm. in diameter. If sunlight is available, the experiment may be performed in parallel light. Obtain an axial image with each lens, tilt the lens, and refocus. In general it will be difficult to observe the comatic images without tilting the lens to so large an angle that astigmatism will also be present.

Make as accurately as possible a drawing of the comatic images with each lens. For which, if any, of the lenses or mirrors used, is coma absent?

Curvature of the Field and Distortion.—For simple lenses these aberrations are marked with objects having large area. It is difficult, however, to distinguish between curvature of the field and astigmatism. The distortion due to a doublet of two convex lenses will be examined. Select two equal double-convex lenses of about 6 cm. aperture and 15 cm. focal length, each mounted in a tube so that the two may be placed different distances apart by sliding the lens tubes into another one which fits them tightly. For the source use a blackened photographic plate ruled with a rectangular grid of scratches about 1 cm. apart. This is to be backed with a sheet of thin white paper and illuminated from behind with a strong source of light.

Measure the change in focus for regions of the image field at different distances from the axis. This will give the curvature of the field. Measure also the difference in magnification for different zones. This will give the distortion. Plot both the curvature and the distortion separately as ordinates on a single sheet of graph paper, against the distance from the axis as abscissa.

Chromatic Aberration.—Mount the plano-convex lens used in the determination of spherical aberration with a concentrated filament for a source. With a red filter, measure the focal distance. Repeat with a blue filter. The difference in focus is a measure of the chromatic aberration. Repeat the experiment with an ordinary achromatic doublet.

EXPERIMENT 4

MEASUREMENT OF INDEX OF REFRACTION BY MEANS OF A MICROSCOPE

Apparatus.—This consists mainly of a microscope mounted horizontally on a carriage in fairly accurate ways so that it is capable of horizontal motion of a few centimeters. The distance moved is measured by means of a linear scale and a micrometer head graduated to thousandths of a millimeter. In case the movable carriage and micrometer are not available, a tenth-millimeter scale may be attached to the horizontal microscope and the distance it is moved may be measured by means of a second, vertical, microscope focused on the scale and equipped with a micrometer eyepiece. In some cases high-grade microscopes are equipped with micrometers capable of measuring the focusing distance with great accuracy, so that no auxiliary measuring microscope is needed.

There should also be an adjustable stand on which specimens and cells may be mounted in front of the horizontal microscope, and a source of light, preferably diffuse.

Part A.   Refractive Index of a Glass Block.—The block to be examined should be one for which the index can also be measured

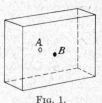

Fig. 1.

by means of the grazing incidence method (see Experiment 7) and should therefore be a rectangular block with one end and two sides polished. The distance between the sides A and B (Fig. 1) is measured with a micrometer caliper to hundredths of a millimeter. Sprinkle a few grains of lycopodium powder on the surfaces. The microscope is first focused on a grain at A, and its position read, then on a grain at B, and a reading taken. Since the angles of incidence of the rays entering the microscope are very small, to a high degree of approximation the distance the microscope is moved between readings is equal to the actual distance AB divided by the index of refraction of the glass. From this the index may be calculated.

Part B.   Refractive Index of a Liquid.—Use one of the liquids to be examined in Experiment 7. First, on the inside walls of a dry cell with parallel glass walls like that shown in Fig. 2, sprinkle a little lycopodium powder and measure the distance between the walls by the method described in Part A. In this case, however, the distance moved by the microscope between readings will be the actual separation of the inner walls of the cell. Then remove the powder from the inner walls and sprinkle a little on the outer walls, and repeat the measurements. Then, without moving the cell, place the liquid in it, and re-measure the distance (apparent) between the outer walls. If a is the apparent distance measured between the outer

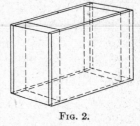

Fig. 2.

walls without the liquid, b the apparent distance between them with the liquid, and c the actual distance between the inner walls, then

$$n = \frac{c}{c - (a - b)}.$$

Answer the following questions:

1. How many figures after the decimal place in the value of n are you justified in retaining? Explain your answer.

2. What error in Part A would be introduced by having an angle of 5 deg. between the normal to the plane surfaces and the axis of the microscope?

3. What error in Part B would be introduced under the same conditions?

4. Justify the assumption involved in the statement that the angle can be substituted for its sine in making the measurements in this experiment.

EXPERIMENT 5

THE PRISM SPECTROMETER

Apparatus.—A spectrometer equipped with a Gauss eye-piece, a prism of approximately 60 deg. refracting angle, an extra slit to be fitted over the telescope objective, a white light source, a mercury arc, a helium source.

The adjustment of the spectrometer should be made first according to the directions in Appendix IV. It is recommended that the student read through these directions with a view to understanding their purpose, rather than follow them line by line without appreciating the significance of each operation.

After the spectrometer is in adjustment, read the following experimental directions and make sure that each can be carried out without modification of the spectrometer.

Part A. To Measure the Refracting Angle of the Prism.—A prism is a fragile piece of equipment, easily chipped on its corners and edges so that its usefulness is impaired. It

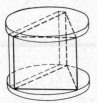

may be protected by mounting as shown in Fig. 1. If the base is somewhat larger than shown and equipped with three leveling screws, it will be easier to use. Adjust the prism table so that the faces of the prism are parallel to the vertical axis of the spectrometer. (It is essential for this experiment only that the faces be perpendicular to the telescope axis, but it is assumed that the latter has been adjusted with reference to the axis of the spectrometer.)

F I G . 1.—A mount to protect the prism, consisting of two circular metal plates held firmly together by a rectangular p l a t e against which the base of the prism is set.

Method 1.—Set the telescope perpendicular to one of the prism faces, using the Gauss eyepiece (see Sec. **7-3**), and record the angle on the graduated circle. Repeat for the other prism face. The difference between the two readings, subtracted from 180 deg., gives the refracting angle A of the prism.

CAUTION: in making this and all other readings it is essential that both verniers (or reading microscopes) be used. It is assumed that the telescope axis intersects the principal axis of the spectrometer, but this may not be exactly so. Any slight error in this respect may be eliminated by reading both verniers. This is illustrated by the following numerical example.

	First Vernier	Second Vernier
First prism face................	276° 25′ 15″	96° 27′ 32″
Second prism face.............	35 25 45	215 29 10
180° − A.....................	119° 0′ 30″	119° 1′ 38″
Mean........................	119° 1′ 4″	
A..........................	60° 58′ 56″	

Each setting in this and other observations should be made four or five times and the mean value taken.

Method 2.—Project the light through the slit and collimator lens (white light will do) and set the prism on the table with the refracting edge at the center as in Fig. 2. Set the telescope in position I so that the reflected image of the slit *in good focus* is exactly at the intersection of the cross hairs. Repeat for position II. The angle between the two settings of the telescope is twice the prism angle.

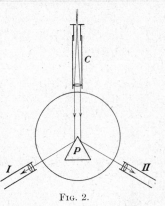

Fig. 2.

Part B. To Find the Index of Refraction and Dispersion Curve of the Prism by the Use of the Angle of Minimum Deviation.—For this part of the experiment a discharge tube containing helium and mercury in correct quantities to yield spectra of approximately equal strengths is excellent, although two separate sources may be used.   If the helium source is not available, some other such as hydrogen or neon may be used, or even sunlight. All that is required is a dozen or so easily distinguishable lines throughout the range of the visible spectrum. *Do not use a slit that is too wide.* The spectrum lines should be so narrow that they appear as sharp lines with no perceptible evidence of the width of the slit. A table of wave-lengths of suitable elements is given in Table I, page 443.

With the prism removed, and a mercury source in front of the slit, set the telescope and collimator in line so that the image of the slit falls exactly on the cross hairs, and record the angle of the telescope. Then place the prism on the table as in Fig. 3. Do not move the collimator, but set the prism so that the light from the slit completely fills one face of the prism. Swing the telescope to one side and look directly at the spectrum in the other face of the prism. Rotate the prism table and prism about the vertical axis, first in one direction, then in the other, watching the spectrum at the same time. It will be noted that as the prism is rotated, the spectrum changes position, but for a particular angle of the prism the direction of motion of the spectrum reverses. That is, if the prism and collimator occupy the position shown in Fig. 3, as the prism is turned clockwise, the spectrum will first seem to move to the right and then, reversing its motion, move toward the left, while the prism continues to rotate in the same sense as before. Locate the position of minimum deviation roughly in this way, swing the telescope into the field of view, and repeat the rotation of the prism back and forth over a smaller range until the position of minimum deviation for the green mercury line (wave-length 5.461×10^{-5} cm.) is accurately determined. The angle between this setting of the telescope and that recorded without the prism will be Δ, the angle of minimum deviation for 5461 angstroms. Calculate the index of refraction for this wave-length by means of eq. 8-5, page 89. Next obtain Δ for each of several bright lines through-

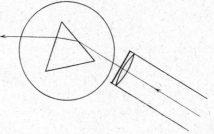

Fig. 3.

out the range of the visible spectrum, and calculate the corresponding indices of refraction. Plot the values of the index thus obtained against the wave-lengths, and obtain the dispersion curve. It is customary for manufacturers to specify for a particular glass the value of the index for the sodium doublet, whose average wave-length is 5893 angstroms. Obtain the value of the index of refraction for this wave-length from your curve and compare it with the value provided by the instructor.

The dispersive power of a glass between the Fraunhofer C and G lines is given by the equation

$$\omega = \frac{n_G - n_C}{n_D - 1}. \tag{1}$$

Using the wave-lengths of the Fraunhofer C, D, and G lines (from Sec. **6-14**), find n_C, n_D, and n_G from your dispersion curve, and calculate the value of ω. This result should also be compared with one provided by the instructor.

Calculate also the values of the Cauchy constants n_0 and B from the following equations:

$$n_0 = \frac{n_1\lambda_1^2 - n_2\lambda_2^2}{\lambda_1^2 - \lambda_2^2}; \qquad B = \frac{\lambda_1^2\lambda_2^2 \cdot (n_2 - n_1)}{\lambda_1^2 - \lambda_2^2}. \qquad (2)$$

Part C. The Resolving Power of the Prism.—In order to apply Rayleigh's criterion it would be necessary to select two spectrum lines which are sufficiently close together so that they are just seen as distinct lines in the spectrometer under the best conditions.   However, resolving power is shown by eq. 8-14 to be proportional to the equivalent thickness of the prism and thus to the width of the beam of light falling upon it.   Hence we may choose any suitable pair of lines, such as the yellow pair in the mercury spectrum, 5770 and 5790 angstroms, which are much farther apart than those which are just resolved by the full prism, and decrease the width of the beam of parallel light passing from the collimator through the prism and thence to the telescope. This can be done by placing over the collimator or telescope lens in a vertical position a second slit whose width may be varied. This slit is then to be closed until the lines, each of which will appear to widen, are just on the point of becoming indistinguishable.   Carefully remove the second slit and measure its width a' with a microscope or comparator.   The resolving power of that part of the prism thus used is given by

$$R' = \frac{a'}{a} \cdot R, \qquad (3)$$

where a is the width of the beam of light intercepted by the full prism face and R is the resolving power of the prism.   But from geometry it is evident that w, the width of the face upon which the light is incident is given by

$$w = \frac{t}{2 \sin (A/2)},$$

and also, at minimum deviation,

$$a = w \cos i' = w \cos i;$$

hence,

$$R = \frac{R'w \cos i}{a'}. \qquad (4)$$

Now we can calculate R' for the width a', from the fundamental definition of resolving power, *i.e.*,

$$R' = \frac{\lambda}{d\lambda}.$$

Thus, by eq. 3, R can be obtained from the experimental results.

For the average wave-length used, calculate also the value of R for the entire prism from

$$R = \frac{2Bt}{\lambda^3}$$

and compare it with the experimental result. Compute from $R = aD$ where D is the dispersion of the prism, the values of the resolving power for several wave-lengths.

EXPERIMENT 6
THE SPECTROPHOTOMETER

Spectrophotometers which make possible the comparison of the intensities of sources over small ranges of wave-length may be constructed in various ways. Two forms will be described here, in both of which the actual comparison is effected by the use of polarized light.

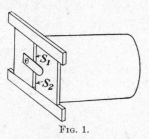

Fig. 1.

The Glan Spectrophotometer.—This instrument is similar to the ordinary spectrometer, but has certain modifications making possible the comparison of two sources. The light from one of these passes directly into the upper portion S_1 of the slit (Fig. 1), while that from the other is directed into the lower portion S_2 by means of a total reflecting prism. Inside the collimator tube, at a suitable distance from the slit, is placed a Wollaston prism (see Sec. **13-10**). This prism divides the light from each of the sources into two beams which are polarized so that the directions of their plane vibrations are perpendicular to each other. These four beams are refracted by an ordinary 60-deg. prism set on the spectrometer table, so that four parallel spectra are formed, one above the other. The middle two of these which we may call spectrum 2 and spectrum 3 are from S_1 and S_2 or *vice versa*, and consist of light vibrations which are in perpendicular planes. Spectra 1 and 4 do not appear in the field of view of the eyepiece. Between the collimator lens and the refracting prism is placed a polarizing prism of the Glan type, in which the faces are inclined so that the transmitted beam undergoes no sidewise displacement as the prism is rotated. When this polarizing prism is oriented so as to transmit the full intensity of light reaching it from source 1, it will transmit none of the light from source 2, and when rotated through 90 deg. from this position, it will transmit all the light reaching it from source 2 and none from source 1. At intermediate angles, some of the light from each source will reach the eye, and for one particular angle

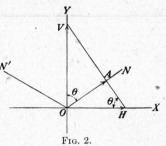

Fig. 2.

of the polarizing prism the intensities of the two spectra will be equal for a given wave-length region. It is this particular angle which must be determined experimentally for each part of the spectrum.

Referring to Fig. 2, and considering only the two middle spectra, let us suppose that the coordinate axis X represents the direction of vibration of the plane-polarized beam from source 1, transmitted by the Wollaston prism, while Y represents the direction of vibration of the beam so transmitted from source 2. Let OH and OV represent respectively the amplitudes of these vibrations. Then the ratio of these amplitudes is given by $\tan \theta = OV/OH$. If the Glan polarizing prism is oriented so that its plane of transmission is in the direction ON, making an angle θ with OY, the component OA of the amplitude OV will represent that part of the light from source 2 which will reach the eye. Similarly only the light represented by the amplitude component OA of OH will reach the eye, so that for the spectral region under observation the intensities of the two spectra will be the same. This will also be true if the polarizing prism is oriented so that its plane of transmission is parallel to ON'. Since the intensity is proportional to the square of the amplitude, it follows that when the Glan polarizer is set so that the two spectral regions have the same intensity, the ratio of the intensities of the two original sources is given by

$$\frac{\text{Intensity 2}}{\text{Intensity 1}} = \tan^2 \theta, \tag{1}$$

where θ is the angle between the setting of the polarizing prism for equal intensities and the setting for complete extinction of the light from source 1.

An ordinary spectrometer may be converted into a Glan spectrophotometer with a few changes. Across the middle of the slit is placed a strip which blocks the light and effectively divides the slit into an upper and a lower portion. The Wollaston prism is inserted in the tube so that the images from S_1 and S_2 (Fig. 1), coincide vertically. It should be possible to rotate the Wollaston through a small angle about the optical axis, and to move it along the collimator tube a short distance in either direction. A nicol in a holder having a circle preferably graduated in four quadrants is fitted on the end of the collimator tube between the lens and the refracting prism. The eyepiece is equipped with a pair of long slit jaws which may be opened wide enough so as to permit a view of the entire spectrum, or closed so as to permit the transmission of a band of only about 25 to 30 angstroms. This slit, or diaphragm, should be mounted at the focal plane of the eyepiece.

Part A. The Comparison of Continuous Spectra.—The distribution of intensities of a number of sources may be compared with that of a standard lamp. While an accurate standard may be used, it is neither necessary nor advisable for ordinary class studies. It is satisfactory to use instead an ordinary new 40-watt Mazda lamp as an arbitrary standard. To this a sticker should be affixed near the base to indicate the side of the lamp from which the light is to be taken throughout a series of measurements, since the brightness of such a lamp is not the same when viewed from different directions. With this improvised standard several sources may be compared, as, for instance, an old-fashioned carbon filament lamp, a ruby lamp, a gasoline Welsbach lamp, or sunlight. The intensity distribution in the light from a second 40-watt, 110-volt lamp operated on 135 to 150 volts may also be studied, if voltages higher than 110 are available, or a lamp of lower rated voltage than 110 may similarly be overrun.

To place the two spectra exactly one above the other, a mercury arc or other bright-line source may be used in front of the slit with the total reflection prism removed. If the bright lines due to light passing through S_1 and S_2 are not exactly in line, the Wollaston prism should be rotated slightly until the spectra coincide vertically.   At the same time, if the two spectra are not exactly edge to edge, a slight displacement of the Wollaston prism may be made along the tube to bring them together without overlapping or separation.

The prism which refracts the light is next to be calibrated. Setting it for minimum deviation approximately for the yellow, using any convenient lines, such as the sodium lines or the mercury lines, the angle of the telescope should be plotted against wave-length for a number of positions in the spectrum.   Either sunlight or ordinary laboratory sources will serve for this purpose. It is not necessary to read the angle of the telescope closer than $\frac{1}{4}$ deg. for any setting, since the comparisons to be made later are of regions of the spectrum several angstroms in width. Enough readings should be taken, however, so that a graph may be made, with wave-lengths as abscissas and telescope settings as ordinates.   After the points are plotted, a smooth curve should be drawn through them, so that for any subsequent position of the telescope the corresponding wave-length may be quickly read from the graph.

Next set up the standard lamp and the source to be compared with it.   If clear glass lamps are used, a piece of finely ground glass should be placed between each lamp and the slit, and as close to the former as possible without the risk of breakage by heat.   Glass ground to a sufficiently fine grain may be made by grinding lantern-slide cover glasses with fine carborundum, or emery, and water, using a flat piece of iron as a tool.   When the lamps are accurately in place and the zero position of the polarizing prism determined, set the telescope on a region in the red end of the spectrum, rotate the polarizing prism until the spectra of the two sources appear the same intensity, and record the setting of the polarizer.   Make several settings for each position in the spectrum, and average their values.   Then move the telescope to successive regions of the spectrum about 100 or 200 angstroms apart, and make similar observations.   Calculate the intensity ratios by means of eq. 1, and plot the values obtained.   (Remember that the telescope gives an inverted image of the slit.

Part B.   Absorption of Colored Transmitting Substances.— Using the same adjustments as in Part A, allow the light from the standard source to pass through both parts of the slit, and place a piece of didymium glass about 5 mm. thick over the lower part. Measure and plot the relative transmissions for each spectral region as outlined above. Other substances whose absorption may be measured are solutions of potassium permanganate, cobalt chloride, and thin films of metal evaporated or otherwise deposited on glass. A very useful chart of the transmissions of about 50 substances is to be found on page 16 of Wood's "Physical Optics," 1911 edition. Extensive tables of the spectral transmissions of substances are also to be found in the "Handbook of Chemistry and Physics," published by the Chemical Rubber Company, and others are procurable from the Corning Glass Works, the Eastman Kodak Company, and Jena Glass Works (Fish-Schurman Company, agents).

Part C. (**Optional**) **Relative Intensities of Bright Lines in a Spectrum.**—By using a slit of sufficient width so that each bright line from a source such as the mercury arc appears as a narrow rectangle of light, the intensities of lines in discontinuous spectra may be compared with the spectrum of a white-light source. This comparison, however, cannot be used to obtain the relative intensities within the discontinuous spectrum itself unless the distribution of intensity in the white-light source is known. While this distribution can be measured for any continuous spectrum, it is perhaps best to use a standardized and calibrated white-light source for this part of the experiment.

A tungsten ribbon lamp operated at a sufficiently high temperature may be said to radiate in accordance with the Wien distribution law, which may be written

$$E_\lambda = \frac{c_1}{\lambda^5} e^{-c_2/\lambda T},$$

where E_λ is the energy radiated for a particular wave-length λ, T is the absolute temperature, and c_1 and c_2 are constants. The value of c_2 is commonly taken as 1.433 cm.-deg. On p. 363 is a calibration for brightness temperature of a special standard lamp, made of a tungsten ribbon filament.

This lamp, operated on a current of 26 to 28 amp., may be said to approximate a black body. Hence, by Wien's law, the energy distribution in its spectrum may be calculated. If this distribution is known, it is possible to obtain with a fair degree of accuracy the distribution of intensity in the visual part of a

spectrum which is compared with it.   However, the student is
to be warned against undertaking this part of the experiment

RELATION BETWEEN CURRENT AND TEMPERATURE

Current, amp.	Brightness temperature, °K.
13.0	1,484
15.5	1,667
18.5	1,856
22.5	2,076
27.0	2,300
32.5	2,549

without careful supervision by the instructor, since calibrated
lamps are expensive and may easily be ruined.

In reporting this experiment, answer the following question:
In adjusting the Wollaston prism so that the two spectra are
exactly edge to edge, it will probably be found that when they
are so adjusted in the red, they will overlap in the blue or *vice
versa*.   Explain why this should be so.

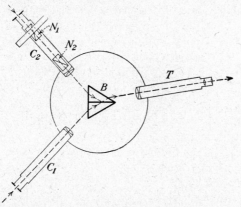

FIG. 3.—The Brace-Lemon spectrophotometer. C_1 and C_2, collimators; N_1 and
N_2, nicols; T, telescope; B, Brace prism.

The Brace-Lemon Spectrophotometer.—Another type of spectrophotometer which may be used with considerable precision is
the Brace-Lemon, illustrated in Fig. 3.   It has two identical
collimators, in one of which are set two Glan polarizing prisms.
The prism nearer the collimator lens is fixed in azimuth, while
the other may be rotated.   The dispersive instrument is a Brace
compound prism made of two 30-deg. prisms.   On one of these
is deposited an opaque coat of suitable metal of high reflecting

power, which covers the middle section of the prism face, the dividing edges between this coat and the unobstructed portions of the face being perpendicular to the refracting edge of the prism. Sometimes the reflecting coat is deposited on one half of the prism face, the upper or lower, and the remaining half left transparent. The two 30-deg. prisms are then sealed together with Canada balsam, so that the reflecting coat is between the two halves of the compound prism.

This instrument has the advantage that when the compound prism is properly made and adjusted with reference to the optical path of the light, the dividing line between the two spectra to be compared is rendered invisible.

In order to make a comparison of two sources, one of them is set before each slit, and the rotatable prism, whose zero position has been previously determined, is turned until the intensities in a given spectral region are the same.

Since the Brace compound prism is fragile and the adjustments must be made very exactly, it is perhaps desirable that the instrument be of a fixed form, and not adjustable by the student. In case adjustments are necessary, they may be made as follows:

1. The spectrometer should be adjusted with the Brace prism removed in the same manner as for any similar instrument, the essential requirements being that the axis of each collimator and that of the telescope should be perpendicular to the vertical axis of the instrument, and that the axis of rotation of the telescope should coincide with that vertical axis.

2. The rotatable polarizing prism N_1 should be set for maximum transmission; *i.e.*, its plane of transmission should be set parallel to that of N_2.

3. The Brace prism should be replaced, leveled so that its faces are parallel to the vertical axis, and set at the proper height. It should then be set for minimum deviation for the yellow.

4. The prism should be calibrated in the manner outlined for the Glan spectrophotometer, and a calibration curve constructed by means of which the approximate wave-length region be found for any angle of the telescope.

5. The collimator slits should be the same width. For this purpose, it is essential that each should be provided with a micrometer head. It will be necessary to determine the zero, *i.e.*, the setting for which no light passes through the slit, for each micrometer, since the slit may not be closed when the head reads zero.

6. The two spectra must then be made to coincide vertically. This may be done with the aid of a mercury arc from which the light is reflected into both collimator tubes. Two arcs may be used, one in front of each collimator. If the spectral lines from one are displaced sideways with respect to those from the other, unclamp the collimator tube containing the Glan prisms, and rotate it slightly to eliminate the displacement. Be sure to reclamp the tube.

The measurements may be made in the same manner as outlined for the Glan spectrophotometer.

EXPERIMENT 7
INDEX OF REFRACTION BY TOTAL REFLECTION

There are several *refractometers, i.e.,* instruments for the measurement of refractive index, which make use of the principle of total reflection. Perhaps the best known is that of Abbe, which gives excellent results, especially for liquids. But since the use of a commercial Abbe refractometer would give the student very little practice in optical manipulation, an experimental arrangement using the same principles is employed, in which the means of measuring the angles is an ordinary spectrometer.

Before doing the experiment, Sec. **8-7** should be read carefully.

Apparatus.—A pair of flint-glass prisms of high index of refraction, which may profitably be mounted as shown in Fig. 1, a rectangular block of glass with all sides polished, a number of liquids whose indices are to be measured, a spectrometer, a monochromatic source, and an ordinary condensing lens of about 2 in. aperture and 6 or 8 in.

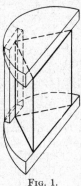

Fig. 1.

focal length. *Handle the glass pieces carefully as they are fragile and difficult to replace.*

Part A. The Index of a Glass Prism.—The spectrometer must be in adjustment as in Experiment 5, with the telescope focused for parallel light. See that the prisms are thoroughly clean and place one of them on the spectrometer table. If it is necessary to clean them, it can be done either with alcohol or ordinary commercial acetone. The use of good soap and lukewarm water is also recommended. Using a Gauss eyepiece, measure the refracting angle of the prism. Move the collimator to one side, or, if it is rigidly mounted, rotate the prism table. Adjust the source and condensing lens so that a broad beam illuminates the entire diagonal face of the prism. Looking into the face AB (Fig. 2) at the illumination, with the telescope swung to one side, rotate the prism table until the field of view observed at e is divided by a sharp vertical line on one side of which the field is not illuminated. It is essential that no light from the source fall on the side BC, which can be covered with a screen of cardboard. The bright side of the field will obviously coincide with light which is incident upon the diagonal face at angles less than 90 deg., and in the case illustrated in Fig. 2 it will be on the left of the field of view. As the table and prism are rotated, the

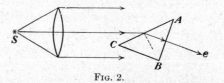

Fig. 2.

bright field will become narrower and will be seen to have a sharp vertical edge. A precaution to be taken at this point is to be sure that this apparent division between light and dark is not an image of the boundary of the source itself. This can be done by shifting the source or condenser lens slightly from side to side, observing carefully meanwhile to see whether the apparent division also moves. The telescope is now to be swung into the field of view, and the cross hairs set accurately on the line of division. Record the setting of the telescope on the divided circle. Then by means of the Gauss eyepiece set the telescope perpendicular to the face AB of the prism and record the angle. The difference between these two settings will be the angle i' of eq. 8-19. The index of refraction may now be found by means of eq. 8-20 since the medium in this case is air, the index of which is practically unity. It is given by the following equation:

$$n_g{}^2 = \frac{(\sin i' + \cos A)^2}{\sin^2 A} + 1.$$

Since the angle i' may be either on the left- or right-hand side of the normal to the surface AB, it may be either positive or negative; in the illustration in Fig. 2 it is positive.

Part B. Index of Refraction of a Liquid.—Liquids which may be conveniently tested are: Distilled water, glycerin, and cedar oil which has been prepared for oil immersion in microscopes. Put a drop of the liquid whose index is to be measured on the diagonal face of one of the prisms, and lay the other gently on it, so that the two form a rectangular block. *Do not press them*

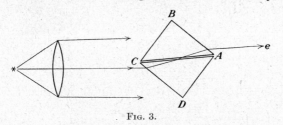

Fig. 3.

together tightly. Set them on the prism table and illuminate as shown in Fig. 3. Rotate the table until the division of the field into light and dark areas is in the field of view, as in Part A. The selection of the dividing boundary will be aided in this case by the fact that interference fringes are formed in the thin film of liquid between the prisms. These fringes will in general appear tangent to the boundary, as in Fig. 4. If the prisms are pressed together too tightly, the fringes will be so sharp and

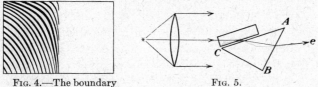

Fig. 4.—The boundary is the vertical division in the middle.

Fig. 5.

conspicuous as to make the setting of the cross hairs on the boundary difficult. As in Part A, record the setting of the telescope for the boundary and the normal to the surface. Remember that i' may be either negative or positive. By means of eq. 8–19 the index of refraction of the liquid may be calculated.

Part C. Index of Refraction of a Glass Plate.—Thoroughly clean the 45 deg. prisms. Put on the surface of one of them a drop or two of some liquid whose index is higher than that of the glass plate, and place the block gently on the face *AC*, as shown in Fig. 5. Liquids suitable for the purpose are: Methylene iodide, index 1.74; α-monobromnapthalene, index 1.66; aniline, index 1.56. Locate the boundary between the light and dark fields as before. It will be distinguished as in Part B by the presence of interference fringes. There may be two boundaries, one corresponding to the index of the glass block, the other to the index of the liquid. The one to be chosen is that corresponding to the smaller index. Carry out the measurements as in Part B, and calculate the index of refraction for the glass block by means of eq. 8-19.

EXPERIMENT 8

WAVE-LENGTH DETERMINATION BY MEANS OF FRESNEL'S BIPRISM

The theory of the Fresnel apparatus is to be found in Secs. **10-6** and **10-7.**

Apparatus.—An optical bench about 2 m. long, a mercury arc, a filter transmitting only 5461 angstroms, an accurate slit, a biprism mounted in a rotatable holder provided with a circular rack so that the biprism may be rotated about an axis perpen-

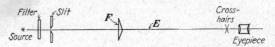

FIG. 1.—Arrangement of apparatus for use of Fresnel biprism.

dicular to the common prism base, a high power micrometer eyepiece with cross hairs, an achromatic lens of about 30 cm. focal length and 5 cm. aperture. On account of the dimness of the fringes, it is advisable to perform this experiment in a separate room, or in a space sufficiently screened so that there is no disturbance from other light sources.

Part A.—The apparatus is shown in Fig. 1. Be careful to place the biprism not more than about 35 cm. from the slit. Make sure that the cone of light from the slit covers the biprism, and have the slit quite narrow. Adjust all parts so that the optical axis is horizontal and centered with respect to each part. Set the common face *F* of the biprism toward the slit and perpendicular to the direction of light. This may be done with sufficient accuracy by sighting down the biprism and, if need be, getting the image of the slit which is reflected from *F* into coincidence with the slit opening. Move the eyepiece along the bench out of the way and place the eye at E in the figure. A very fine pattern of fringes will be seen between the two virtual images of the slit. Next place the eyepiece, previously accurately focused on the cross hairs, at E and look through it. Be sure of at least four settings. Let s_1, s_2, s_3, s_4, and s_5 be those fringe positions on the left-, and s_1', s_2', s_3', s_4', and s_5' be those on the right-hand side of the pattern. Suppose also that s_1' is the 30th fringe from s_1. Then the value of e obtained from

$$e_1 = \frac{s_1 - s_1'}{30}$$

is 30 times as accurate as that obtained by measuring the distance between any two consecutive fringes, since any lack of precision in making the settings is divided by 30. Thus five independent determinations of e may be made, each of a high degree of accuracy, from which a final average value of the spacing of the fringes may be obtained.

To measure d, place the lens between the biprism and the eyepiece. If the distance from slit to eyepiece is more than four times the focal length of the lens, there will be two positions of the lens for which real images of the slit will be in focus at the plane of the cross hairs. With the eyepiece micrometer, measure the separations d_1 of the virtual images for the first position, and d_2 for the second position. The value of d is given by

$$d = \sqrt{d_1 \times d_2}.$$

By means of equation 10-9 calculate λ.

Hand in the answers to the following in your report:

a. Derive the equation $d = \sqrt{d_1 \times d_2}$.
b. Enumerate the possible sources of error in your result.
c. Calculate the probable error of your final result for λ.

Part B. (Optional.) The Use of Parallel Light.—If a lens is placed between the slit and the biprism with its principal focus at the slit, parallel light will be incident upon the latter. The position of the lens should be determined with great care. This can be done by using a telescope, previously adjusted for parallel light, in place of the eyepiece, with the biprism removed. With the telescope in place, move the lens until a sharp image of the slit is in good focus at the cross hairs. Replace the biprism and micrometer eyepiece, and measure e as in Part A.   Since the wave-length with parallel light may be calculated by means of eq. 10-11, the only remaining measurement is that of the angle 2δ, between the virtual images.   This may be obtained with a telescope which can be turned about a vertical axis and whose angle of rotation can be measured with great accuracy.   The angle of rotation may be measured by means of a mirror mounted on the telescope so that the deviation of a beam of light may be found, or the telescope may be equipped with a micrometer and scale.

Part B may also be done on a spectrometer, in which case the biprism is mounted at the center of the spectrometer table and the angles measured on the divided circle.

Part C.   (Optional.)   Measurement of λ with Fresnel Mirrors.—In case a biprism is not available, a pair of mirrors may be used, inclined at a very small angle.   In this case the observations are the same as in Part A for the biprism, except that instead of d, the angle α between the mirrors is to be found and λ calculated by means of eq. 10-5.

EXPERIMENT 9

MEASUREMENT OF DISTANCE WITH THE MICHELSON INTERFEROMETER

The theory of this instrument is presented in Secs. **11-4, 5, 6,** and **7.**

Apparatus.—A Michelson interferometer, equipped with three plane mirrors A, B, and B' as shown in Fig. 1, a mercury arc, a filter transmitting only the green mercury line 5461 angstroms, a white-light source.

Adjustment of the Interferometer.—The mirrors A, B, and B' should have good reflecting surfaces.   If they are made of glass, metallic coatings may be deposited by one of the methods outlined in Appendix V.   The dividing plate C, which should be cut from the same plane parallel plate as the compensator D, may have on its front surface (nearer the observer) a semi-transparent metallic coat which will transmit half the light to B and B' and reflect half to A.   This mirror should not be handled unnecessarily as the half coat is fragile and easily rubbed off.   Fringes may be obtained without the half coat, and even with surfaces of poor reflecting power at A, B, and B', but the beginner will find it much easier to work with good mirrors.

After the source and condenser lens are set as indicated in Fig. 1 for good illumination of the mirrors, the fringes may be found. From theory it is seen that the position of formation of the fringes depends upon the relative distances of A and B from C. If these distances are the same, not only will the fringes be formed at a position corresponding to good reading distance from the eye, but for monochromatic light as well as for white light the *visibility* will be near maximum. The first step, therefore, is to move the carriage supporting A by means of the main screw until AC and BC are about equal. A match stick may then be mounted by means of laboratory wax vertically at M.

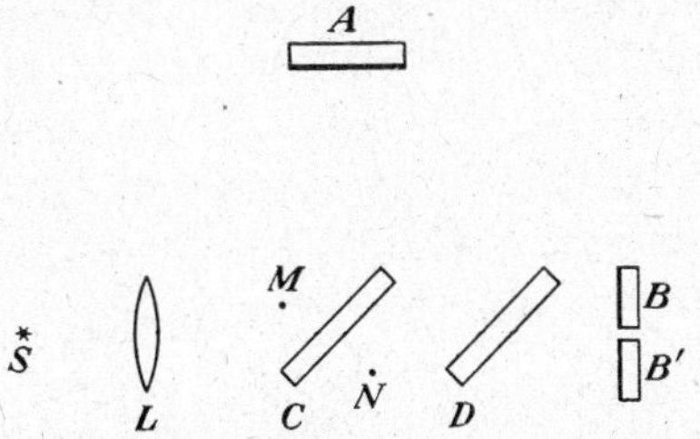

Fig. 1.

The image of the end of the stick should appear in the center of the field of B. Cover B' with a card. There will be seen four images of the stick. Two of these are due to light divided at the metal-coated surface at C and two are due to light divided at the other surface of the plate C. The first two are easily distinguished since they are more distinct. By means of the adjusting screws behind B, bring them into coincidence, whereupon the fringes should appear. Some manipulation may be required before the fringes are actually seen, since they will probably be very narrow at first. Once they are seen, move the adjusting screws behind B carefully until the fringes are of suitable width. About 20 in a field 2 cm. wide is usually a satisfactory spacing. If the fringes are not straight, it means either that the surfaces are not plane, or that the distances AC and BC are not equal. Ruling out the first possibility, the fringes may be made straight by turning the main screw which moves the carriage of A in either direction. The screw should be turned until the curvature of the fringes in one direction is pronounced and then reversed until the curvature is in the other direction. The position sought can then be found between narrow limits. If the fringes change their slope while this is done, the track on which the carriage moves is not clean, and should be wiped with a clean cloth and a little oil. B' may now be adjusted in the same manner, and a distance in front or behind B of about 0.1 mm.

Different purposes may be served in this experiment, some of which require more elaborate adjustments than are possible with the instrument as described. It should be kept in mind, however, that the procedure is satisfactory, no matter how simple, if it teaches the student how to manipulate the interferometer and understand its basic principles. The purpose of this experiment, therefore, is to assist in the understanding of the optical phenomena. To demonstrate the accuracy obtainable in comparison with that of a micrometer microscope, the distance between the mirrors B and B' will be measured.

Part A. Comparison of the Measurement of Distance by Fringe Counting and by a Micrometer Microscope.—For this

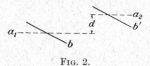

Fig. 2.

it will be necessary to have a micrometer microscope rigidly attached to the bed of the interferometer and focused on a fine line or ruling at right angles to the motion of A, and on a

plate attached to the carriage of A. A tenth-millimeter scale ruled on glass may be used.

If B and B' are parallel, the virtual sources with which we may replace them are indicated in Fig. 2 by the parallel lines b and b'. The dotted line a_1 is the virtual source which replaces A when white-light fringes are obtained in A and B. When white fringes are obtained in the common field of A and B', the mirror will have been moved through the distance d to a position indicated by the virtual source a_2. This distance can be measured roughly, (1) by means of the micrometer head on the main screw which moves A, (2) by the micrometer microscope, and (3) by counting the number of monochromatic fringes which pass a point in the field of view. Since the total path distance introduced by method (3) between B and B' is $2d$, we have $2d = n\lambda$, where n is the number of fringes which pass a given point in the field.

It is necessary to locate the positions of A for which white-light fringes are obtained in turn in B and B'.   This can be done by the following steps:

1. Adjust B and B' until the fringes in both are straight, of equal width, and parallel.

2. Using a white-light source held between the mercury arc and the interferometer, move A back and forth slightly until the white-light fringes appear in either B or B'.   (There may be some lost motion in the bearings of the main screw, but the angle of turn required to take this up may be easily found by observing the monochromatic fringes.) If white-light fringes are found in B first, and B' is farther away from C than B, next move A to correspond to the position of B' and find the white-light fringes.   It should then be possible to move A from one position to the other two or three times so as to get the corresponding angle of turn on the micrometer head of the main screw.

3. With the white-light fringes in view in either B or B', take up the lost motion in the direction which will bring them into the other field.

It is now necessary to establish a fiducial point for counting fringes.   This can be done elaborately in a variety of ways, but a satisfactory arrangement is a pair of wires, one fixed at M and one at N (Fig. 1).   If the head is kept in a position so that these two are superposed, there should be no mistake in counting fringes because of a shift of the point of view.   (For persons of normal vision, or with good accommodation, there will be no difficulty in seeing the fringes and the wires clearly; for persons who are farsighted, it may be necessary to mount between the eye and the interferometer a lens of 15 to 25 cm. focal length.)

Set the moving cross hair of the micrometer microscope on the ruled line or scratch on the carriage at A, repeating the setting several times in the same direction, and recording each observation.

Count the monochromatic fringes which pass as the main screw is turned slowly until the black central fringe seen in B' is coincident with the fiducial mark.   For slow turning of the screw there is usually provided an auxiliary worm gear which can be brought to bear against the edge of the micrometer head. If the distance between B and B' is 0.1 mm., the number of fringes of the green mercury line (5.461×10^{-5} cm.) which pass should be about 367.

Again set the moving cross hair of the micrometer microscope on the ruled line, which will have been moved, repeating the setting several times as before. The distance through which the ruled line and hence the mirror A has been moved should be

$$d = \frac{n\lambda}{2},$$

where n is the number of fringes counted.

Repeat the count, moving A in the opposite direction. Also repeat the settings on the ruled line with the micrometer microscope.

Answer the following questions:

1. Compare the accuracy of your observations by the two methods.

2. In making the preliminary adjustments with the mercury arc, did you notice some fringes, elliptical in shape, superposed on the fringes to be measured? If so, attempt an explanation of their origin.

3. Remove the compensating plate D, and look for the white-light fringes. To what is their appearance due? What do you conclude regarding the function of the compensating plate?

Part A′. The Use of Circular Fringes.—If circular fringes are used, it will not be necessary to use any fiducial mark, since these fringes are formed when the mirrors are parallel. Hence, no matter where the eye is placed in the field of view, the fringes will suffer no changes in diameter. Hence there is no difference of phase introduced by an accidental shifting of the head. In this case, it is necessary to count the fringes which appear from or disappear into the center of the system as one of the mirrors is moved. It is a little harder to count circular fringes, how-ever, unless the light is strictly monochromatic, especially when the path difference $AC - BC$ is small. If the path difference is small the circular fringes are very large, and for zero path difference they cannot be distinguished at all. Under these circumstances it will be impossible to keep accurate count.

Part B. The Calibration of a Scale.—If mirrors B and B' are mounted on a carriage which may be moved in accurate ways by a screw in the same fashion as is mirror A, the distance BB' may be used to step off some other distance which is several times BB'. This may be done by moving A from coincidence with B to coincidence with B', then moving B and B' until B is once more in coincidence with A, and so on until the full distance in the larger step is measured. If this larger distance is not an even multiple of BB', some difficulty is experienced, unless the remainder can be measured by an independent method. Suppose, for instance, the larger distance is the spacing between two scale marks on a standard millimeter scale. Then

$$K = n(BB') + \text{a fraction of } BB',$$

where K is the larger distance, n is the whole number of times BB' is stepped off. The fraction may be measured in the manner already described by a count of monochromatic fringes.

Part B′. The Calibration of a Scale. Alternative Method.— In case the interferometer is one with only a single mirror at B, a tenth-millimeter scale may be calibrated with a not excessively large fringe count. A scale ruled on glass with divisions of 0.1 mm. is recommended. This can be attached to the carriage of A, and extended beyond the bed of the interferometer so that it may be illuminated from beneath, with a vertical microscope equipped with a micrometer eyepiece directly above the scale. It is recommended that a point of light or small source be used, placed so as to give, in effect, dark-field illumination. In other words, instead of placing the source directly on the optical axis of the microscope, place it so that the light diffracted by the scale divisions is seen in the microscope.

White-light fringes are not needed. Instead, straight fringes of monochromatic light may be used. The procedure is to set the moving cross hair of the micrometer microscope on the image of one of the scale divisions S_1. Several settings should be made and the average of the micrometer readings taken. Then mirror A is moved until the micrometer cross hair is over another scale division S_2, the fringes being counted meanwhile. It is important to realize, however, that bringing the cross hair of the micrometer microscope into coincidence with S_1 and S_2 in the ways described above are not comparable procedures. The setting on S_1 is the average of a number, rapidly made, while that on S_2 can be made only once, since fringes are being counted, and is then made *slowly*. Consequently the distance from S_1 to S_2 measured in this way may be in error. This possibility of error can be checked by setting the cross hair once more on S_2 by turning the micrometer head, making several such settings in the identical manner in which the cross hair was formerly set on S_1. Any difference is to be added or subtracted from the rated scale distance $S_2 - S_1$. For instance, suppose that when the micrometer microscope was originally set on S_1 the average of the readings on the head was 87.5, the pitch of the micrometer screw being 1 mm. That when the corrective setting was finally made on S_2, the average of the readings on the head turned out to be 88.8. The difference in the settings is 0.013 mm. This amount is to be added to or subtracted from the rated distance between S_2 and S_1, depending on whether increased readings on the head correspond to an advance of the cross hair toward S_2 or a motion back toward S_1.

Another method which may be successful if it is practiced before the experiment is under way is as follows: Start counting fringes *a little before* the cross hair reaches S_1, and when the observer at the microscope decides the cross hair is just on S_1, note the extent of the count. Also, continue counting *a little after* the cross hair is seen to reach S_2. If n_1 is the number in the count as the cross hair passes S_1, and n_2 is the number in the count as it passes S_2, then $n_2 - n_1$ is the number of fringes corresponding to $S_2 - S_1$.

$$(S_2 - S_1) = (n_2 - n_1)\frac{\lambda}{2}.$$

Obviously, if the rated distance $S_2 - S_1$ is known accurately, the wave-length of the light may be found, instead of the scale being calibrated.

EXPERIMENT 10

MEASUREMENT OF INDEX OF REFRACTION WITH A MICHELSON INTERFEROMETER

Theory.—If a plane-parallel plate of index of refraction n is inserted normal to the path of one of the beams of light traversing the arms of a Michelson interferometer, the increase of optical path introduced will be $2(n - 1)t$, where t is the thickness of the plate. The factor 2 occurs because the light traverses the plate twice. For monochromatic light of wave-length λ, the difference of path introduced is $N\lambda$, where N is the number of fringes displacement introduced when the plate is inserted. Hence, if a

Michelson interferometer is adjusted for white-light fringes, a parallel plate of index n inserted in one of the paths, and a count made of the number of fringes which cross the field when equality of optical path is reestablished, it would be possible to measure n with a high degree of accuracy. This is not a satisfactory method of measuring the index of refraction, first, because N is too large a number to be conveniently counted unless the plate is very thin; second, because it is extremely difficult to determine the center of a white-light-fringe pattern when the two arms of the interferometer contain unequal thicknesses of glass. If, however, a parallel plate in one of the arms is rotated through a small measured angle, the path of the light will be changed, and the number of fringes N corresponding to this

change may be counted. The exact method of performing this experiment will be described in a later paragraph.

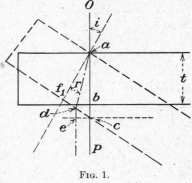

Fig. 1.

The change of path through the glass plate depends upon the thickness of the plate, the angle through which it is turned, and the index of refraction. The last of these three may be calculated if the other two are measured. Let OP (Fig. 1) be the original direction of the light normal to plate of thickness t. The total optical path between a and c for the light going in one direction is $nt + bc$. After the plate is rotated through an angle i, this optical path has been increased to $ad \cdot n + de$. Hence the total increase of optical path, since the light travels over the path twice, is

$$2(ad \cdot n + de - nt - bc) = N\lambda. \qquad (1)$$

But

$$ad = \frac{t}{\cos r},$$

$$de = dc \sin i = (fc - fd) \sin i = t \tan i \sin i - t \tan r \sin i,$$

$$bc = \frac{t}{\cos i} - t.$$

So,

$$\frac{nt}{\cos r} + t \tan i \sin i - t \tan r \sin i - nt - \frac{t}{\cos i} + t = \frac{N\lambda}{2}.$$

Using Snell's law, $n \sin r = \sin i$, this may be reduced to

$$n[(1 - \cos i)2t - N\lambda] = (2t - N\lambda)(1 - \cos i) + \frac{N^2\lambda^2}{4t}. \quad (2)$$

Since the last term is small compared to the others, it may be neglected, leaving for the index of refraction

$$n = \frac{(2t - N\lambda)(1 - \cos i)}{2t(1 - \cos i) - N\lambda}. \quad (3)$$

In the experiment, two such plates, P_1 and P_2, are used, one in either arm of the interferometer. These are made only half as high as the mirrors A and B so as to permit the observation in the field of view above them of fringes unaffected by the change of angle i. The use of two plates insures equal optical paths in the two arms, at all times when the angles of these plates with the direction of the light beams are the same, making possible the observation of white-light fringes through the plates when they are tilted at the same angle with the beam.

First, by the method outlined in Experiment 9, obtain in the upper part of the field vertical white-light fringes. This had better be done with the half plates P_1 and P_2 already in place, as inserting them afterward may be the cause of an accidental displacement of the other parts of the interferometer. With the white light fringes obtained, next set P_1 and P_2 normal to the light path as nearly as can be done while looking down on the instrument. Then, while observing the fringes, turn P_1 slowly until the fringes appear also in the lower part of the field. Now observe what happens if half plate P_2 is rotated a slight amount in one direction. If the lower fringes move completely out of the field and do not return, rotate P_2 in the other direction. What will usually happen is that either in turning one way or the other the fringe system will be displaced a number of fringes, say, to the right, and then move in the opposite direction. This indicates that the half plate P_1 was not, in the rough adjustment of the plate normal to the light path, set normal with sufficient precision. Hence it is to be rotated by such an amount that eventually the white-light fringes in the lower part of the field will move continuously out of the field in one direction upon a turn of P_2 in one sense, and out of the field in the same direction with a turn of P_2 in the opposite sense, without returning in either case. If the half plates P_1 and P_2 are cut from the same parallel plate, *i.e.*, are of exactly the same thickness, the white-light fringes should coincide in the upper and lower parts of the field.

Sometimes it is impossible to obtain the adjustment described in the preceding paragraph. This may be due to the fact that one of the half plates is "leaning" slightly in its frame, a condition which may be corrected by rocking the plate slightly. Another reason for lack of adjustment may be that the half plates are not cut from a parallel plate, but from one which has a slight wedge shape, the two sides being out of parallelism by a fringe or two. In this case the fringes in the upper and lower parts of the field of view of the interferometer may not be parallel, and one of the plates should be turned over in its frame.

After the white-light fringes extend across both the upper and lower portions of the field, and the half plates are precisely normal to the beams, turn P_1 through an angle of about 15 deg. This should be done in the direction in which the last adjustment of that plate was made, so that there is no lost motion to be taken up. (If no micrometer attachment is available for determining exactly the angle that P_1 is turned through, a small mirror fastened to the cell for P_1 and facing in the direction of a telescope and scale placed about 6 ft. away may be used. The angle will then be measured in the conventional manner with the telescope and scale.) Having turned P_1, and measured its angle, slowly turn Q_2 through the same angle, meanwhile counting fringes to the number (N) of monochromatic light which pass a selected point in the field, until the white-light fringes reappear in the lower part of the field and coincide with those in the upper. For this purpose, the green line of mercury may be used, and a source of white light be held or clamped in such a way that part of the field is illuminated by it. Thus the monochromatic fringes may be observed to pass, and at the same time the white-light fringes will be detected when they appear. An excellent check on the value of N is then to turn P_2 in the opposite direction, meanwhile counting fringes, until the white-light fringes once more appear in coincidence. P_2 will then have been turned through twice the angle i, and the number of fringes in this second count should be $2N$.

Remove P_2 and measure its thickness t with a micrometer caliper.   Then calculate the value of n, using eq. 3.

Answer the following questions:

1. What percentage of error is introduced in the measurement of the index of refraction by an error of 10 min. of arc in the measurement of the angle through which P_2 is turned from the normal position?

2. What percentage of error is introduced in the measurement of the index by an error of 0.005 mm. in the thickness of P_2?

3. What percentage of error is introduced in the measurement of the index by an error in the count of N of five fringes?

4. Would any appreciable improvement in the result be obtained by retaining the last term in eq. 2?

EXPERIMENT 11

THE RATIO OF TWO WAVE-LENGTHS WITH THE MICHELSON INTERFEROMETER

Read Sec. **11-7** for the discussion of visibility fringes.

Apparatus.—A Michelson interferometer, a mercury arc, a filter of didymium glass about 5 mm. thick, aqueous solutions of copper nitrate, cobalt sulphate, and nickel acetate, an assortment of gelatin filters, a condensing lens.   Uranine may be substituted for the solution of cobalt suphate.

Part A.—The solutions are to be prepared of sufficient density so that the combined filter will permit the transmission of only λ4358 and λ5461.   It is essential that these be of about the same visual intensity.   The transmission of the filter can be tested with a direct-vision spectroscope or a spectrometer and 60-deg. prism.   Of the stronger mercury lines, copper nitrate transmits only those from λ4046 to λ5790, inclusive.   Nickel chloride cuts out λ4046 and λ4071.   Didymium glass cuts out λ5770 and λ5790, and cobalt sulphate or uranine cuts out the faint green line λ4916.   These solutions may be mixed together in a filter cell about 1 cm. thick, or better still, in separate cells.   If there is any precipitate present, the addition of a little hydrochloric acid will remove it.

Adjust the interferometer for white-light fringes.   With the mercury arc and the combined filter the succession of maxima and minima will be clearly seen. Count the number of fringes from the minimum closest to the center of the white-light pattern to the thirtieth minimum away. Obtain by division an average number of fringes N between any two consecutive minima. N will not necessarily be a whole number. The ratio of the two wave-lengths will be given by $\dfrac{N \pm 1}{N}$. Since this ratio is so far from unity, N being small, it will be necessary to try both the positive and negative signs.

Part B.—Remove the didymium glass and substitute a filter which transmits only $\lambda 5770$ and $\lambda 5790$. This may be composed of an orange gelatin filter with an aqueous solution of cobalt sulphate. Since the two wave-lengths are almost the same, many fringes (between 200 and 300) must pass the field of view in passing from one position of maximum visibility to another. Moreover, at minimum visibility the counting of the fringes will be impossible or nearly so. Instead it will be necessary to rely on the accuracy of the main screw which moves the carriage.

First calibrate the screw by turning the micrometer head through about one-tenth of a turn, counting the fringes meanwhile. Then set for the first position of minimum visibility next to the position of zero path difference, and read the micrometer. Turn the screw until the twentieth minimum comes into the field, keeping track meanwhile of the total number of turns of the screw. The fractional part of a turn may be read from the micrometer. The total number of fringes which have passed may thus be calculated.

Since the screw may not possess an accuracy warranting this calculation, an alternative method is suggested as a check. Substitute a filter transmitting only the green line of mercury, and turn the screw through exactly one revolution, counting fringes meanwhile. This will determine the pitch of the screw. (If this is already accurately known, the foregoing will not be necessary.) Then, if, say, the screw was turned through 3.32 turns in passing from one minimum of visibility to a distant one for $\lambda 5770$ and $\lambda 5790$, since the distance moved is equal to $N\lambda/2$, we have

$$\frac{2 \times 3.32 \times 0.05}{0.0000578} = N,$$

where the pitch of the screw is taken as 0.05 cm. and the average wave-length is used. In the example, the number of fringes is about 5743, corresponding to the passage from a given minimum to the twenty first from it. Hence 5743/21, or 273.48 fringes would pass in going from one minimum to the next, and 273.48/274.48 is the ratio of the wave-lengths. For the accuracy possible it is not material whether in $(N \pm 1)/N$ the + or − sign is used. Assuming the correct value for the longer wave-length to be 5790.66, the value for the shorter becomes 5769.56. The correct value is 5769.60.

EXPERIMENT 12

THE FABRY-PEROT INTERFEROMETER

In the discussion of the theory of this instrument in Sec. **11-8** it has been pointed out that the use of multiple beams instead of double beams to produce interference results in a great decrease in the width of the interference maxima. Thus the observer is permitted to see, distinctly separated, the interference fringes due to two or more radiations. Since, however, for each monochromatic radiation, the interference pattern consists of a set of concentric rings, there is no direct method of finding out which of two wave-lengths may be the larger. For instance, in the interference pattern of the complex mercury line $\lambda = 5461$ illustrated in Fig. 11-17, it is not immediately possible to say whether the faint fringes shown are of shorter or longer wave-length than the brighter ones. If, however, however, two radiations already well known are used, the ratio of their wave-lengths may be found.

Apparatus.—A Fabry-Perot interferometer with one plate on a movable carriage so that it may be moved perpendicular to its face by means of a screw, a mercury arc, a condensing lens, and a filter transmitting only 5770 and 5790 angstroms.

Since the sharpness of the fringes depends on the number of reflections between the two plates, care should be taken to see that the reflecting coats are as bright as possible. Aluminum deposited on the plates by evaporation is exceedingly durable. The coats of metal should be much thicker than half coats in order to insure high reflecting power. Care should be taken to see that the ways in which the carriage moves are clean and free from dust.

In finding the fringes, which are circular, it is best to have the separation between the mirrors as small as possible, since then the diameters of the innermost fringes are very large.

Do not jam the mirrors together.

Set up the mercury arc and condensing lens so that the entire area of the plates is well illuminated. Hold a pencil or match stick between the rear mirror and the lens, and manipulate the adjusting screws in front of the interferometer until the manifold images of the stick coincide. The fringes will then be seen, probably poorly defined and as if astigmatic. Careful adjustment is then made by turning the screws, which change the tilt of the fixed mirror, meanwhile observing whether the diameters change as the eye is moved from side to side and up and down. If on moving the eye to the left, the circles become larger, the distance between the mirrors on the left is greater than that on the right, and further adjustment should be made. In this manner, get the two mirrors as nearly parallel as possible. Then run the movable carriage back a few millimeters and see if the parallelism is lost. If, to any appreciable extent, it is, the ways must be cleaned again or other necessary steps taken to improve the mechanical performance.

Next insert the filter transmitting only the two wave-lengths to be observed. A tentative turn or two of the main screw will show that, as the carriage moves, single and double fringes alternate. If the metallic coatings are not very thick, the resolving power will be less, and instead of definite doubling of the fringes, there will be simply a decrease in visibility of the interference pattern.

The radius of any circular fringe increases as the mirrors are moved apart, and decreases as they are brought together. A bright fringe for a given wave-length λ_1 has a radius which depends on the separation of the mirrors, the orders of interference of the fringe, and the wave-length, as given by the equation

$$2e \cos i = P_1 \lambda_1,$$

where e is the separation of the mirrors, P_1 is the order of interference, or number of wave-lengths difference of path between two interfering beams, and i is the angle subtended by the radius of the fringe. Hence, if there is another longer wave-length λ_2

whose fringes have the same radii as λ_1, *i.e.*, if the fringes for the two are exactly superposed, then

$$2e \cos i = P_2\lambda_2.$$

As the distance between the two mirrors is increased, in passing from one position of coincidence to the next, the change in N_2 will be one less than the change in N_1. Hence, if N is the number of fringes which appear at the center of the pattern as the distance is increased, then

$$(N - 1)\lambda_2 = N\lambda_1.$$

Actually, the wave-lengths are so nearly alike that it is not possible to tell which set of fringes belongs to the longer, and the procedure is to count the number of fringes which appear at the center between two successive coincidences (or maxima of visibility) and obtain the ratio of the wave-lengths by the equation

$$\frac{\lambda_1}{\lambda_2} = \frac{N \pm 1}{N}.$$

If one of the wave-lengths is known, the other may be calculated. Determination of the point at which the fringes are exactly superposed is difficult. However, the error in this determination can be reduced by counting from one maximum or point of superposition to the fifth or sixth from it, and obtaining a mean value for N. An alternative procedure is to count from the position of minimum visibility instead. If the fringes are very sharp, this will correspond to the position where the two sets are midway between each other, with dark rings of equal width and blackness between them.

EXPERIMENT 13

MEASUREMENT OF WAVE-LENGTH BY DIFFRACTION AT A SINGLE SLIT

For the theory of diffraction by a single slit, see Sec. **12-8.**

It is evident from eq. 12-5 that the intensity obtained by diffraction of light through a single slit becomes zero for values of $\varphi = m\lambda/a$, where a is the width of the slit and m is an integer. Since $\varphi = \sin i \pm \sin \theta$, satisfactory experimental conditions will exist if i is made zero, so that $\sin \theta = m\lambda/a$. It must be remembered, however, that eq. 12-5 is based on the assumption that the light illuminating the slit is collimated, so that the pattern is one obtained by Fraunhofer diffraction.

Apparatus.—A spectrometer, a mercury arc, a filter for the transmission of the green mercury line 5461 angstroms, an auxiliary slit. (In case a spectrometer is not available for this experiment, satisfactory results may be obtained if the primary slit, upon which the light of a mercury arc is focused through a filter, is placed at a distance of about 20 ft. from a laboratory telescope, which has an auxiliary slit fitted over its objective. The telescope must be capable of rotation about a vertical axis, and there must be provided also some method for measuring this rotation to an accuracy of about 5 sec. of arc. The use of a spectrometer is advised.)

If a filter transmitting only the green line is not available or if its use dims the light too much, the light from the collimator may first be passed through a prism, and thereafter the green line allowed to fall upon the auxiliary slit.

With a spectrometer correctly focused so that an image of the primary slit is at the plane of the cross hairs, and a satisfactory filter, or prismatic dispersion, set the auxiliary slit with its jaws at the center of the spectrometer table so that the plane of the jaws is perpendicular to the beam of light from the collimator. Adjust the width of the auxiliary slit so that the fringes are distinct and of measurable width. Frequently there is difficulty in getting sufficient light intensity to permit accurate settings on the diffraction minima. In this case it is not good practice to open the primary slit at the source end of the collimator too wide, since this results in a blurring of the pattern. The primary slit should be closed to as small dimensions as will afford good *visibility* of the fringe pattern. Proper shielding of the instrument from extraneous light, and allowing time for the eye to become accustomed to conditions, will be of advantage.

It is recommended that before observations are begun, the auxiliary slit be removed carefully and its width measured by means of a micrometer microscope or comparator. This may be done afterward, but in case there is any danger of altering the slit width by moving it, time will be saved by finding it out at the start.

The quantities to be measured are the width a of the auxiliary slit and θ the angle between two successive minima. Since the angle to be measured is very small, sin θ may be put equal to θ, so that $\pm \theta = m\lambda/a$, from which θ may be calculated. The easiest settings to make are obviously those on minima which are close to the middle of the pattern where the intensity is greatest. However, increased accuracy may result if as many minima as possible are measured, and a weighted mean of the resulting value of θ be found. If the light is not too faint, it should be possible to set on eight or ten minima on either side. In case difficulty is experienced in seeing the cross hairs when they are set on minima, flashing a utility light of low brightness into the telescope will help.

As in other experiments, there should be several settings made for each position of the telescope, and the mean taken in each case. It is possible to obtain a final average value of θ by simply subtracting the mean value of each setting from the mean value of the next contiguous one, thus obtaining several values of θ which may be averaged. It should be pointed out, however, that the result thus obtained is not the mean of independent observations. Furthermore, the observations are not of equal weight. A better practice is to subtract the setting on the first minimum on one side from the first minimum on the other side of the central image, yielding a value twice θ, and assign to it a weight of 2; then subtract the setting on the second minimum on the one side from the setting on the second minimum on the other side, yielding a value four times θ, with a weight of 4, and so on, as far out as minima can be distinguished. This practice of weighting, however, which assumes that all the observations are of equal difficulty, should be modified in the present case since the minima become progressively more difficult to distinguish as one goes further out from the center of the pattern. The following modification is suggested. Suppose the settings on the two seventh minima are as follows:

Side	Angle of telescope (degrees omitted)	Deviation from mean
Left:		
(1)	42′ 15″	9″
(2)	41′ 8″	58″
(3)	42′ 27″	21″
(4)	42′ 34″	28″
Mean 42′ 6″		±23.5″

Side	Angle of telescope degrees omitted	Deviation from mean
Right:		
(1)	17' 2''	21''
(2)	16' 27''	14''
(3)	16' 38''	3''
(4)	16' 37''	4''
Mean	16' 41''	±10.5''

Suppose, similarly, the settings on the two sixth minima have values of the mean deviation of ± 18.2 and ± 7.6 sec. Then obviously the value of θ determined from the seventh minima is *not* $14/12$ times as accurate as that determined from the sixth, and should not be weighted as much in arriving at a mean. If the results obtained by the student are such that he is in doubt as to the proper procedure, he should consult the instructor before arriving at a final determination of θ.

Having found a and θ, calculate the value of the wave-length of the light used.

Repeat the experiment for a different value of a.

Answer the following questions:

1. What error in the wave-length is caused by an uncertainty of 0.005 mm. in the width of a? What percentage of error?

2. What error in the wave-length is caused by an uncertainty of 25 sec. of arc in the value of θ? What percentage of error?

3. What error is due to both these uncertainties combined? What percentage of error?

EXPERIMENT 14

THE DOUBLE-SLIT INTERFEROMETER

The theory involved in this experiment is to be found in Sec. **12-9,** on Diffraction through Two Equal Slits.

Apparatus.—A good laboratory telescope with an objective of about 25 to 35 cm. focal length, provided with a high-power eyepiece. In front of the objective is to be mounted a specially constructed double slit, each opening of which can be adjusted in width over a range of about 3 mm. This double slit must have bilateral motion, so that the slits may be separated to any distance between about 6 and 30 mm. The telescope should preferably be mounted in a snug fitting tube, so that it may be rotated about its axis, in order to adjust the double slits to a vertical position. If this is not feasible, the double slit should be rotatable. A single slit to be used as a source, accurately round pinholes, filters, and a mercury arc are also needed. A rotatable biprism is necessary for Part E, in case that part is done.

Adjustments.—Set the single slit in a vertical position, and illuminate it with a mercury arc, provided with a filter to permit the passage of the green line λ5461. An image of the arc must be projected on the slit, so that the latter is truly a source with respect to the observing telescope. The single slit and the double slits must be vertical, or at least parallel to each other.

It will be necessary to adjust the width of the single slit so that the resulting interference pattern can be made to disappear (or reach a minimum visibility) within the range of motion of the double slit. Obviously, from the equation

$$w = \frac{l\lambda}{d}, \tag{1}$$

in which w is the slit width, and l the distance between the source slit and the telescope, a rough preliminary calculation of the most desirable value of w will save a great deal of time. For a value of l of about 8 m. and a separation d of the double slits of about 1.5 cm., w would be about 0.3 mm.

The double slits should be equal in width. A suitable width, for other dimensions given, is about 1 mm., although a smaller width can be used if there is sufficient light intensity. A greater width will, of course, result in a more brilliant image, but the diffraction pattern from each slit will be narrower, and the number of fringes in the brightest portion of the image will be less. When the telescope is correctly focused, the image seen in the eyepiece will be similar to the two-slit diffraction pattern seen in Fig. 12-14*b*, except that there will usually be more and narrower interference fringes. As will be seen from the theory, the number and spacing of the interference fringes will depend upon the ratio of the common width of the double slits to the width of the opaque space between them.

Part A.—With proper illumination on the slit, and the maximum intensity of the cone of light directed to the telescope, adjust the source slit to a width between 0.2 and 0.3 mm. Focus the telescope on the slit and mount the double slit in front of the objective, so that the source slit and the double slits are parallel. Fringes should be seen. Beginning with the widest separation, slowly reduce the separation of the double slits until the fringes disappear. Record the distance from center to center of the double slits at this point, and continue narrowing the separation until the last disappearance is observed. It is sometimes difficult, especially for the beginner, to detect the point of disappearance, because (a) the slit source may be slightly wedged-shaped, in which case disappearance will not occur simultaneously along the fringes; (b) the fringes are so narrow that they are indistinct; (c) the two slits are not of the same width, and only a *minimum* visibility is attained. In case of failure to observe disappearance or to identify it as a first-order disappearance, the theoretical separation d of the double slits may be approximately calculated by eq. 1, to aid in the observations.

White light may be used instead of the mercury arc, since the order of interference is quite small. In this case, in the calculation of w from eq. 1, the value of λ to which the eye has maximum sensitivity should be used. For most eyes this is between 5.5×10^{-5} and 5.7×10^{-5} cm. Make several determinations of d and l and calculate w and the mean error of observation.

Measure the width of the single slit carefully with a micrometer microscope, a traveling microscope, or a comparator, repeating the measurements for different places on the slit. Replace the single slit in its former position in the optical train.

Part B.—Set the double slit at a separation of about 1 to 2 cm. and vary the width of the single slit slowly, observing the successive widths for which the fringes disappear. For this purpose it is desirable that the slit be equipped with a micrometer head for quick reading. If this is not available, the width for each disappearance must be measured as before. The widths observed should be multiples of some value which, within experimental error, will be the value of w obtained in Part A. The allowable error of the experimental determination of w by observation of the disappearance of the fringes in Parts A and B is between 2 per cent and 8 per cent, depending upon the care and skill of the operator and the precision of the mechanical parts.

Part C.—Remove the double slit and the eyepiece and substitute a micrometer eyepiece. Can you measure the width of the slit? If so, with what accuracy? What limits the accuracy in this case? Compare the accuracy of this measurement with the ones made in Parts A and B.

Part D.—Remove the single slit and substitute a pinhole in a thin metal sheet. Use white light for greater intensity. In this case the angular diameter is given by $1.22\lambda l/d$, when the fringes disappear.

Part E.—Place the rotatable biprism over the pinhole so that the two images seen through the biprism just touch edges when viewed through the telescope without the double slit. Replace the double slit, orient it to the angle of the biprism, and measure the separation of the two virtual images by the disappearance of the fringes as before. The distance between the centers of the two virtual images of the pinhole is given by $a = 0.61\lambda l/d$. Repeat Part C for this source.

EXPERIMENT 15

THE DIFFRACTION GRATING

The theory of this experiment is to be found in Sec. **12-12**.

Apparatus.—A spectrometer, a mercury arc, a helium discharge tube, a plane diffraction grating of the reflection type, a Gauss eyepiece. If only a transmission grating is available, the following procedure must be modified slightly.

Adjust the spectrometer as directed in Appendix IV. Place the mercury arc in front of the slit, which may be opened to a width of about 0.5 mm. By looking at the face of the collimator lens, make sure that the entire lens is filled with light. Set the grating on the spectrometer table so that (a) its plane contains the main vertical axis of the spectrometer, (b) the cone of light from the collimator is centered on the ruled area of the grating, (c) the rulings are parallel to the axis of the spectrometer, (d) the slit is parallel to the rulings.

Adjustments for (a) and (b) may be initially made by simple inspection, with the telescope swung out of the way. To insure that the axis actually lies in the surface, the Gauss eyepiece method may be used. Assuming that the telescope is in adjustment so that its axis cuts, and is perpendicular to, the axis of the spectrometer, the latter will be parallel to the grating surface when the image of the cross hairs reflected from the surface of the grating coincides with the cross hairs themselves.

Before making adjustment (c), fasten a wire or match across the middle of the slit, and set the spectrometer table so that the angle of incidence is between 50 and 60 deg. Then each line of the spectrum, in as many orders as can be reached on both sides of the central image (direct reflection), should be examined through the telescope. When the middle of the slit stays the same height in the field of view, the rulings are parallel to the axis.

Before attempting adjustment (d), ascertain whether the slit is in a fixed position, or if it may be rotated. If the former is the case, do not risk damaging it by forcing rotation. If rotatable about the axis of the collimator, turn it until the image of the obstacle is sharpest; then the slit will be parallel to the rulings.

At this point it is well to caution the student that precise adjustments and observations are not possible unless the telescope is properly focused on the spectrum lines. Remember also that even if the instrument is fitted with so-called achromats, the focal lengths will not be the same for all wave-lengths. It is also well to find out if the grating has Rowland or Lyman ghosts.[1] If these exist, they should be ignored in making the observations.

Before continuing, narrow the slit until the lines are as sharp as possible. This stage will be reached when closing the slit further makes no apparent change in the width of a line but simply a reduction in the intensity.

Part A.—With the foregoing adjustments made, next find the setting in angle on the circle of the spectrometer, (a) when the telescope is normal to the grating, (b) when the central image (direct reflection) is on the cross hairs, (c) when each strong line of the mercury spectrum, in each order which can be reached, is on the cross hairs. Tabulate these data. In the first column put the order of the spectrum; in the second, the wave-lengths; in the third, the angles. From settings (a), (b), and (c) the values of i and θ may be found and put in columns four and five. The grating equation is

---

[1] Rowland ghosts are false images of a spectrum line, grouped symmetrically on both sides of the line; they are usually faint in low orders. Lyman ghosts are false orders of spectra occurring at angles θ for which m is not a whole number (see eq. 1). Both types are due to irregularities in the ruling of the grating.

$$\sin i \pm \sin \theta = \frac{m\lambda}{d}, \tag{1}$$

in which i is the angle of incidence, θ the angle of diffraction, m the order, λ the wave-length, and d the grating space. From eq. 1 and the observed data, the *wave-lengths* of the lines may be calculated if the *grating space* is known, or *vice versa*. The negative sign is used when the spectrum is on the same side of the normal to the grating as the central image.

Part B. Resolving Power.—Since $R = \lambda/d\lambda$ when the limit of resolution is reached, the resolving power is found by determining the limit of resolution which, according to Rayleigh's criterion, is reached when two spectrum lines are a distance apart such that the central maximum of the diffraction (or interference) pattern of one line falls upon the first minimum of the other. With the particular grating used, it would be difficult to find two spectrum lines which just fulfill this requirement. Moreover, it is essential that the entire grating be uniformly illuminated. The procedure is, then, to find the resolving power r of a small width w of the grating, and calculate R for the entire grating from the relation

$$R = r \cdot \frac{\text{entire width } W \text{ of grating}}{\text{width } w \text{ illuminated to obtain } r}. \tag{2}$$

In order to use only a small portion of the grating, place over the telescope lens an auxiliary slit. When this is closed to a width a, the value of w is given by $w = a/\cos \theta$.

At this stage the student should make sure that he has a satisfactory source of a close pair of lines. For moderately low resolving power the yellow doublet of mercury at 5770 and 5790 angstroms is suitable, but if the grating has rulings as close as, say, 5000 to the centimeter, its resolving power will be so high that the auxiliary slit width must be very small. For the ordinary reflection grating, therefore, the sodium doublet at 5890 and 5896 angstroms is most satisfactory. There are many sources of this light, perhaps the most brilliant being that obtained when an oxygas flame is trained on a small piece of pyrex tubing held on an iron rod about $\frac{1}{8}$ in. in diameter. If oxygen is not available, a well-adjusted air-gas flame and soft glass tubing will do.

With the proper source in operation in front of the first slit, close down the auxiliary slit until the two lines of the doublet can just be observed separately. Make several trials. Carefully remove the auxiliary slit and measure its width a with a microm-eter microscope. Find θ and calculate w.

The resolving power of part of the grating is given by

$$r = \frac{\lambda}{d\lambda} \tag{3}$$

where $d\lambda$ is the separation between two lines just resolved and λ is their mean wave-length. Substitute this value of r in eq. 2 and calculate R. Compare this result with the value given by $R = mN$, where m is the order and N is the total number of rulings on the grating.

Part C. Dispersion.—This is defined as $D = d\theta/d\lambda$. Calcu-late D from the values of θ for two close lines such as the mercury yellow lines, and compare it with D obtained from

$$D = \frac{m}{d \cos \theta}.$$

Discuss the errors and their probable origin, in your determina-tions of the wave-lengths.

Part D. The Transmission Grating.—The foregoing direc-tions are for a reflection grating of fairly high dispersion. In case only a transmission replica is available, the directions will apply with slight modifications. Instead of the angle of the direct reflection, that of the transmitted beam, *i.e.*, at 180 deg. from the collimator setting, must be used. Also, in eq. 1 the positive sign is used if the diffracted light is on the same side of the normal as the incident beam. Other modifications may be suggested by the instructor.

Part E. The Concave Grating.—In case only a concave grat-ing is available, essentially the same quantities may be found by experiment, but the procedure will be quite different, depend-ing on the type of mounting used. There are three general ways of mounting a concave grating:

a. The Rowland Circle.—If light is incident at an angle i with the normal to the grating, then the position of the *astigmatic* spectral line is given by the equation for the *primary* astigmatic focus (eq. 6-8), with θ, the angle of diffraction, substituted for

i', and n and n' put equal to unity. Solved for the distance s' to the spectral line, this equation becomes

$$s' = \frac{\rho s \cos^2 \theta}{s(\cos \theta + \cos i) - \rho \cos^2 i},\qquad(4)$$

where ρ is used instead of r for the radius of curvature of the grating. If $s = \rho \cos i$, then $s' = \rho \cos \theta$, and the grating, the slit, and the spectral line lie on a circle called the *Rowland circle* shown in Fig. 1. Mountings in which the slit, grating, and part or all of the Rowland circle are arranged in a fixed position are

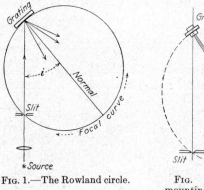

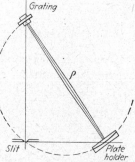

FIG. 1.—The Rowland circle.

FIG. 2.—The Rowland mounting. The straight lines intersecting at the slit are the tracks A and B.

called *Paschen mountings*. To measure wave-lengths with this mounting it is necessary to know accurately the angles i and θ for each line. The method by which these may be found can be worked out by the instructor.

b. The Rowland Mounting.—From the geometry of the circle it follows that two lines which intersect at right angles at the slit will cross the circle, one at the center of the grating, the other at a point in the focal plane for which θ in eq. 4 is zero, as shown in Fig. 2. When the grating and eyepiece (or photographic plateholder) are mounted on the extremities of a bar of length ρ, this may be slid along two tracks A and B (Fig. 2) and different parts of the spectrum observed. This is called the *Rowland mounting* and has the advantage that for small angles θ' on either side of the normal, the dispersion is uniform. From eq. 1 and the constants of the instrument the wave-length of a line exactly on the normal may be found, after determining i and θ. This may be repeated for each line, or else the dispersion may be found for a small region near the normal, and an interpolation method used.

c. The Eagle Mounting.—Sometimes it is convenient to set the grating so as to utilize the diffracted light which is returned directly back along the same path as the incident beam, or nearly so, as shown in Fig. 13-35 for a prism instrument. This type of mounting is little used except for photographic spectroscopy. In case it is necessary to use it for visual determinations of wave-length, it is recommended that Baly, "Spectroscopy," Vol. I, be consulted.

EXPERIMENT 16

SIMPLE POLARIZATION EXPERIMENTS

The theory of this experiment is to be found in Chap. XIII.

Apparatus.—A polariscope[1] of design similar to that supplied by the Gaertner Scientific Co., illustrated in Fig. 1, a white light with diffusing bulb, a monochromatic source such as a mercury arc and filter for λ5461, or a sodium burner (which need not be very bright), a supply of the polarizing materials mentioned in the directions given below.

Procedure.—1. Make a dot on a piece of white paper and over it place a rhomb of calcite 1 cm. thick or more. Rotate the rhomb and identify the *o*- and *e*-rays. Which travels the faster through the crystal? This may be determined by seeing which image appears to be nearer the upper face. The one which travels the slower should be nearer. Why? Does this identify calcite as a positive or negative crystal? Check your conclusions with the theory in Chap. XIII.

2. Tilt the rhomb so that the light is transmitted in a direction nearly parallel to the optic axis. If a crystal is at hand which is flattened and polished in two planes cut perpendicular

---

[1] Less expensive devices are sold in which the analyzer and polarizer consist of the patented substance "polaroid." These are extremely useful, but cannot be used for so wide a variety of experiments as the older polariscopes unless they are completely equipped and have polaroid of the best quality sealed between good optical glass plates. These experimental directions are written for a complete polariscope, and may be modified by the instructor if only a simpler device is available.

to the optic axis, so much the better. What do you observe regarding the apparent positions of the two images when viewed in this direction?

3. Arrange the frosted-bulb white-light source and a screen with an opening *o* as shown in Fig. 2. The instrument may be vertical or at any convenient angle.

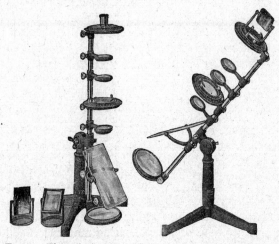

FIG. 1.—The polariscope. (*Courtesy of Gaertner Scientific Co.*)

4. Adjust mirror *m* (Fig. 2) at such an angle with the axis of the instrument that the light through the opening *o* is incident at about 57 deg. Mirror *m* is then the *polarizer*. At the upper end set the blackened mirror *m'* which will then act as the *analyzer*. Set *m'* so that the beams *om*, *mm'*, and *m'e* (Fig. 2) are in the same plane. Rotate *m'* about a horizontal axis so that the angle of incidence of *mm'* is about 57 deg. Then turn *m'* about an axis parallel to *mm'*, watching the reflected light meanwhile. The light should be extinguished when *m'e* makes an angle of 90 deg. with *om*.

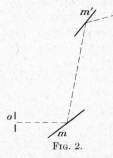

FIG. 2.

If extinction is not complete, a slight adjustment of the angles of *m* and *m'* may make it so.

5. Remove *m'* and substitute the pile of plates at an angle of 57 deg. with *mm'*. Look through these from above and rotate

about an axis parallel to *mm'* as before. At which angle is the extinction most complete? This illustrates the almost complete polarization by successive transmission through successive surfaces, each one of which is at the polarizing angle.

6. Remove the pile of plates and substitute the Nicol prism as an analyzer. Rotate this about axis *mm'* until the light is extinguished. Then place the rhomb of calcite on a rotable holder in the path *mm'*. Rotate the calcite until the ordinary ray is extinguished. Then rotate the analyzer until the *o*-ray reappears and the *e*-ray is extinguished. Do the results of these observations confirm the statement that the *plane of vibration* of the *o*-ray is perpendicular to the principal section of the calcite and that of the *e*-ray is parallel to it? Explain in detail.

7. Replace the white-light source with a monochromatic source. Remove the rhomb of calcite, turn the analyzer to extinction, and replace the rhomb with a half-wave plate for the wave-length of the source. What do you observe when the *half-wave plate is rotated?* Set the plate at the position for extinction, record the angle, and turn it in either direction through about 25 deg. Then note the setting in angle of the nicol, turn the nicol until the light is extinguished once more, and note the angle through which the nicol has been turned. This angle should be twice 25 deg., or 50 deg. From the fact that the analyzer *can* extinguish plane-polarized light incident upon and transmitted by a half-wave plate, what do you infer regarding the nature of the light vibration so transmitted?

8. Remove the half-wave plate, set the analyzer for extinction, and replace the half-wave plate with a quarter-wave plate, set at any angle at random. Now rotate the analyzer. Can you extinguish the light? If so, turn the quarter-wave plate through an angle of about 15 deg. and try again.

Remove the quarter-wave plate, set the nicol for extinction, replace the quarter-wave plate set for extinction, and note the direction of its principal section as indicated by the line on its face. What angle does it make within the direction of vibration of the light incident upon it? Now turn the quarter-wave plate through 45 deg. Upon rotating the nicol, what happens to the transmitted light? Does your observation confirm the statement that a quarter-wave plate, with its principal section at 45 deg. to the plane of vibration of plane-polarized light incident upon it, changes the plane-polarized to circularly polarized light?

9. Replace the quarter-wave plate with a small sheet of cellophane. What do you conclude regarding the optical characteristics of cellophane? Wrinkle the cellophane and observe what happens to the transmitted light. What precautions does this suggest in the use of wave plates? Replace the monochromatic source with white light, and repeat the observations with cellophane.

10. Replace the cellophane with a cube of ordinary glass about 1 cm. on a side. Are there any variations in the light transmitted through different parts? Now put a small laboratory clamp on the sides of the cube, and squeeze it. Observe that the effect of strains in an optically isotropic medium is to render it anisotropic.

11. Replace the glass cube with a section of calcite cut perpendicular to the optic axis. Observe the change in the pattern as the analyzer is rotated. Replace the white light with monochromatic light and repeat these observations with the section of calcite. Keeping in mind that the light is *divergent*, explain the *rings* and *brushes* seen. Because many nicols have too small a field, this experiment with the calcite section may be performed more easily with disks of polaroid used as analyzer and polarizer, instead of the polariscope.

12. Use a sodium source. Remove the calcite crystal, set the analyzer for extinction, and replace the calcite with a section of quartz about 5 mm. thick cut perpendicular to the optic axis. The light will reappear. Record the position of the analyzer and turn it to extinction once more. Does the angle through which it was turned confirm the statement that light transmitted along the optic axis of quartz has its plane of vibration rotated an angle to 21.7 deg. for every millimeter of thickness? Keep in mind that both right- and left-handed-rotatory quartz exist. Which is the specimen you have used?

13. Make either a half-wave or quarter-wave plate of mica or cellophane and submit it to the instructor for approval. Since λ5461 is so universally used, it is better to use the mercury source. If mica is used, it may be split with a fine needle. If cellophane, use the thickness ordinarily used for cigar wrappers. More than one layer may be necessary. Two with the directions

of the striae at an angle of about 45 deg. make a fairly satisfactory quarter-wave plate.

EXPERIMENT 17

ANALYSIS OF ELLIPTICALLY POLARIZED LIGHT WITH A QUARTER-WAVE PLATE

The theory of elliptically polarized light and of wave plates contained in Sec. **13-11** should be read carefully before this experiment is begun.

Apparatus.—A spectrometer equipped with two graduated circles to fit over the collimator and telescope lenses, a third circle to be mounted as described later, a quarter-wave plate, preferably for Hg-5461, a Wollaston prism, two nicols, a Gauss eyepiece, and a mercury arc with a filter transmitting only the green line at 5461 angstroms. If a spectrometer table is not available, the essential elements of a collimator and telescope may be clamped on some suitable mounting or optical bench, since the experiment is performed with no deviation of the beam. The description following will assume the use of a spectrometer. Polaroids may be used instead of nicols, provided they are mounted in good quality optical glass.

The experiment consists of producing a beam of plane-polarized light with a nicol and changing this to elliptically polarized light with a thin sheet of mica; then analyzing the light thus produced, to find the orientation and eccentricity of the ellipse. To this end, it is desirable to mount all the polarizing parts in the space between the collimator and telescope lenses. One of the circles can be clamped over the telescope lens, one over the collimator, and the third attached either to the telescope or collimator tube by an arm, as shown in Fig. 1, Exp. 18.[1]

The Wollaston prism is used to accomplish the preliminary orientation of the nicols. With the collimator and telescope in line, and the slit vertical, place the Wollaston in the circle over the collimating lens, and rotate it until the two images of the slit are superposed in a vertical line. Now clamp a circle over the telescope lens, fasten its index at zero and put in it a Nicol

---

[1] If space prevents this, the middle circle may be over the telescope lens, and the third circle be placed at the eyepiece end of the telescope, but this is not so desirable. If it is so done, the nicol in the third circle may be put between the field and eye lenses of the eyepiece.

prism with its plane of transmission approximately horizontal. This plane may be previously found by extinguishing, with the nicol, skylight reflected at the angle of complete polarization (about 57 deg.) from a plate of glass, the plane of transmission then being vertical. With the index clamped, turn the nicol *slightly* until one of the images of the slit is extinguished. Determine this position as accurately as possible. Replace the Wollaston with a nicol, having clamped the index at zero, and turn it in the tube until the other image is extinguished. The planes of transmission of the polarizer and analyzer are now respectively vertical and horizontal. Keeping them crossed, mount the λ/4 plate in the third (middle) circle, and turn it until the light is extinguished once more. Retaining all positions, fasten firmly over the end of the polarizer a thin piece of mica. This may be done with a little wax or plasticine. The light will be restored, indicating that the mica transmits elliptically polarized light. There is, of course, the possibility that the mica may be a quarter- or half-wave plate, but this is not probable and may be guarded against beforehand. Now proceed as follows:

a. Set the analyzer at the position for minimum intensity.

b. Turn the λ/4 plate through about 5 deg. and reset the analyzer for minimum intensity. This intensity will be either greater or less than that in (*a*). If it is *less*, the λ/4 plate was turned in the right direction. If it is greater, then

c. Repeat (*b*), turning the λ/4 plate in the other direction and find a position of *less* minimum intensity than in (*a*). In any case,

d. Orient the λ/4 plate and analyzer to the positions for which extinction occurs. Call α the total angle through which the analyzer has been turned from its position before the mica was introduced, and call β the corresponding total angle through which the λ/4 plate has been turned. The axes of the ellipse are at the angle β with that of the planes of transmission of the polarizer and analyzer when crossed. If the slit of the spectrograph is accurately vertical and the preliminary adjustment with the Wollaston was accurately made, these planes of transmission are respectively vertical and horizontal.

The ratio of the amplitudes in these directions is given by $\tan (\alpha - \beta)$.

Make a graph of the elliptical vibration, orienting the ellipse with reference to the planes of transmission of the nicols as X- and Y-axes.

Answer these questions:

1. Suppose the mica had been a quarter-wave plate; could the experiment have turned out as described?   Explain.

2. Suppose it had been a half-wave plate; then could the analysis of elliptically polarized light have been carried out?   Explain.

EXPERIMENT 18

THE BABINET COMPENSATOR

Read carefully Section **13-12.**

Apparatus.—A polarizer and analyzer, a Babinet compensator of the Jamin type, a quarter-wave plate, a spectrometer, a white-light source, and a source of monochromatic light such as a mercury arc with a filter to transmit 5461 angstroms.   If a

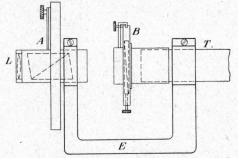

Fig. 1.—The Babinet-Jamin compensator B and analyzing nicol A, mounted at the eye end of the telescope tube.

spectrometer is not available, a pair of ordinary laboratory telescopes may be used, if the experiment is one in which the state of polarization to be examined is produced by transmission as through a quarter-wave plate.   In any experiment in which an angle of reflection is to be measured, the spectrometer is essential.   For convenience, the instructions will assume the use of a spectrometer.

The polarizer is mounted at the slit end of a spectrometer collimator.   At the eyepiece end of the telescope is mounted the Babinet compensator.   Beyond this, as shown in Fig. 1, is mounted the analyzer.   The eye end of the analyzer should be equipped with a simple magnifyer of such focal length that in sharp focus are the cross hairs of the Babinet compensator. In some cases, instead of cross hairs, there are ruled two parallel lines on one of the wedges, perpendicular to the long edge of the wedge. The telescope and collimator should be adjusted for parallel light so that the image of the polarizing nicol will also be at the focal plane of the magnifyer.

It is supposed that light in some unknown state of polarization is to be examined. For the purpose of class room experiment, this may be produced by using a λ/4 plate oriented to such an angle that the light is elliptically polarized. The collimator and telescope should in this case be clamped in line.

Part A. To Find the Phase Difference between the Components of the Elliptical Polarization.—The instrument must first be adjusted. Use a source of white light (the unfiltered mercury arc will do in this case). Remove the compensator, and set the analyzer for extinction. The compensator is equipped with two adjustments: (*a*) One wedge may be moved with respect to the other; (*b*) the entire compensator may be rotated about the optical axis of the instrument. Rotate the compensator so that the pointer is on one of the 45-deg. marks, and replace it so that the wedges are parallel or perpendicular to the plane of transmission of the analyzer. This will be the case when the fringes disappear. Clamp the compensator tightly on the draw tube and rotate the wedge 45 deg. This will give the position of maximum distinctness of the fringes. Place the cross hairs on the central fringe which is black. Replace the white light with monochromatic light. Now move the wedge until the next black fringe is under the cross hairs and record the distance moved. This distance may be called $2s$ corresponding to a difference of phase of 2π and a path difference of λ. Now introduce a plate of mica or a λ/4 plate between the polarizer and analyzer so that the light incident on the compensator is elliptically polarized. In general the axes of the ellipse will not be parallel to the principal section of either wedge, and the fringes will be shifted. But it should be made certain that the polarization of the light transmitted by the λ/4 plate is elliptical and not circular or plane. Move the wedge until the dark fringe is once more under the cross hairs. Calling the distance moved x, we have the corresponding difference of phase

$$\varphi = 2\pi\frac{x}{2s}.$$

This is, however, the amount by which the phase difference is changed by passage through the compensator (see eq. 13-7). Hence

$$2\pi\Delta = \pi\frac{x}{s}. \tag{1}$$

Part B.   To Find the Position of the Axes of the Ellipse.—Let plane-polarized light fall on the compensator and move the wedge through a distance $s/2$, having previously calibrated the micrometer driving the wedge by measuring the distance $2s$ between the dark fringes.   Then the cross hairs will be over a position at which the phase difference is $\pi/2$, corresponding to a retardation of $\lambda/4$.   Now let the elliptically polarized light fall once more on the compensator.   In general the middle black band will not be under the cross hairs, but it may be brought there by rotating the compensator.   It will usually be necessary to rotate the analyzer also, to obtain maximum distinctness of the fringes. The axes of the elliptically polarized light are now parallel to the axes of the wedges.

Part C.   The Ratio of the Axes of the Ellipse.—The situation will now be as shown in Fig. 13-21. OA and OB are parallel to the axes of the two wedges, OC is the direction of the principal section of the analyzer, and the direction of vibration of the light which is extinguished at the central fringe is DD'.   If the analyzer is rotated through the angle θ, the fringes will disappear, since for this position the compensator will act like a quarter-wave plate.   The tangent of θ will be the ratio of the axes of the elliptical polarization.   In the illustration the longer axis is in the direction OA.

EXPERIMENT 19

ROTATORY POLARIZATION OF COMMON SUBSTANCES

Read Secs. **13-19** and **20**.

There are many *polarimeters* designed solely for the measurement of the rotatory powers of optically active substances, especially for the measurement by this means of the purity of sugar.   When the graduated circle of the analyzer is calibrated in terms of purity instead of degrees the instrument is called a *saccharimeter*. In the absence of a special instrument, a polarimeter may be constructed by arranging the necessary optical parts as shown in Fig. 1, which depicts essentially the *Laurent* polarimeter.

M is a filter which gives approximately monochromatic light, *P* is the polarizing nicol (or polaroid), *A* is the analyzer, mounted in a graduated circle. At *W* is located some half-shade device such as the Laurent half-shade plate described in Sec. **13-23**. With this device, the settings of the analyzer are made not for extinction but by turning the analyzer to the angle where the two halves of the field are of equal brightness. Accordingly, *W*

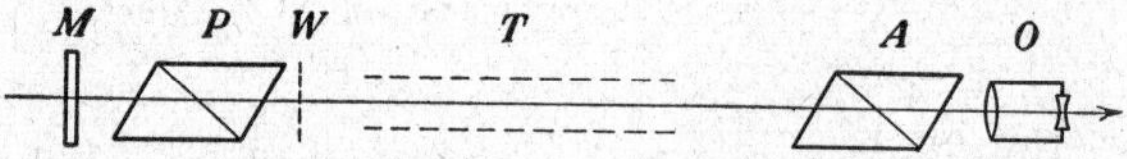

Fig. 1.—The arrangement of the Laurent polarimeter.

should be mounted so that a slight adjustment of its angle about the axis of the instrument should be permitted, in order to obtain sufficiently high brightness in the field of view. The ocular *O* is really a very short focus telescope focused on the dividing line of the Laurent half-shade plate. At the position *T* may be placed either a tube or cell of solution, or a crystal specimen whose rotatory power is to be determined.

If the green line of mercury is to be used for a source, *M* may be omitted. If sodium light is used, *M* should be a cell with flat sides containing a solution of potassium bichromate, which stops the blue ordinarily found in such a source.

A very bright sodium source is obtained by training the flame from an oxygas glass blowers' torch upon a small piece of pyrex tubing supported horizontally on a steel rod. For moderate intensity, the new General Electric sodium lamp may be used. The use of Hg-5461 or Na-5893 should depend upon the range of wave-length for which the Laurent half-shade plate is suitable, and for what wave-lengths the known values of specific rotation are available. Since the making of a half-wave plate from mica is within the skill of the average student, it is suggested that 5461 be used wherever possible.

With the source and filter in place, focus *O* upon the division in the half-shade plate and adjust the latter slightly until, with the analyzer set for equality of the two halves of the field, the greatest brightness is obtained. At least five settings of the analyzer for equality should be recorded, and the average taken. The analyzer should then be rotated through 180 deg. and the process repeated. These two settings 180 deg. apart are the zero settings of the polarimeter. Then the various specimens to be tested may be inserted at T and the analyzer rotated until equality of the two halves is once more attained. Each determination of this position should be made at least five times, and the average recorded, repeating after rotation through 180 deg.

It should be remembered that the insertion of a medium at T changes the optical path and throws O out of its focus upon the dividing line of W, so that refocusing is necessary.

Sometimes the angle of rotation is so large that it is not immediately known whether the rotation of the plane of vibration is clockwise or counterclockwise. A second observation may be made with a shorter length of substance or, in the case of solution, with smaller concentration, to determine this point. Or, the rotation may be observed with both the 5461 line of mercury and the 4356 line. The rotation of the plane is usually *smaller* for the *red* than for the *blue*.

Part A. The Optical Rotation of Quartz.—The rotation is proportional to the thickness of quartz traversed (in the direction of the optic axis), and depends upon the wave-length and slightly upon the temperature. If the angle of rotation φ for the green mercury line is known, that for sodium light may be found from the equation

$$\varphi_{(5893)} = \varphi_{(5461)} \times 0.85085. \tag{1}$$

The temperature effect is given by

$$\varphi_t = \varphi_0(1 + 0.000144t) \text{ between } 4° \text{ and } 50°C.$$

The value of $\varphi_{(5461)}$ at 20°C. for a plate 1 mm. thick cut perpendicular to the optic axis is 25.3571 deg. of arc.

It should be kept in mind that quartz occurs both right-handed and left-handed. The specimen used should be examined with white light between crossed nicols to make sure that it is not cut from a twinned crystal.

Part B. The Rotatory Power of Pure Cane Sugar.—In this case the so-called direct method may be used, which supposes that the sample of sugar contains no impurities which are also optically active.

With a good analytical balance weigh out 26 gm. of pure cane sugar (rock candy), which has been previously pulverized and dried in a desiccator for about 24 hr., or over sulphuric acid *in vacuo*. Mix this thoroughly with distilled water, allowing none of the sugar to be lost, in a graduate to make exactly 100 c.c. The most scrupulous cleanliness and exactness in measurement should be observed. Keep the solution covered to avoid loss by evaporation.

Fill a tube 20 cm. long with the sugar solution, having first determined exactly what the length of the column of liquid will be. Record the mean of several determinations of equality in the two halves of the field. Repeat after rotating the analyzer through 180 deg. The *specific rotation* is given by

$$\left[\alpha\right]_{\lambda}^{t°\text{C.}} = \frac{a}{lc}, \tag{2}$$

where λ is the wave-length used, a is the observed rotation in degrees of arc, l the length of the solution in *decimeters*, and c the concentration in grams per 100 c.c. of solution. The value of $\left[\alpha\right]_{5893}^{20°\text{C.}}$ for cane sugar (sucrose, $C_{12}H_{22}O_{11}$) is 66.45 deg. of arc. Since it is a little difficult to make observation at exactly 20°C., a correction of 0.02 deg. of arc may be subtracted from the experimentally determined value for each degree centigrade above 20°C.

The rotation ratio for sucrose, analogous to that given in eq. 1 for quartz, is

$$\varphi_{(5893)} = \varphi_{(5461)} \times 0.84922. \tag{3}$$

Part C (Optional).—The purity of a commercial sample of cane sugar may be tested by the method outlined in Part B. The sample should be prepared in the same manner as in Part B, except that the solution should be a little stronger than 26 gm. to each 100 c.c. of water, until it is certain that there will be no turbidity. If the solution is slightly turbid, it may be clarified as follows: Make a saturated solution of alum in water. Pour into about two thirds of it a slight excess of ammonium hydroxide and then pour in enough of the remaining one third to get a slightly acid reaction. Add to the sugar solution only a drop at a time. Too much will, because of the change in concentration, introduce an error which cannot be neglected. The remaining water should now be put in to bring the concentration to specifications.

Substituting the value of α obtained for this sample into eq. 2, calculate the value of c, and the percentage of purity.

Part D (Optional).—The methods described above make no provision for the errors possible due to the presence of optically active impurities. For this purpose, the *invert method* is used. Take 100 c.c. of the solution prepared in Part C, and add drop by drop 10 c.c. of concentrated hydrochloric acid, specific gravity 1.2 (38.8 per cent solution), shaking meanwhile. Since the reaction is delayed, set this aside for not less than 24 hr. and keep the temperature at 20°C. or over. Dilute the invert solution to 200 c.c. Measure the rotation as before, and multiply it by 2, because of the reduced concentration. Calculate c as directed in Part C.

The result obtained in this manner will be more accurate than by the direct method, provided the invert solution is properly made.

Part E (Optional).—Measure the rotations of several optically active substances.

EXPERIMENT 20
VERIFICATION OF BREWSTER'S LAW

From Fresnel's laws of reflection, in Secs. **13-13** and **14,** which should be read carefully before this experiment is begun, it follows that for transparent isotropic media $\tan i_p = n$, an equation known as Brewster's law. The angle i_p is that for which $i + r = 90$ deg. This affords an experimental method of determining n, the principal difficulty being that it is required to find the angle of a Nicol prism, or other analyzer, at which extinction of a polarized beam occurs.

It is also possible to measure the change, upon reflection, of the direction of vibration of a plane-polarized beam. This change is given by eq. 13-18:

$$- \tan \alpha \, \frac{\cos (i - r)}{\cos (i + r)} = \tan \beta,$$

where α is the angle between the direction of vibration of the incident light and the plane of incidence and β the angle between the direction of vibration of the reflected light and the same plane. If both i and r are known, the values of β for several values of α may be calculated. It is a simple matter to measure i and α, but the measurement of r is difficult. If n is known beforehand from some other experiment, r may be calculated from Snell's law. For this reason it is convenient to use in the experiment a prism or glass block for which the value of n has been quite accurately determined.

Apparatus.—A spectrometer equipped with graduated circles which may be clamped on the telescope and collimator tubes, a

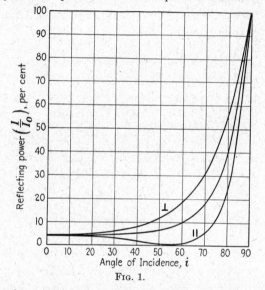

Fig. 1.

pair of nicols to go in the circles, a Gauss eyepiece, sources of white and monochromatic light, and a prism or block of glass whose index is known. Polaroids may be used instead of nicols, but they should be mounted in good optical glass.

Part A.—This consists of a trial determination of n from Brewster's law. Adjust the collimator and telescope for parallel light, and clamp over the telescope lens one of the graduated circles containing a nicol. Open the slit wide. The circle and nicol should be previously examined so that the setting corresponding to the plane of vibration of the transmitted light is known, or a Wollaston prism may be employed as described in Experiment 17. Use a monochromatic source of as high intensity as possible and one for which n is known. On the spectrometer table set the glass prism or block so that the light from the collimator is reflected from one face. *It is important that the face be absolutely clean.* The nicol should be set so that its plane of transmission is parallel to the plane of incidence, *i.e.*, in a horizontal plane. This will insure maximum intensity at the beginning of the experiment. Rotate the spectrometer table slowly and the telescope twice as fast, so as to keep the light in view at all times. Somewhere in the neighborhood of an angle of incidence of 57 deg., depending on the glass used, it should be possible to extinguish the light by turning the nicol. Reference to Fig. 1 shows that this point of extinction is difficult to determine accurately, because the curve of reflection is not symmetrical about the point where $I = 0$. By means of the Gauss eyepiece find the normal to the glass surface. Substitute the value of i_p in Brewster's law and compare the calculated and known values of n.

Part B.—Fit the second nicol into a graduated circle and clamp it over the collimator lens. Orient the nicol so that its plane of transmission makes an angle other than 0 or 90 deg. with the plane of incidence. Use monochromatic light for which n is known. With the analyzer measure β for several values of i on either side of the angle of complete polarization determined in Part A. The angle i should be at intervals of between 2 and 5 deg. To find each β, the analyzer should be set for extinction several times and a mean value recorded. Do not forget to record the position of the normal at each setting i. (To render this unnecessary, it is possible to use a very convenient table, so geared that it turns half as fast as the telescope. Ordinarily this is called a *minimum deviation* table. With this equipment, i need only be measured once.) Make a table of data, with i in the first column, calculated β in the second, and measured β in the third. There should, of course, be a change in the sign of β at the angle of complete polarization. Plot the measured angles of β against the corresponding values of i. The point where the curve crosses the i-axis gives i_p. From this, n may be calculated.

How does the value of n obtained compare with that from Part A? with that from other experiments? What are the chief sources of error in this experiment?

EXPERIMENT 21

THE OPTICAL CONSTANTS OF METALS

The theory of metallic reflection is discussed briefly in Secs. **15-10** and **11**. For a more extended discussion the student should consult Drude, "Theory of Optics," and Wood, "Physical Optics." The principal experimental facts may be summarized as follows:

a. Metals do not completely polarize light at any angle of reflection.

b. Plane-polarized light incident upon a metallic surface is upon reflection changed to elliptically polarized light, unless the plane of vibration is either parallel or perpendicular to the plane of incidence.

c. The ellipticity is due to a phase difference Δ introduced, on reflection, between the components of the vibration parallel and perpendicular to the plane of incidence. The ellipticity is greatest for the angle of incidence φ for which this phase difference $\Delta = \pi/2$. This angle is called the *angle of principal incidence* $\bar{\varphi}$.

d. Circularly polarized light incident at the angle $\bar{\varphi}$ is reflected as plane-polarized light with its plane of vibration making an angle $\bar{\psi}$ with the plane of incidence. The angle $\bar{\psi}$ is called the angle of *principal azimuth*.

As stated in the text, theoretical relationships can be obtained between these angles and the quantities n, the index of refraction of the substance, and κ, the absorption index. These are given in one form with a high degree of approximation in eqs. 15-15, for any value of Δ. In order to make these equations applicable to the experimental conditions described above, Δ is put equal to $\pi/2$, whereupon eqs. 15-15 become

$$\left. \begin{array}{r} \kappa = \tan 2\bar{\psi}, \\ n^2(1 + \kappa^2) = \sin^2 \bar{\varphi} \tan^2 \bar{\varphi}. \end{array} \right\} \tag{1}$$

As will be seen from (*c*) and (*d*) above, there are two experimental methods of determining n and κ. Incident plane-polarized light may be reflected from the surface at the angle $\bar{\varphi}$, and the value of $\bar{\psi}$ determined for which it becomes circularly polarized upon reflection. Or, incident circularly polarized light may be reflected as plane-polarized and the azimuth $\bar{\psi}$ determined for which it is completely extinguished by an analyzer.

Since difference of phase is responsible for the change of polarization, the experiment should be performed, not with white, but monochromatic light.

With n and κ known, the value of the reflectivity R may be calculated by means of eq. 15-10.

Apparatus.—The spectrometer, polarizer, and analyzer used in Experiments 17 and 20, or, the polarizer, analyzer, and Babinet compensator used in Experiment 18. A mercury arc and filter for λ5461. Several plane glass surfaces freshly coated with metals. It is recommended that heavy opaque aluminum, silver, and copper be deposited by evaporation on plane glass surfaces about 2.5 cm. square. If evaporation is not possible, polished plane surfaces may be used, although in the polishing process the surface often takes on foreign matter which changes its character.

Part A. n and κ with the Babinet Compensator.—Set the wedges of the compensator so that the central dark fringe is displaced through a distance which corresponds to a phase difference of one quarter of a complete period. Set the analyzer for maximum blackness of the fringe. Then allow plane-polarized light to fall on one of the coated plates, which should be held securely at the middle of the spectrometer table. Change the angle of incidence by rotating the table, and the telescope twice as fast, until the central dark fringe comes back to the central position. Record this angle of incidence, which is $\bar{\varphi}$. Then turn the analyzer until the central fringe is once more black. This will give the angle $\bar{\psi}$.

Part B.   Alternative Method with Quarter-wave Plate.—With a λ/4 plate change the plane-polarized light transmitted by the polarizer to circularly polarized light. Let this be incident upon the metallic surface, and find the angle of incidence ($\bar{\varphi}$) for which the reflected light is plane-polarized, as determined by the analyzer. Record also the azimuth of the analyzer, *i.e.*, the angle its plane of transmission makes with the plane of incidence.

Substitute the values of $\bar{\varphi}$ and $\bar{\psi}$ found by either of these methods in eqs. 1 to get n and κ.

From eq. 15-10, calculate R, the reflectivity. The following values of n and κ are taken from the International Critical Tables, Vol. V, page 248. They are for *opaque* surfaces. Semitransparent surfaces yield different values. The values of the optical constants of metals vary widely among observers, principally because of the difficulty of obtaining an uncontaminated surface.

	λ	n	κ	R calc.
Silver	4500	0.16	14.5	88.
	5000	0.17	17.1	90.
	5500	0.18	18.8	91.5
	5893	0.18	20.6 ⎱	Different observers
	5893	0.20	17.1 ⎰	
	6000			92.7
	6300	0.20	19.5	
Aluminum	4310	0.78	2.85	
	4860	0.93	3.15	
	5270	1.10	3.39	
	5893	1.44	3.64 ⎱	Different observers
	5893	1.28	3.66 ⎰	
	6570	1.48	3.92	
Copper	5000	1.17	2.03	
	5600	0.855	2.83	
	5893	0.62	4.1 ⎱	Different observers
	5893	0.64	4.08 ⎰	
	6000	0.565	5.51	

EXPERIMENT 22

POLARIZATION OF SCATTERED LIGHT

Read Secs. **15-12** and **13** on the scattering of light and its polarization.

Apparatus.—A spherical liter flask, a 500-watt projection lamp, a cylindrical shield of metal with a slot in one side about 2 cm. wide. A Nicol prism or polaroid in a graduated circle. A little hyposulphite of soda and some concentrated sulphuric acid.

Clean the flask and put in it about a quarter of a teaspoonful of hyposulphite of soda. Half fill the flask with distilled water and shake it to dissolve the hyposulphite of soda and also to get rid of the bubbles which gather on the sides. In a graduate mix about 0.5 c.c. of concentrated sulphuric acid with 100 c.c. of distilled water, and wait till it clears. Set the lamp in a vertical position, base down, put the shield around it, and set the flask so that the broad wedge of light through the slot falls on the hyposulphite of soda solution.

Mount the nicol (or polaroid) so that it may be swung about a vertical axis permitting analysis of the state of polarization of the solution at any angle.   For this purpose the flask may be set on the table of a spectrometer, and the nicol and graduated circle on a short tube put in place of the telescope.   This is not necessary, since the nicol may also be mounted on a stand which can be shifted from one position to another.

With the analyzer, observe the scattered light perpendicular to the beam and estimate the amount of polarization.   Make the

Fig. 1.

same estimate of the polarization in the direction (nearly) of the beam.   The light will be too bright to look at directly, and it will be best to look instead at an angle of about 20 deg. with the direct beam.   Repeat these observations with a red filter in the path of the beam.

Pour in the dilute acid and give to the flask a slight rotating motion to produce a vortex in the liquid.   If this is done successfully, the precipitation will take place mostly in the center of the flask, as shown in Fig. 1.

With the nicol set so as to observe the liquid at right angles to the beam, note the increase of polarization as precipitation increases.   Occasionally make the same observations at other angles to the beam.

Write a description of what you have observed, noting especially the degree of polarization before and after the acid was poured in the flask, the growth in polarization, the direction of vibration of the scattered light, the color effects, and any other effects you have seen.

EXPERIMENT 23

THE FARADAY EFFECT

For the theory of this experiment, read Sec. **16-6**.

Apparatus.—In order to produce the rotation of the plane of vibration of a light beam traversing a medium in a magnetic field, it is necessary to have a coil of considerable field strength. While such coils are not ordinarily part of the equipment of a light laboratory, they actually cost far less than many pieces of optical equipment and may be used for a variety of purposes, in laboratory instruction, lecture demonstration, and research. A coil with a hollow cylindrical center, having a field strength of about 1,000 gauss, will produce a measurable Faraday effect in a column of carbon bisulphide 15 cm long. The field at the center of a single solenoid of length L and radius R, due to current I through n turns per centimeter, is given by

$$H = 4\pi n I \frac{L}{\sqrt{L^2 + R^2}}, \qquad \text{(gauss)}$$

and for many layers of turns, there will be a value of H for each layer. For successful operation over any but very short periods of time, the coil should be water-cooled. There are different systems of water cooling, a common one being the insertion every 5 or 10 cm. along the coil of a hollow disk through which water flows at a good rate. Unless the laboratory is equipped for the construction of a properly insulated and water-cooled coil, it is wiser to purchase one of sufficient strength, exactly as telescopes, spectrometers, microscopes, and other accessories are purchased.

The remaining items of apparatus consist of a polarizer and analyzer, a graduated circle for the latter, a half-shade plate, a mercury arc and filter, or a sodium source. The use of sodium is not recommended as more precise determinations are possible with Hg-5461. Tubes for containing liquids may be similar to those used for the sugar experiment, Experiment 19, Part B.

A satisfactory tube can be made by cutting a heavy-walled tube of pyrex to the appropriate length with a hot wire and grinding the ends flat. Or, if glass-blowing equipment is available, the ends of a section can be moulded into a flange about 5 mm. wide which can be ground flat. After grinding, on the ends should be sealed circular disks of good quality glass. A good sealing material which is acid-proof and impervious to ordinary solvents is Insa-lute Adhesive Cement. If it is desired to use a separate tube of some permanence for each liquid, one end disk may be sealed on, given time for the cement to set, then, with the tube in a vertical position, liquid may be poured in almost to the top of the tube, and the other end sealed on. The small amount of air thus enclosed will not cause any difficulty. If the tube is to be emptied and refilled, it should have a side opening

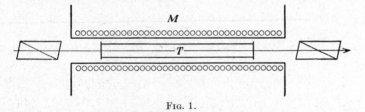

Fig. 1.

which can be corked up, but which should not be so long as to interfere with the insertion of the tube in the coil. Great care should be taken to avoid the ignition or explosion of any volatile liquid used.

Part A.—Arrange the apparatus as shown in Fig. 1. Since the field is not uniform at the ends of the coil, it is suggested that the coil be about 30 cm. long, with a hollow cylindrical center about 5 or 6 cm. in diameter. The tubes of liquid should be about half as long. Since, however, the experiment is not expected to produce rigorously accurate results, no harm is done if they are longer.

Determine the rotation θ for carbon bisulphide. The Verdet constant R for carbon bisulphide is 0.0441. Substitute θ and R in the equation $\theta = RlH$ (in minutes of arc) where l is the length of the liquid column in centimeters, and calculate H. Repeat for distilled water, whose Verdet constant is 0.0130.

Part B (Optional).—Measure the indices of refraction and dispersion of carbon bisulphide in a hollow prism, with walls of good optical glass free from strains, over the range from about 4300 to 6000 angstroms by the method of Experiment 5. Find the value of $dn/d\lambda$ for $\lambda 4356$ and $\lambda 5461$ of mercury, and for the sodium lines. Find the angle of rotation θ, and substitute θ, λ, $dn/d\lambda$, e, m, and c in the equation

$$\theta = -\frac{e}{2mc^2}H \cdot l \cdot \frac{\lambda dn}{d\lambda}$$

and thus calculate H.

In each case a good filter is desirable, as the color effects due to dispersion of rotation are pronounced.

Part C (Optional).—If facilities permit, an exceedingly interesting experiment is to measure the rotation due to a semi-transparent iron film in a magnetic field. With the evaporating outfit (Appendix V) deposit a thin film of iron on one half of a circular disk of good optical glass about 1 in. in diameter, and free from strains. A coat which transmits between one half to one fourth of the light is satisfactory. Fasten this in a support which will hold it in a position normal to the field and place it at the middle of the coil. Measure the rotation produced by the glass alone and that by the iron coating and the glass, subtract the first from the second, to obtain the rotation due to the iron film. Since the angle will be very small, the experiment should be regarded only as qualitative, and as a demonstration of the rotatory power of iron. A field of 5000 gauss or over will be required for this experiment.

APPENDICES

APPENDIX I

A COLLINEAR RELATION USEFUL IN GEOMETRICAL OPTICS

For an ideal optical system, a point-to-point, line-to-line, and plane-to-plane correspondence between object and image may be expressed in terms of coordinate geometry by the equations

$$\left.\begin{aligned}
x' &= \frac{a_1x + b_1y + c_1z + d_1}{ax + by + cz + d}, \\
y' &= \frac{a_2x + b_2y + c_2z + d_2}{ax + by + cz + d}, \\
z' &= \frac{a_3x + b_3y + c_3z + d_3}{ax + by + cz + d},
\end{aligned}\right\} \tag{1}$$

in which x, y, and z represent the coordinates of an object point and x', y', and z' the coordinates of the conjugate image point. We may conventionally prescribe that the object space be placed on the left, with positive directions to the *right* and *up*, while the image space be on the right with positive directions to the *left* and *up*.

This general relationship can be limited for ideal *symmetrical coaxial* optical systems. A symmetrical optical system is one in which each reflecting or refracting surface is generated by rotating an element of the surface about the optic axis. In such a system, for any plane of incidence containing the optic axis, the magnification in, and position of, the image plane will always be the same for a given object plane. Hence we need consider only the xy- and $x'y'$-planes, the optic axes being in the x- and x'-directions. Equations 1 may accordingly be simplified to

$$\left.\begin{aligned}
x' &= \frac{a_1x + b_1y + d_1}{ax + by + d}, \\
y' &= \frac{a_2x + b_2y + d_2}{ax + by + d}.
\end{aligned}\right\} \tag{2}$$

A second property of symmetrical optical systems is that a change in the size alone of the object causes no change in the *position* of the image, but only a conjugate change of size. This means that a change in the value of y in eqs. 2 must cause no change in x', but only in y'. As the equations stand, this is not true, but it can be made true by putting b, b_1, a_2, and d_2 each equal to zero, reducing the equations to

$$x' = \frac{a_1 x + d_1}{ax + d}, \quad \text{and} \quad y' = \frac{b_2 y}{ax + d}. \quad (3)$$

These may be solved for x and y, obtaining

$$x = \frac{d_1 - dx'}{ax' - a_1}, \quad \text{and} \quad y = \frac{y'(ad_1 - a_1 d)}{b_2(ax' - a_1)}. \quad (3')$$

Now the coefficients a, d, a_1, d_1, and b_2 are values for a particular optical system depending on the radii of curvature of the surfaces, their distance apart, and the indices of refraction of the media. Furthermore, the linear equation $ax + d = 0$ obviously represents the principal focal plane in the object space, since it places x' at infinity. Likewise the equation $ax' - a_1 = 0$ represents the principal focal plane in the image space. By the substitutions $x = x_1 - \dfrac{d}{a}$ and $x' = x_1' + \dfrac{a_1}{a}$, the origins are shifted to the principal focal points. The resulting equations are

$$\left.\begin{aligned} x_1 x_1' &= \frac{ad_1 - a_1 d}{a^2}, \\ \frac{y'}{y} &= \frac{b_2}{ax_1}. \end{aligned}\right\} \quad (4)$$

We may further simplify eqs. 4 by putting

$$\frac{ad_1 - a_1 d}{a^2} = ff', \quad \text{and} \quad \frac{b_2}{a} = f,$$

where f and f' are constants depending upon the radii of curvature of the surfaces, their distances apart, and the indices of refraction of the media, so that finally, dropping the subscripts,

$$xx' = ff', \quad \text{and} \quad \frac{y'}{y} = \frac{f}{x} = \frac{x'}{f'}. \quad (5)$$

Equations 5 hold for any ideal optical system in which the foregoing limitations placed on the general collinear relation exist.

APPENDIX II

THIRD-ORDER CORRECTION FOR SPHERICAL ABERRATION FOR A THIN LENS IN AIR

From Fig. 2-1,

$$\frac{n'}{n} = \frac{\sin \varphi}{\sin \varphi'} = \frac{a + r_1}{b} \cdot \frac{b'}{a' - r_1}. \tag{1}$$

But by the cosine law,

$$b^2 = (a + r_1)^2 + r_1^2 - 2(a + r_1)r_1 \cos \alpha \tag{2}$$

and

$$b'^2 = (a' - r_1)^2 + r_1^2 + 2(a' - r_1)r_1 \cos \alpha. \tag{3}$$

By expansion, $\cos \alpha = 1 - \dfrac{\alpha^2}{2!} + \dfrac{\alpha^4}{4!} - \dfrac{\alpha^6}{6!} + \cdots$. Neglecting higher powers of α than the second, and substituting for α its approximate value h/r_1,   *what is h*

$$b^2 = a^2 + \frac{(a + r_1)h^2}{r_1}. \tag{4}$$

and

$$b'^2 = a'^2 - \frac{(a' - r_1)h^2}{r_1}. \tag{5}$$

Using the binomial theorem

$$(x + y)^n = x^n + nx^{n-1}y + \cdots$$

for $n = 2$, considering the right-hand member of eq. 4 to be $2xy$, $y = \dfrac{a + r_1}{r_1} \cdot \dfrac{h^2}{2a}$ and, to a sufficient degree of approximation, considering h to be small,

$$b = a\left[1 + \left(\frac{1}{r_1} + \frac{1}{a}\right)\frac{h^2}{2a}\right], \tag{6}$$

and, similarly,

$$b' = a'\left[1 - \left(\frac{1}{r_1} - \frac{1}{a'}\right)\frac{h^2}{2a'}\right]. \tag{7}$$

Substituting eqs. 6 and 7 in eq. 1,

$$\frac{n_1}{a} + \frac{n_2}{a_m'} = \frac{n_2 - n_1}{r_1} + \frac{h^2}{2}\left(\frac{1}{r_1} + \frac{1}{a}\right)\left(\frac{1}{r_1} - \frac{1}{a'}\right)\left(\frac{n_2}{a} + \frac{n_1}{a'}\right), \tag{8}$$

in which n_2 and n_1 have been substituted for n' and n, and the subscript m is used to indicate the image distance with a single surface. This substitution is made in order to facilitate the application of the results to the case of a lens in air, in which case $n_1 = n_3 = 1$ and $n_2 = n$.

Since in view of the approximation already made h is small with respect to the other dimensions, we can substitute for a' wherever it occurs in the coefficient of h^2 the value derived from the first-order equation,

$$\frac{n_1}{a} + \frac{n_2}{a'} = \frac{n_2 - n_1}{r_1},$$

whence

$$\frac{n_1}{a} + \frac{n_2}{a_m'} = \frac{n_2 - n_1}{r_1}$$
$$+ \frac{h^2}{2}\left(\frac{1}{r_1} + \frac{1}{a}\right)\left(\frac{n_1}{n_2 r_1} + \frac{n_1}{n_2 a}\right)\left(\frac{n_2^2 - n_1^2}{n_2 a} + \frac{n_1 n_2 - n_1^2}{n_2 r_1}\right). \quad (9)$$

For the second surface of the lens, the distance to the virtual object from the vertex is $-a_m'$, hence the equation analogous to eq. 8 for this surface is

$$-\frac{n_2}{a_m'} + \frac{n_3}{a_k'} = \frac{n_3 - n_2}{r_2}$$
$$+ \frac{h^2}{2}\left(\frac{1}{r_2} - \frac{1}{a_m'}\right)\left(\frac{1}{r_2} - \frac{1}{a'}\right)\left(-\frac{n_3}{a_m'} + \frac{n_2}{a'}\right), \quad (10)$$

where a_k' is the distance from the lens to the focus for the rays intersecting the lens at a distance h from the axis. Since h is small, we can substitute for a_m' wherever it occurs in the coefficient of h^2 the value of a_m' derived from

$$-\frac{n_2}{a_m'} + \frac{n_3}{a'} = \frac{n_3 - n_2}{r_2},$$

whence for the second surface,

$$-\frac{n_2}{a_m'} + \frac{n_3}{a_k'} = \frac{n_3 - n_2}{r_2}$$
$$+ \frac{h^2}{2}\left(\frac{1}{r_2} - \frac{1}{a'}\right)\left(\frac{n_3}{n_2 r_2} - \frac{n_3}{a' n_2}\right)\left(\frac{n_3^2 - n_2 n_3}{n_2 r_2} - \frac{n_3^2 - n_2^2}{a' n_2}\right). \quad (11)$$

For the case of a lens in air, $n_1 = n_3 = 1$ and $n_2 = n$.   Substituting these values in eqs. 9 and 11,

$$\frac{1}{a} + \frac{n}{a_m'} = \frac{n-1}{r_1} + \frac{h^2}{2}\left(\frac{n-1}{n^2}\right)\left(\frac{1}{r_1} + \frac{1}{a}\right)^2\left(\frac{n+1}{a} + \frac{1}{r_1}\right), \quad (12)$$

and

$$-\frac{n}{a_m'} + \frac{1}{a_k'} = \frac{1-n}{r_2} + \frac{h^2}{2}\left(\frac{n-1}{n^2}\right)\left(\frac{1}{r_2} - \frac{1}{a'}\right)^2\left(\frac{n+1}{a'} - \frac{1}{r_2}\right). \quad (13)$$

The sum of eqs. 12 and 13 is

$$\frac{1}{a} + \frac{1}{a_k'} = (n-1)\left(\frac{1}{r_1} - \frac{1}{r_2}\right)$$
$$+ \frac{n-1}{n^2}\cdot\frac{h^2}{2}\left[\left(\frac{1}{r_1} + \frac{1}{a}\right)^2\left(\frac{n+1}{a} + \frac{1}{r_1}\right)\right.$$
$$\left. + \left(\frac{1}{r_2} - \frac{1}{a'}\right)^2\left(\frac{n+1}{a'} - \frac{1}{r_2}\right)\right]. \quad (14)$$

For paraxial rays,

$$\frac{1}{a} + \frac{1}{a'} = (n-1)\left(\frac{1}{r_1} - \frac{1}{r_2}\right). \quad (15)$$

Hence,

$$\frac{1}{a'} - \frac{1}{a_k'} = -\frac{n-1}{n^2}\cdot\frac{h^2 K}{2},$$

where K is the quantity in the large brackets $\left[\;\right]$ in eq. 14.   The difference between the focal lengths for paraxial rays and those intersecting a lens a distance h from the axis may be written

$$a_k' - a' = -a'^2\cdot\frac{n-1}{n^2}\cdot\frac{h^2 K}{2}, \quad (16)$$

provided the difference between a_k' and a' is small enough so that for their product may be substituted a'^2.

APPENDIX III

DERIVATION OF EQUATIONS FOR ASTIGMATIC FOCAL DISTANCES AT A SINGLE REFRACTING SURFACE

In Fig. 1 let O be an object point, not on the axis, in the plane containing the line element AP of a single spherical refracting surface and C, its center of curvature. Then if coma is absent, all the rays which have the same inclination u as OP with OC will intersect the line OC extended in a point such as I_2. Let

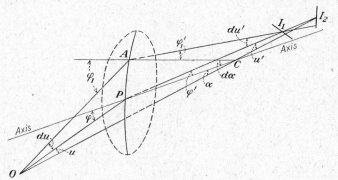

Fig. 1.

$OP = s$, and $PI_2 = s_2$. Then, from the law of sines, in triangle OPI_2

$$\frac{s}{\sin u'} = \frac{s_2}{\sin u} = \frac{OI_2}{\sin (\varphi - \varphi')};\tag{1}$$

in triangle OPC

$$\frac{s}{\sin \alpha} = \frac{r}{\sin u} = \frac{OC}{\sin \varphi};\tag{2}$$

and in triangle PCI_2

$$\frac{r'}{\sin u'} = \frac{s_2}{\sin \alpha} = \frac{CI_2}{\sin \varphi'}.\tag{3}$$

From eq. 2,

$$OC = \frac{r \sin \varphi}{\sin u};\tag{4}$$

from eq. 3,

$$CI_2 = \frac{r \sin \varphi'}{\sin u'}.\tag{5}$$

Adding eqs. 4 and 5,

$$OC + CI_2 = OI_2 = \frac{r \sin \varphi}{\sin u} + \frac{r \sin \varphi'}{\sin u'}. \tag{6}$$

Substituting this value of OI_2 in eq. 1 and using the first and last members of eq. 1,

$$\frac{s}{\sin u'} = \frac{r}{\sin (\varphi - \varphi')}\left[\frac{\sin \varphi}{\sin u} + \frac{\sin \varphi'}{\sin u'}\right]. \tag{7}$$

From the first and second members of eq. 1, $\sin u = (s_2 \sin u')/s$, whence eq. 7 becomes

$$\frac{s}{\sin u'} = \frac{r}{\sin (\varphi - \varphi')}\left[\frac{s \sin \varphi}{s_2 \sin u'} + \frac{\sin \varphi'}{\sin u'}\right]. \tag{8}$$

Expanding $\sin (\varphi - \varphi')$ and substituting for $\sin \varphi$ its value from Snell's law, *i.e.*,

$$\sin \varphi = \frac{n'}{n} \sin \varphi', \tag{9}$$

eq. 8 may be written

$$\frac{n}{s} + \frac{n'}{s_2} = \frac{n' \cos \varphi' - n \cos \varphi}{r}. \tag{10}$$

This gives the distance s_2, measured from the surface, of the sagittal or secondary focus.

Consider next two rays, OP and another adjacent ray OA. Since they are refracted by the surface at different distances from the intersection of OC with the surface they will, after refraction, intersect at a point I_1 not on OC extended. Let the angle between OA and OC be $u + du$, that between AI_1 and PI_1 be du', and let $PI_1 = s_1$. Since from the figure

$$\varphi = \alpha + u, \quad \text{and} \quad \varphi' = \alpha - u',$$

by differentiation it follows that

$$d\varphi = d\alpha + du, \quad \text{and} \quad d\varphi' = d\alpha - du'. \tag{11}$$

Considering the angles du, du', and $d\alpha$ to be equal to their sines, it follows from the law of sines that

$$du = \frac{PA \cos \varphi}{s}, \quad du' = \frac{PA \cos \varphi'}{s_1}, \quad d\alpha = \frac{PA}{r}, \tag{12}$$

whence, in eq. 11,

$$d\varphi = PA\left(\frac{1}{r} + \frac{\cos\varphi}{s}\right), \quad \text{and} \quad d\varphi' = PA\left(\frac{1}{r} - \frac{\cos\varphi'}{s_1}\right). \quad (13)$$

Differentiation of Snell's law in eq. 9 gives

$$n\cos\varphi\,d\varphi = n'\cos\varphi'\,d\varphi', \quad (14)$$

and on substituting the values of $d\varphi$ and $d\varphi'$ from eq. 13 this becomes

$$n\cos\varphi\left[\frac{1}{r} + \frac{\cos\varphi}{s}\right] = n'\cos\varphi'\left[\frac{1}{r} - \frac{\cos\varphi'}{s_1}\right],$$

which may be written

$$\frac{n\cos^2\varphi}{s} + \frac{n'\cos^2\varphi'}{s_1} = \frac{n'\cos\varphi' - n\cos\varphi}{r}. \quad (15)$$

This gives the distance s_1, measured from the surface, of the tangential or primary focus.

APPENDIX IV

ADJUSTMENT OF A SPECTROMETER

Spectrometers vary widely in their adaptability to a variety of uses, precision and ease of adjustment, and consequently in cost. For most of the experiments in this book a moderately expensive instrument will serve as well as the most costly to demonstrate the principles of optics. The precision to be desired is perhaps greatest in the case of the experiments on the index of refraction of a prism and the dispersion of prisms and gratings. There are certain minimum requirements to be met by any instrument. The optical parts should be of good quality, the mechanical construction should be rigid and sufficiently massive to prevent flexure, and the graduated circle should permit an accuracy of setting at least to 5 sec. of arc.

The essential parts of a spectrometer are: A circle graduated in degrees of arc, equipped either with verniers or micrometer microscopes with which angles may be read; a rotatable table on which prisms or other optical parts may be set; a collimator and slit; and a telescope. The ideal arrangement is to have each one of these four parts independently rotatable on a cone or axis, but arranged so that the table, the collimator, and the telescope may either be clamped to the mounting or to the graduated circle. Sometimes the verniers (or microscopes) are fixed to the arm of the telescope so that they rotate with it, while the table, the collimator, or both, may be clamped to the graduated circle. In any case, the user of the spectrometer should study the demands made by any particular experiment before proceeding with its performance.

When in adjustment, the telescope and collimator tubes should be set so that no matter what their angle about a vertical axis may be, their axes are always perpendicular to, and intersect, the main vertical axis of the spectrometer. A satisfactory instrument will be equipped with devices to make this possible. Moreover, when in adjustment, the slit of the collimator should be at the principal focus of the collimator lens, and the telescope cross hairs should be at the principal focus of the telescope objective.

1. Adjustment of the Telescope for Parallel Light.   *Method 1.*—Remove the telescope from the spectrometer and point it at a bright object, such as a lamp globe or the sky. With the eye previously accommodated to distant vision, slide the eyepiece in or out in the draw tube, keeping the position of the cross hairs fixed until the cross hairs appear sharp. This will insure that the experimenter makes observations with a minimum of eyestrain. It is well, perhaps, as a final adjustment, to pull the eyepiece out to the point beyond which the cross hairs appear to become slightly blurred. Next point the telescope through an *open* window at some object a few hundred feet away, and rack the cross hair and eyepiece together in or out until a distinct image is seen. Try this several times. Make sure that the eyepiece has a sufficiently snug fit in the drawtube so that it will not slip too freely and destroy this adjustment.

Method 2.—This involves the use of a Gauss eyepiece, without which several experiments cannot be performed. It is described in detail in Sec. **7-3** and is illustrated in Fig. 7-4. Its relation to the spectrometer is illustrated in Fig. 1. Light from a source will thus be reflected past the cross hairs through objective O. If it is then reflected from a plane surface M, such as the face of a mirror or prism, directly back into the collimator, an image of the cross hairs will appear. Provided the cross hairs are at the principal focus of O, this image will be in the same plane. When the cross hairs and their image are both in sharp focus, with no parallactic displacement, the telescope is in correct adjustment for parallel light.

2. Adjustment of the Collimator for Parallel Light.—The collimator and the telescope should next be set so that their axes are coincident and intersect the vertical axis of the spectrometer. This may first be done roughly by sighting along the tubes. A finer adjustment may be made by the use of a block set on the prism table with a vertical edge at the center of the table, sighting past it with the slit and eyepiece removed, without disturbing the position of the cross hairs. Replace the

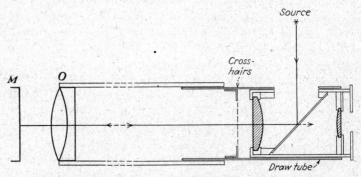

Fig. 1.—Sketch of a telescope equipped with a Gauss eyepiece

eyepiece and slit, taking care to bring the former once more into correct focus on the cross hairs. Open the slit to a convenient width, say a millimeter or less. Rack the slit in or out until a sharp image of it is at the plane of the cross hairs without parallactic displacement. The collimator will then be adjusted for parallel light.

2a. Alternative Method of Focussing a Spectrometer. Schuster's Method.—If neither a distinct object nor a Gauss eyepiece is available, the following method, due to Schuster, may be employed.

Use the mercury arc with filter for 5461 angstroms, or a sodium source. Adjust the telescope and collimator in a straight line across the center point of the spectrometer table. Put the prism so that it has maximum illumination from the collimator and orient it to the position of minimum deviation (see Sec. **8-1**). Rotate the prism slightly to the other side of minimum deviation following the image with the telescope, and focus the collimator for sharpest image. Repeat the alternations of rotating and focusing, first telescope and then collimator, until turning the prism causes no change of focus. When this condition is reached, the rays from any point on the slit are parallel in passing through the prism.

3. Adjustment of the Telescope so that Its Axis Is Perpendicular to the Axis of the Spectrometer.—For this purpose it is desirable to provide a plane-parallel plate coated on both sides with a reflecting metallic surface. If a plane-parallel plate is not available, a plate with one side plane and metallically coated may be used instead. The plate should be mounted in a metal holder like that shown in Fig. 2, so that it may be set firmly on the spectrometer table and the possibility of breaking may be minimized. If the base is made somewhat larger than shown, and three adjusting or leveling screws are inserted, its usefulness will be increased. Set this plate so that the telescope may be pointed to either face without interfering with the collimator or verniers. Illuminate the cross

Fig. 2.

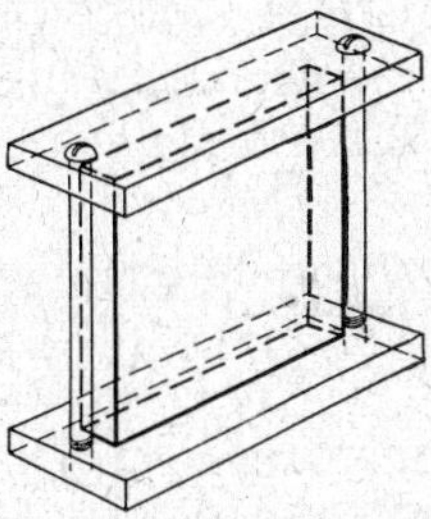

hairs by means of the Gauss eyepiece, and manipulate the telescope and table until an image is reflected back into the field of view. At first this will be difficult as some experience is needed to insure good illumination of the cross hairs. A good procedure is to look directly into the mirror with the telescope swung to one side so that the image of the eye appears at about the same level as the center of the objective and at a point in the mirror directly over the center of the table. Then swing the telescope to position between the eye and the mirror. Then move the telescope from side to side slightly with different adjustment of the telescope leveling screws until a glimpse is caught of the circular area of illumination reflected back through the telescope. When the image is located, it will probably be either too high or too low. Bring it into coincidence with the cross hairs by adjusting the telescope leveling screws for one-half of the correction and the table leveling screws for the other half. Then rotate the telescope through 180 deg. until it is pointing to the other side of the mirror, and repeat the adjustment. After several corrections of position on either side, the image of the cross hairs should coincide with the cross hairs themselves, no matter on which side the telescope may be. It should be noted that, although the mirror *surface* is in adjustment, the table may not be, so that the substitution of a prism or grating may necessitate some further leveling. The telescope, however, should now be correctly set so that its axis is perpendicular to, and intersects, the principal axis of the spectrometer.

In some cases the axis of rotation of the table is not coincident with the axis of the instrument. The adjustment above is, however, the most useful one. In case it is desired simply to adjust the telescope perpendicular to the axis of the *table*, this may be done by moving the *mirror and table* through 90 deg. between adjustments with the Gauss eyepiece.

The collimator may now receive its final adjustment. Set the telescope and collimator in a straight line pointing toward a light source so that the slit, in a vertical position, coincides with the intersection of the cross hairs. Place a hair, toothpick, or fine wire across the slit and on a level with the center of the collimator tube, and adjust the leveling screws of the latter until the shadow of the obstacle coincides with the intersection of the cross hairs. Sometimes the slit length and eyepiece magnification are such that no obstacle is required, both ends of the slit being in view at the same time.

An alternative method is to rotate the slit to a horizontal position for leveling the collimator. This is not generally recommended, since often there is no provision for free rotation of the drawtube of the slit. Forced rotation of the slit may then tend to destroy some defining pin in the tube, or wear the threads of the connection between the drawtube and the slit so that the latter may no longer be definable in a vertical position.

APPENDIX V

PREPARATION OF MIRROR SURFACES

1. Chemical Deposition of Silver.—For this method the student is referred to the "Handbook of Chemistry and Physics," published by the Chemical Rubber Publishing Co. The method is tedious and uncertain and should not be used unless the more satisfactory evaporation method cannot be used.

2. Deposition by Evaporation.—This is by far the most satisfactory method, and can be used for the greatest variety of substances. Since the essential parts of the apparatus are a tungsten coil which can be raised electrically to a high temperature, an enclosure in which the pressure can be reduced to approximately a cathode-ray vacuum, and a rack for supporting the plate to be coated, quite simple apparatus can be utilized. The writer has obtained good surfaces, for use in a small interferometer, by making use of a liter flask into which was sealed temporarily a glass plug carrying the leads to the heating coil, the vacuum being obtained with an oil pump and a trap of outgassed charcoal. However, such devices are only temporary, and the laboratory in which much optical work is to be done should be provided with a more permanent equipment, such as is illustrated in Fig. 1.

A base plate of steel is mounted firmly on a stand, table, or rigid shelf. The base plate should be thick enough to withstand the force of atmospheric pressure on its lower surface, with a wide margin of safety. For a bell jar of 6 in. diameter the plate should be cold-rolled steel ½ in. thick, and thicker for larger jars. Through the plate are drilled a hole about 1 in. in diameter for evacuation and two or more holes about 3 in. apart for the terminals.

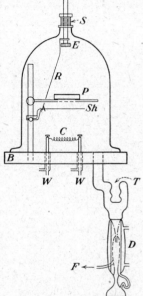

FIG. 1.—Evaporating apparatus. *B*, base plate; *WW*, water-cooled electrodes; *T*, liquid air or CO_2 trap; *D*, diffusion pump; *F*, to fore pump; *P*, plate to be coated; *Sh*, shield; *R*, glass rod for moving shield; *S*, sylphon; *E*, testing electrode; *C*, heating coil.

While two terminals are sufficient for most purposes, three permit the use of two heating coils which may be used for different metals. The terminals should be water-cooled so as to prevent overheating, a suggested design being shown in Fig. 2. Ordinary automobile spark plugs screwed into the base plate from above have been used in place of water-cooled terminals, but they are short-lived.

The bell jar should be of good quality and ground with emery on the base plate. The neck should preferably be of the type which can be fitted with a stopper. On this is fastened with some suitable cement such as deKhotinsky, sealing wax, shellac, or glyptal, a disk of brass with a rod extending through it, to act as a terminal for a high-voltage discharge from a spark coil. The base plate may serve as the other terminal. This discharge is useful for testing the vacuum.

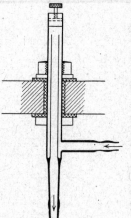

FIG. 2.

A very useful device, not absolutely necessary, is a sylphon about 2 in. long soldered to the lower side of the disk. This is then firmly sealed to the top of the jar. The rod which acts as the high-tension terminal is made quite long, and equipped on its lower end with a glass extension. The rod may then be flexed so as to explore, with the glass end, a considerable area inside the bell jar. The writer has used this device for steering a glass shield in and out between the heating coil and the surface to be coated.

Instead of a bell jar, a large cylinder of metal is sometimes used, with a heavy glass plate sealed on top. This plate may also be of metal, in which case one or more windows about 2 in. in diameter should be put in.

A stand S (Fig. 1) of convenient size is used inside the bell jar. On this may be mounted the mirror to be coated, suspended face down on a thin sheet of metal cut to size and shape.

The diffusion pump, preferably a three-stage type with a cooling trap T built into its upper end, as shown in Fig. 1, should be equipped at its upper end with a ½-in. flange to be sealed on the lower side of the base plate. It is absolutely essential that this pump be held rigidly. A convenient method is to make the base plate the top of a table, the four legs being ordinary water pipe about 1 in. in diameter. Large flanges fitted to the tops of these pipes may then be screwed directly to the base plate. The diffusion pump is then clamped in place to the legs with large laboratory clamps, and sealed to the base plate.

An ordinary Hyvac pump will serve as a fore pump. In case a diffusion pump cannot be obtained, one or more charcoal traps may be used to aid in the evacuation of the jar. This process is, however, slow and tedious, especially since it is sometimes necessary to make several trials for a desired coat.

The trap T in the top of the diffusion pump must be filled with a cooling solution or liquid air, to prevent mercury vapor from rising into the bell jar and contaminating the metal deposit. A satisfactory cooling solution is made by packing the trap with dry ice and slowly pouring ordinary commercial acetone over it. A small stopcock may be sealed to the upper part of the pump just below the flange to admit air to the jar.

The heating coil should be of tungsten for evaporating most metals. For a few with low boiling points, such as antimony, it may be of nickel. A suitable diameter for tungsten wire is 30 mils. It may be wound while red-hot into a helix to be mounted horizontally. The winding can be done on a steel rod about $\frac{1}{8}$ in. in diameter or slightly larger. Some have a preference for a cone-shaped helix to be mounted vertically, acting as a sort of pot into which the metal is placed. The exact form of the heating coil should be dictated by practical considerations and experience, as its form is not important for ordinary mirror coating.

There should be a large rheostat used in series with the heating coil, to control the current, and fuses inserted in the circuit for safety. The heating current may be 110 volts alternating current.

After the coil is made and clamped in place, it should be preheated in a high vacuum to get rid of the oxide on its surface. The sylphon attachment mentioned above is useful in this operation, as it eliminates opening the bell jar and pumping down again after loading the coil with metal. Always after the coil is heated, sufficient time should elapse for it to cool before admitting air, so that oxidation is avoided.

Aluminum is by far the best metal for mirror surfaces. It should be as pure as possible. Pure aluminum may be procured in pellet form which can be conveniently spaded into the coil. Some aluminum contains copper, which may be dissolved out with nitric acid. Some workers use pure aluminum wire which is fastened in small lengths to turns of the tungsten helix.

To render the apparatus airtight, the bell jar should be put in place and moved slightly to grind out any particles of dust which might adhere to its lower flange. Then, before pumping is started, the edge should be sealed with plasticine. A special plasticine in which apiezon oil is used is excellent, as the oil has a very low vapor pressure. For most work, however, ordinary plasticine will serve. Hot paraffine wax may also be used.

The high-tension test coil for testing the vacuum may be an ordinary ½-kva. transformer, with a rating of about 10,000 volts across the secondary. A satisfactory vacuum for evaporation is reached when no discharge is possible between the upper terminal and the base plate. When this vacuum is attained, turn on the heating current slowly, making sure the cooling water is flowing through the terminals.

A suitable deposit is a matter of experience.

3. Deposition by Cathodic Sputtering.—The same bell jar as for evaporation may be used, except that to the electrode at the top of the bell jar should be attached firmly a disk of the metal to be sputtered. The disk should be slightly larger than the metal to be sputtered. This disk is to be the cathode of a high-tension discharge. A suitable source is the ½-kva. transformer mentioned in Sec. 2 above, but in this case the second terminal in the apparatus must either be a small point shielded from the mirror surface or it must be removed as far as possible from the mirror surface. This may be accomplished by having a side tube of about 1 in. diameter sealed to the tube connecting the base plate and the diffusion pump, just below the flange. This side tube should be about 6 in. long and have an aluminum electrode sealed into the end of it.

Sputtering must be done with a higher pressure than evaporation. This pressure may be calibrated roughly by the width of the cathode dark space, which grows as the pressure drops. A dark space of about 3 cm. indicates a satisfactory pressure. The mirror to be coated should be mounted face up, below the cathode, and just inside the cathode dark space.

Aluminum does not sputter well. Silver may be used successfully, and is by far the best metal if this method of deposition is to be used. The exact amount of deposit for a suitable mirror is a matter of experience. Sputtering is found to be most successful in an atmosphere of some rare gas, such as helium, argon, or neon.

Additional details of cathodic sputtering and evaporation may be found in the following articles:

"Making of Mirrors by the Deposition of Metal on Glass," *Bureau of Standards Circular* 389, 1931 (chemical deposition and cathodic sputtering).

Jones, E. G., and E. W. Foster, "Production of Silver Mirrors by Kathodic Sputtering," *Journal of Scientific Instruments (London)*, **13,** 216, 1936.

Williams, R. C., and G. B. Sabine, "Evaporated Films for Large Mirrors," *Astrophysical Journal*, **77,** 316, 1933.

Strong, John, "Aluminizing of Large Telescope Mirrors," *Astrophysical Journal*, **83,** 401, 1936 (evaporation).

APPENDIX VI

MAKING CROSS HAIRS

One of the time-honored methods of making cross hairs is to fasten spider-web strands, silk fibers, or similar filaments on a metal holder with fast-drying cement, such as shellac. Another method, especially useful where two or more lines close together and parallel are desired, is to rule them with a diamond on a glass disk. Both of these methods involve a considerable amount of technical skill, and the second requires

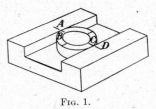

Fig. 1.

apparatus which is often beyond the means of the laboratory. Recently it has been discovered that filaments spun of some quick-drying cement make excellent cross hairs.

A small drop of fresh Duco is squeezed on the end of a match stick or pencil, touched immediately to one side of the holder, and drawn into a fine filament which is laid across the other side of the holder so that it sticks there. Since this often results in a filament which does not have a uniform diameter in the field of view of the telescope, the following modification is recommended: Make out of wood or metal a small frame as shown in Fig. 1, in which the holder is held securely, with the surface on which the cross hairs are to be mounted slightly above the upper surface of the frame. The fresh Duco is touched at A, drawn quickly to a filament which is lowered to points B and C on the holder, and fastened at D. Then a small drop of Duco is laid on the filament at B and C to anchor it securely. The Duco must be quite fresh or it will not spin properly. With a little practice, extremely fine cross hairs can be made in this manner. It is recommended that the entire operation be carried on under a hand magnifier or equivalent lens mounted in position above the frame.

APPENDIX VII

STANDARD SOURCES FOR COLORIMETRY[1]

It is recommended that three illuminants A, B, and C as described below, be adopted as standards for the general colorimetry of materials.

A. A gas-filled lamp operated at a color temperature of 2848°K.

B. The same lamp used in combination with a filter consisting of a layer, 1 cm. thick of each of two solutions B_1 and B_2, contained in a double cell made of colorless optical glass. The solutions are to be made up as follows:

Solution B_1:

Copper sulphate ($CuSO_4.5H_2O$)............	2.452 grams
Mannite [$C_6H_8(OH)_6$].....................	2.452 grams
Pyridine (C_5H_5N).......................	30.0 c.c.
Water (distilled) to make.................	1000.0 c.c.

Solution B_2:

Cobalt ammonium sulphate [$CoSO_4.(NH_4)_2SO_4.6H_2O$]...............	21.71 grams
Copper sulphate ($CuSO_4.5H_2O$)............	16.11 grams
Sulphuric acid (sp. gr. 1.835).............	10.0 c.c.
Water (distilled) to make.................	1000.0 c.c.

C. The same lamp used in combination with a filter consisting of a layer, 1 cm. thick of each of two solutions C_1 and C_2, contained in a double cell made of colorless optical glass. The solutions are to be made up as follows:

[1] Taken from T. SMITH and J. GUILD, "The C.I.E. Colorimetric Standards and Their Use," *Transactions of the Optical Society, London*, **33**, 73, 1931–1932.

Solution C_1:

  Copper sulphate ($CuSO_4.5H_2O$)............ 3.412 grams
  Mannite [$C_6H_8(OH)_6$].................... 3.412 grams
  Pyridine (C_5H_5N)....................... 30.0 c.c.
  Water (distilled) to make................ 1000.0 c.c.

Solution C_2:

  Cobalt ammonium sulphate
   [$CoSO_4.(NH_4)_2SO_4.6H_2O$]............... 30.580 grams
  Copper sulphate ($CuSO_4.5H_2O$)........... 22.520 grams
  Sulphuric acid (sp. gr. 1.835)............ 10.0 c.c.
  Water (distilled) to make................ 1000.0 c.c.

It is also recommended that the following spectral-energy distribution values for each of these illuminants shall be used in computation of colorimetric quantities from spectrophotometric measurements.

Source A. The spectral distribution of energy from this source may be taken for all colorimetric purposes to be that of a black body at a temperature of 2848°K. The value assumed for Planck's constant c_2 is 14,350 micron-deg.

SPECTRAL DISTRIBUTION OF ENERGY; SOURCES B AND C

Wave-length, angstroms	Relative energy		Wave-length, angstroms	Relative energy	
	B	C		B	C
3700	15.2	21.6	5500	101.0	105.2
3800	22.4	33.0	5600	102.8	105.3
3900	31.3	47.4	5700	102.6	102.3
4000	41.3	63.3	5800	101.0	97.8
4100	52.1	80.6	5900	99.2	93.2
4200	63.2	98.1	6000	98.0	89.7
4300	73.1	112.4	6100	98.5	88.4
4400	80.8	121.5	6200	99.7	88.1
4500	85.4	124.0	6300	101.0	88.0
4600	88.3	123.1	6400	102.2	87.8
4700	92.0	123.8	6500	103.9	88.2
4800	95.2	123.9	6600	105.0	87.9
4900	96.5	120.7	6700	104.9	86.3
5000	94.2	112.1	6800	103.9	84.0
5100	90.7	102.3	6900	101.6	80.2
5200	89.5	96.9	7000	99.1	76.3
5300	92.2	98.0	7100	96.2	72.4
5400	96.9	102.1	7200	92.9	68.3

Sources B and C. The spectral distributions of energies for these sources, as computed from the spectrophotometric measurements of the transmission of the filters made by Messrs. Davis and Gibson of the Bureau of Standards, are tabulated on p. 437.

APPENDIX VIII

THE FRESNEL INTEGRALS

In Sec. **12-6** a vector-polygon method has been described by which the amplitude of the distribution due to any part of a

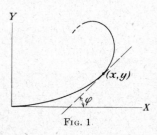

FIG. 1

light wave may be evaluated. When the separate elements of the disturbance are taken small enough, the vectors representing them become a curve which for an unobstructed wave front is the Cornu spiral (Fig. 12-9) of which a drawing to scale is included in this appendix. Cornu originally constructed this spiral by plotting the values of Fresnel's integrals, which may be derived in the following manner:

Consider such a curve (Fig. 1) representing the summation of a number of elements of amplitude of a wave disturbance. Let x and y be the coordinates of an element of disturbance dS. Then the angle ϕ between the x-axis and the tangent to the curve is the phase of the element dS. We may write

$$\cos \phi = \frac{dx}{dS}, \qquad \sin \phi = \frac{dy}{dS},$$
$$x = \int \cos \phi \, dS, \qquad y = \int \sin \phi \, dS. \qquad (1)$$

It is now necessary to evaluate ϕ and dS in terms of an actual wave front. For this purpose we may consider a cylindrical wave front W originating at a line source L (Fig. 2), perpendicular to the paper. It is required to find the intensity at a point O on the screen. By the cosine law, and substituting for θ its approximate value s/a,

$$c^2 = (a + b)^2 + a^2 - 2a(a + b) \cos \frac{s}{a},$$

or

$$c^2 = b^2 + \frac{a+b}{a}s^2, \quad \text{approximately,}$$

or

$$c - b = \frac{a+b}{2ab}s^2. \tag{2}$$

This is sufficiently accurate when θ is small.

The difference of phase between the disturbance at O due to its pole and that due to dW is measured by $(c-b)/\lambda$, so that, if the first is given by $\sin 2\pi t/T$, the second is given by

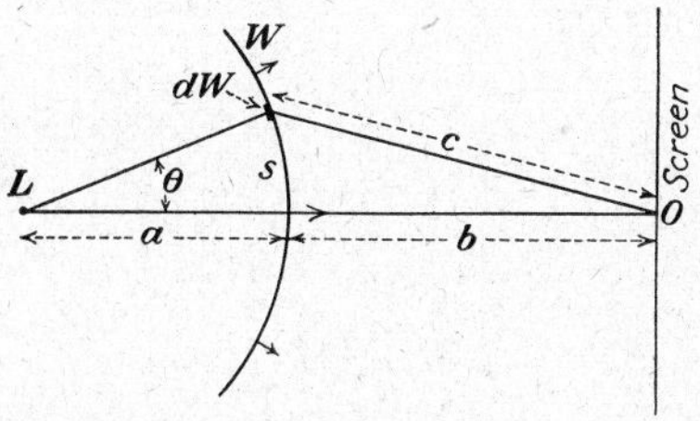

$$\sin 2\pi\left(\frac{t}{T} - \frac{c-b}{\lambda}\right)dW$$

Fig. 2.

and the entire disturbance due to all the elements by

$$D = \int \sin 2\pi\left(\frac{t}{T} - \frac{c-b}{\lambda}\right)dW. \tag{3}$$

The integral is taken between limits appropriate to the particular case.

The amplitude contributed to O by an element of the wave front dW is proportional to its area, inversely proportional to the distance c from dW, and depends also on the obliquity of the wave front. If we neglect these considerations and assume merely that the amplitude due to any element is proportional to the length of the element, then we may identify dW in eq. 3 as dS in eqs. 1. Similarly the phase angle ϕ may be related to the path difference $(c-b)$, for $\phi = \frac{2\pi}{\lambda}(c-b)$, so that by eq. 2

$$\phi = \pi\frac{(a+b)s^2}{ab\lambda}.$$

Substituting v^2 for $(a+b)s^2/ab\lambda$, we may now write the expression for the intensity I due to the wave front in terms of the x and y coordinates given in eqs. 1:

$$I = x^2 + y^2 = \frac{ab\lambda}{a+b}\left[\left(\int \cos\frac{\pi v^2}{2}dv\right)^2 + \left(\int \sin\frac{\pi v^2}{2}dv\right)^2\right]. \tag{4}$$

The integrals in eq. 4 are known as *Fresnel's integrals*. They have been evaluated by Gilbert,[1] and appear in the following table.

TABLE OF FRESNEL'S INTEGRALS

v_1	$\int_0^{v_1} \cos \frac{\pi v^2}{2} dv$	$\int_0^{v_1} \sin \frac{\pi v^2}{2} dv$	v_1	$\int_0^{v_1} \cos \frac{\pi v^2}{2} dv$	$\int_0^{v_1} \sin \frac{\pi v^2}{2} dv$
0.0	0.0000	0.0000	2.6	0.3889	0.5500
0.1	0.1000	0.0005	2.7	0.3926	0.4529
0.2	0.1999	0.0042	2.8	0.4675	0.3915
0.3	0.2994	0.0141	2.9	0.5624	0.4102
0.4	0.3975	0.0334	3.0	0.6057	0.4963
0.5	0.4923	0.0647	3.1	0.5616	0.5818
0.6	0.5811	0.1105	3.2	0.4663	0.5933
0.7	0.6597	0.1721	3.3	0.4057	0.5193
0.8	0.7230	0.2493	3.4	0.4385	0.4297
0.9	0.7648	0.3398	3.5	0.5326	0.4153
1.0	0.7799	0.4383	3.6	0.5880	0.4923
1.1	0.7638	0.5365	3.7	0.5419	0.5750
1.2	0.7154	0.6234	3.8	0.4481	0.5656
1.3	0.6386	0.6863	3.9	0.4223	0.4752
1.4	0.5431	0.7135	4.0	0.4984	0.4205
1.5	0.4453	0.6975	4.1	0.5737	0.4758
1.6	0.3655	0.6383	4.2	0.5417	0.5632
1.7	0.3238	0.5492	4.3	0.4494	0.5540
1.8	0.3337	0.4509	4.4	0.4383	0.4623
1.9	0.3945	0.3734	4.5	0.5258	0.4342
2.0	0.4883	0.3434	4.6	0.5672	0.5162
2.1	0.5814	0.3743	4.7	0.4914	0.5669
2.2	0.6362	0.4556	4.8	0.4338	0.4968
2.3	0.6268	0.5525	4.9	0.5002	0.4351
2.4	0.5550	0.6197	5.0	0.5636	0.4992
2.5	0.4574	0.6192	∞	0.5000	0.5000

From these values the Cornu spiral shown in Fig. 3 was plotted on a large scale and reduced photographically.

The assumptions made in this derivation, that θ is small, and that dW is proportional to the length of the element, are tantamount to the assumption that the effective portion of the cylindrical wave front is really confined to a very small area about the pole of any point O under consideration.

[1] GILBERT, PHILIPPE, *Académie Royale de Belgique*, **31**, 1, 1863. Corrections have been made to his values of the cosine term for v_1 equal to 0.1 and 1.8.

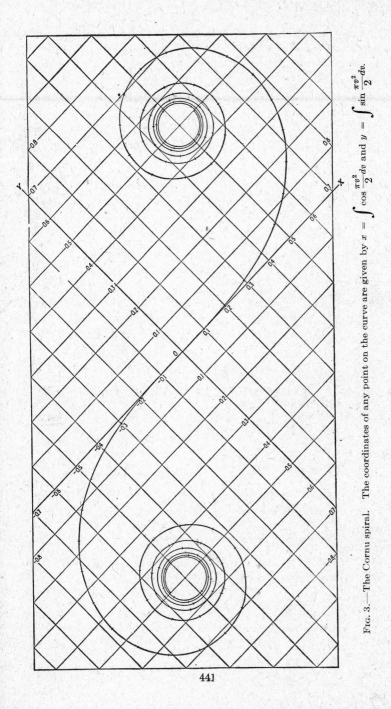

Fig. 3.—The Cornu spiral. The coordinates of any point on the curve are given by $x = \int \cos \frac{\pi v^2}{2} dv$ and $y = \int \sin \frac{\pi v^2}{2} dv$.

TABLES OF USEFUL DATA

TABLE I.—USEFUL WAVE-LENGTHS

The wave-lengths listed are principally those of lines which may be obtained with discharge tubes of helium, hydrogen, neon, mercury; with the mercury arc, or in the spectrum of the sun. Only the stronger lines due to these sources are listed. There are a few, such as the cadmium lines, which may be obtained with an ordinary mercury arc containing an amalgam of mercury and the other metals desired. The values given are in angstroms (1 angstrom = 10^{-8} cm.).

In any particular source there may appear lines fainter than those listed, or lines due to impurities. If the wave-lengths of such lines are measured, they may usually be identified by consulting H. Kayser, "Tabelle der Hauptlinien der Linienspektra aller Elemente," published by Julius Springer, or Twyman and Smith, "Wave-length Tables for Spectrum Analysis," published by Adam Hilger, Ltd. An extensive table of wave-lengths is also included in the more recent editions of the "Handbook of Chemistry and Physics," published by the Chemical Rubber Publishing Co.

Hydrogen

6562.8	H_α
4861.3	H_β
4340.5	H_γ
4101.7	H_δ
3970.1	H_ϵ
3889.0	H_ζ

Helium

7065.2
6678.1
5875.6
5047.7
5015.7
4921.9
4713.1
4471.5
4437.5
4387.9
4143.8
4120.8
4026.2
3964.7
3888.6

Neon

6929.5
6717.0
6678.3
6599.0
6532.9

6506.5
6402.2
6383.0
6334.4
6304.8
6266.5
6217.3
6163.6
6143.1
6096.2
6074.3
6030.0
5975.5
5944.8
5881.9
5852.5
5820.2
5764.4
5400.6
5341.1
5330.8

Mercury

6234.3
6123.5
6072.6
5790.66
5769.60
5460.7
4916.0

4339.2
4347.5
4358.3
4077.8
4046.8
4046.6

Fraunhofer Lines

B	6870.0	O_2
C	6562.8	H
D_2	5895.93	Na
D_1	5889.96	Na
E	5270.1	FeCa
F	4861.3	H
G'	4340.5	H[1]
H	3968.5	Ca II
K	3933.7	Ca II

Miscellaneous

6707.9	Li
6438.5	Cd
6103.6	Li
5895.93	Na
5889.96	Na
5535.5	Ba
5085.8	Cd
4799.9	Cd
4678.2	Cd
3968.5	Ca II
3933.7	Ca II

[1] If the solar spectrum is used, with small dispersion, a wide absorption line also will be seen owing to a blend of Fe and Ca lines, with a mean wave-length of 4307.8 angstroms.

TABLE II.—INDICES OF REFRACTION OF SOME COMMON SUBSTANCES

a. Glasses and Optically Isotropic Substances.—In specifying glass, the manufacturer usually gives n_D, the index for the sodium lines, and also the value of $\nu = (n_D - 1)/(n_F - n_C)$, the indices for several other lines of common sources, and the differences between these and a number of other lines. From these data a dispersion curve may be drawn. In the following table of representative glasses, the indices are given at intervals of 500 angstroms from 4000 to 7500 angstroms, from which the index for any other line may be obtained with an accuracy sufficient for the experiments and problems in this book. For more precise information for a given specimen of glass the manufacturer should be consulted. Detailed information concerning many glasses is to be found in the International Critical Tables.

Wave-length, angstroms	Light crown	Dense crown	Light flint	Dense flint	Heavy flint	Fused quartz	Fluor-ite
4000	1.5238	1.5854	1.5932	1.6912	1.8059	1.4699	1.4421
4500	1.5180	1.5801	1.5853	1.6771	1.7843	1.4655	1.4390
5000	1.5139	1.5751	1.5796	1.6670	1.7706	1.4624	1.4366
5500	1.5108	1.5732	1.5757	1.6591	1.7611	1.4599	1.4350
6000	1.5085	1.5679	1.5728	1.6542	1.7539	1.4581	1.4336
6500	1.5067	1.5651	1.5703	1.6503	1.7485	1.4566	1.4324
7000	1.5051	1.5640	1.5684	1.6473	1.7435	1.4553	1.4318
7500	1.5040	1.5625	1.5668	1.6450	1.7389	1.4542	1.4311

b. Liquids.

Substance	Temperature, °C.	Index with respect to air for D-lines
Water	20	1.3330
Acetone	20	1.359
Ammonia ($d = 0.615$) liquid	16.5	1.325
Benzene	20	1.501
Bromine	20	1.654
Carbon disulphide	18	1.6255
Carbon dioxide	15	1.195
Chloroform	20	1.446
Ethyl ether	22	1.351
Ethyl alcohol	20	1.3605
Glycerin	20	1.474
Methyl alcohol	20	1.329
Toluene	20	1.495

c. The index of refraction of *air* at 0°C. and 760 mm. Hg pressure with respect to a vacuum is 1.0002926.

d. Some Uniaxial Crystals.

Substance	Index for the *D* lines	
	Ordinary ray	Extraordinary ray
Calcite.....................	1.658	1.486
Ice........................	1.3091	1.3104
Quartz.....................	1.54424	1.55335
Tourmaline.................	1.669	1.638
Sodium nitrate.............	1.5874	1.3361
Zircon.....................	1.923	1.968

TABLE III.—REFLECTING POWERS OF SOME METALS

Since the measured reflecting power varies widely with the origin of the surface and its age, these factors should be taken into account in using the figures given below. The values given for silver, aluminum, and gold are compiled from graphical data in an article on the evaporating process by John Strong in *Astrophysical Journal*, **83**, 401, 1936, and are for freshly evaporated opaque coatings. Experience shows that for the visible region the reflecting power of silver diminishes between 15 and 20 per cent in two or three weeks' time. The values for platinum, copper, steel, monel, and speculum are for polished massive metals. In general these have less reflecting power than the evaporated coats of the same metals. Additional data may be found in the International Critical Tables.

λ, angstroms	Percentage reflection of normally incident light							
	Silver	Aluminum	Platinum	Speculum	Steel	Monel	Gold	Copper
2500	34*	80	33	29	33	..	39*	26
3000	9*	85	39	40	37	..	32*	25
3500	74	87	43	51	44	..	28	27
4000	89	89	48	55	50	..	28	31
4500	93	90	55	60	54	56	33	37
5000	95	90	58	63	55	58	47	44
5500	95	89	61	64	55	59	74	48
6000	95	89	64	64	55	60	84	72
6500	96	87	66	65	56	62	89	80
7000	97	87	69	69	57	64	92	83
7500	97	86	69	69	58	66	93	86
8000	97	85	70	70	58	67	95	89

* From other sources than those indicated above.

TABLE IV.—FOUR-PLACE LOGARITHMIC TABLES

	Logarithms										Mean Differences								
	0	1	2	3	4	5	6	7	8	9	1 2 3			4 5 6			7 8 9		
10	0000	0043	0086	0128	0170	0212	0253	0294	0334	0374	4 8 12			17 21 25			29 33 37		
11	0414	0453	0492	0531	0569	0607	0645	0682	0719	0755	4 8 11			15 19 23			26 30 34		
12	0792	0828	0864	0899	0934	0969	1004	1038	1072	1106	3 7 10			14 17 21			24 28 31		
13	1139	1173	1206	1239	1271	1303	1335	1367	1399	1430	3 6 10			13 16 19			23 26 29		
14	1461	1492	1523	1553	1584	1614	1644	1673	1703	1732	3 6 9			12 15 18			21 24 27		
15	1761	1790	1818	1847	1875	1903	1931	1959	1987	2014	3 6 8			11 14 17			20 22 25		
16	2041	2068	2095	2122	2148	2175	2201	2227	2253	2279	3 5 8			11 13 16			18 21 24		
17	2304	2330	2355	2380	2405	2430	2455	2480	2504	2529	2 5 7			10 12 15			17 20 22		
18	2553	2577	2601	2625	2648	2672	2695	2718	2742	2765	2 5 7			9 12 14			16 19 21		
19	2788	2810	2833	2856	2878	2900	2923	2945	2967	2989	2 4 7			9 11 13			16 18 20		
20	3010	3032	3054	3075	3096	3118	3139	3160	3181	3201	2 4 6			8 11 13			15 17 19		
21	3222	3243	3263	3284	3304	3324	3345	3365	3385	3404	2 4 6			8 10 12			14 16 18		
22	3424	3444	3464	3483	3502	3522	3541	3560	3579	3598	2 4 6			8 10 12			14 15 17		
23	3617	3636	3655	3674	3692	3711	3729	3747	3766	3784	2 4 6			7 9 11			13 15 17		
24	3802	3820	3838	3856	3874	3892	3909	3927	3945	3962	2 4 5			7 9 11			12 14 16		
25	3979	3997	4014	4031	4048	4065	4082	4099	4116	4133	2 3 5			7 9 10			12 14 15		
26	4150	4166	4183	4200	4216	4232	4249	4265	4281	4298	2 3 5			7 8 10			11 13 15		
27	4314	4330	4346	4362	4378	4393	4409	4425	4440	4456	2 3 5			6 8 9			11 13 14		
28	4472	4487	4502	4518	4533	4548	4564	4579	4594	4609	2 3 5			6 8 9			11 12 14		
29	4624	4639	4654	4669	4683	4698	4713	4728	4742	4757	1 3 4			6 7 9			10 12 13		
30	4771	4786	4800	4814	4829	4843	4857	4871	4886	4900	1 3 4			6 7 9			10 11 13		
31	4914	4928	4942	4955	4969	4983	4997	5011	5024	5038	1 3 4			6 7 8			10 11 12		
32	5051	5065	5079	5092	5105	5119	5132	5145	5159	5172	1 3 4			5 7 8			9 11 12		
33	5185	5198	5211	5224	5237	5250	5263	5276	5289	5302	1 3 4			5 6 8			9 10 12		
34	5315	5328	5340	5353	5366	5378	5391	5403	5416	5428	1 3 4			5 6 8			9 10 11		
35	5441	5453	5465	5478	5490	5502	5514	5527	5539	5551	1 2 4			5 6 7			9 10 11		
36	5563	5575	5587	5599	5611	5623	5635	5647	5658	5670	1 2 4			5 6 7			8 10 11		
37	5682	5694	5705	5717	5729	5740	5752	5763	5775	5786	1 2 3			5 6 7			8 9 10		
38	5798	5809	5821	5832	5843	5855	5866	5877	5888	5899	1 2 3			5 6 7			8 9 10		
39	5911	5922	5933	5944	5955	5966	5977	5988	5999	6010	1 2 3			4 5 7			8 9 10		
40	6021	6031	6042	6053	6064	6075	6085	6096	6107	6117	1 2 3			4 5 6			8 9 10		
41	6128	6138	6149	6160	6170	6180	6191	6201	6212	6222	1 2 3			4 5 6			7 8 9		
42	6232	6243	6253	6263	6274	6284	6294	6304	6314	6325	1 2 3			4 5 6			7 8 9		
43	6335	6345	6355	6365	6375	6385	6395	6405	6415	6425	1 2 3			4 5 6			7 8 9		
44	6435	6444	6454	6464	6474	6484	6493	6503	6513	6522	1 2 3			4 5 6			7 8 9		
45	6532	6542	6551	6561	6571	6580	6590	6599	6609	6618	1 2 3			4 5 6			7 8 9		
46	6628	6637	6646	6656	6665	6675	6684	6693	6702	6712	1 2 3			4 5 6			7 7 8		
47	6721	6730	6739	6749	6758	6767	6776	6785	6794	6803	1 2 3			4 5 5			6 7 8		
48	6812	6821	6830	6839	6848	6857	6866	6875	6884	6893	1 2 3			4 4 5			6 7 8		
49	6902	6911	6920	6928	6937	6946	6955	6964	6972	6981	1 2 3			4 4 5			6 7 8		
50	6990	6998	7007	7016	7024	7033	7042	7050	7059	7067	1 2 3			3 4 5			6 7 8		
51	7076	7084	7093	7101	7110	7118	7126	7135	7143	7152	1 2 3			3 4 5			6 7 8		
52	7160	7168	7177	7185	7193	7202	7210	7218	7226	7235	1 2 2			3 4 5			6 7 7		
53	7243	7251	7259	7267	7275	7284	7292	7300	7308	7316	1 2 2			3 4 5			6 6 7		
54	7324	7332	7340	7348	7356	7364	7372	7380	7388	7396	1 2 2			3 4 5			6 6 7		
	0	1	2	3	4	5	6	7	8	9	1 2 3			4 5 6			7 8 9		

TABLE IV.—FOUR-PLACE LOGARITHMIC TABLES.—(Continued)

	0	1	2	3	4	5	6	7	8	9	1	2	3	4	5	6	7	8	9
55	7404	7412	7419	7427	7435	7443	7451	7459	7466	7474	1	2	2	3	4	5	5	6	7
56	7482	7490	7497	7505	7513	7520	7528	7536	7543	7551	1	2	2	3	4	5	5	6	7
57	7559	7566	7574	7582	7589	7597	7604	7612	7619	7627	1	2	2	3	4	5	5	6	7
58	7634	7642	7649	7657	7664	7672	7679	7686	7694	7701	1	1	2	3	4	4	5	6	7
59	7709	7716	7723	7731	7738	7745	7752	7760	7767	7774	1	1	2	3	4	4	5	6	7
60	7782	7789	7796	7803	7810	7818	7825	7832	7839	7846	1	1	2	3	4	4	5	6	6
61	7853	7860	7868	7875	7882	7889	7896	7903	7910	7917	1	1	2	3	4	4	5	6	6
62	7924	7931	7938	7945	7952	7959	7966	7973	7980	7987	1	1	2	3	3	4	5	6	6
63	7993	8000	8007	8014	8021	8028	8035	8041	8048	8055	1	1	2	3	3	4	5	5	6
64	8062	8069	8075	8082	8089	8096	8102	8109	8116	8122	1	1	2	3	3	4	5	5	6
65	8129	8136	8142	8149	8156	8162	8169	8176	8182	8189	1	1	2	3	3	4	5	5	6
66	8195	8202	8209	8215	8222	8228	8235	8241	8248	8254	1	1	2	3	3	4	5	5	6
67	8261	8267	8274	8280	8287	8293	8299	8306	8312	8319	1	1	2	3	3	4	5	5	6
68	8325	8331	8338	8344	8351	8357	8363	8370	8376	8382	1	1	2	3	3	4	4	5	6
69	8388	8395	8401	8407	8414	8420	8426	8432	8439	8445	1	1	2	2	3	4	4	5	6
70	8451	8457	8463	8470	8476	8482	8488	8494	8500	8506	1	1	2	2	3	4	4	5	6
71	8513	8519	8525	8531	8537	8543	8549	8555	8561	8567	1	1	2	2	3	4	4	5	5
72	8573	8579	8585	8591	8597	8603	8609	8615	8621	8627	1	1	2	2	3	4	4	5	5
73	8633	8639	8645	8651	8657	8663	8669	8675	8681	8686	1	1	2	2	3	4	4	5	5
74	8692	8698	8704	8710	8716	8722	8727	8733	8739	8745	1	1	2	2	3	4	4	5	5
75	8751	8756	8762	8768	8774	8779	8785	8791	8797	8802	1	1	2	2	3	3	4	5	5
76	8808	8814	8820	8825	8831	8837	8842	8848	8854	8859	1	1	2	2	3	3	4	5	5
77	8865	8871	8876	8882	8887	8893	8899	8904	8910	8915	1	1	2	2	3	3	4	4	5
78	8921	8927	8932	8938	8943	8949	8954	8960	8965	8971	1	1	2	2	3	3	4	4	5
79	8976	8982	8987	8993	8998	9004	9009	9015	9020	9025	1	1	2	2	3	3	4	4	5
80	9031	9036	9042	9047	9053	9058	9063	9069	9074	9079	1	1	2	2	3	3	4	4	5
81	9085	9090	9096	9101	9106	9112	9117	9122	9128	9133	1	1	2	2	3	3	4	4	5
82	9138	9143	9149	9154	9159	9165	9170	9175	9180	9186	1	1	2	2	3	3	4	4	5
83	9191	9196	9201	9206	9212	9217	9222	9227	9232	9238	1	1	2	2	3	3	4	4	5
84	9243	9248	9253	9258	9263	9269	9274	9279	9284	9289	1	1	2	2	3	3	4	4	5
85	9294	9299	9304	9309	9315	9320	9325	9330	9335	9340	1	1	2	2	3	3	4	4	5
86	9345	9350	9355	9360	9365	9370	9375	9380	9385	9390	1	1	2	2	3	3	4	4	.5
87	9395	9400	9405	9410	9415	9420	9425	9430	9435	9440	0	1	1	2	2	3	3	4	4
88	9445	9450	9455	9460	9465	9469	9474	9479	9484	9489	0	1	1	2	2	3	3	4	4
89	9494	9499	9504	9509	9513	9518	9523	9528	9533	9538	0	1	1	2	2	3	3	4	4
90	9542	9547	9552	9557	9562	9566	9571	9576	9581	9586	0	1	1	2	2	3	3	4	4
91	9590	9595	9600	9605	9609	9614	9619	9624	9628	9633	0	1	1	2	2	3	3	4	4
92	9638	9643	9647	9652	9657	9661	9666	9671	9675	9680	0	1	1	2	2	3	3	4	4
93	9685	9689	9694	9699	9703	9708	9713	9717	9722	9727	0	1	1	2	2	3	3	4	4
94	9731	9736	9741	9745	9750	9754	9759	7763	9768	9773	0	1	1	2	2	3	3	4	4
95	9777	9782	9786	9791	9795	9800	9805	9809	9814	9818	0	1	1	2	2	3	3	4	4
96	9823	9827	9832	9836	9841	9845	9850	9854	9859	9863	0	1	1	2	2	3	3	4	4
97	9868	9872	9877	9881	9886	9890	9894	9899	9903	9908	0	1	1	2	2	3	3	4	4
98	9912	9917	9921	9926	9930	9934	9939	9943	9948	9952	0	1	1	2	2	3	3	4	4
99	9956	9961	9965	9969	9974	9978	9983	9987	9991	9996	0	1	1	2	2	3	3	3	4
	0	1	2	3	4	5	6	7	8	9	1	2	3	4	5	6	7	8	9

TABLE V.—TRIGONOMETRIC FUNCTIONS

Natural Sines 0°–45°

°	0′	10′	20′	30′	40′	50′		°	1′	2′	3′	4′	5′	6′	7′	8′	9′
0	.0000	.0029	.0058	.0087	.0116	.0145	.0175	89	3	6	9	12	14	17	20	23	26
1	.0175	.0204	.0233	.0262	.0291	.0320	.0349	88	3	6	9	12	14	17	20	23	26
2	.0349	.0378	.0407	.0436	.0465	.0494	.0523	87	3	6	9	12	14	17	20	23	26
3	.0523	.0552	.0581	.0610	.0640	.0669	.0698	86	3	6	9	12	14	17	20	23	26
4	.0698	.0727	.0756	.0785	.0814	.0843	.0872	85	3	6	9	12	14	17	20	23	26
5	.0872	.0901	.0929	.0958	.0987	.1016	.1045	84	3	6	9	12	14	17	20	23	26
6	.1045	.1074	.1103	.1132	.1161	.1190	.1219	83	3	6	9	12	14	17	20	23	26
7	.1219	.1248	.1276	.1305	.1334	.1363	.1392	82	3	6	9	12	14	17	20	23	26
8	.1392	.1421	.1449	.1478	.1507	.1536	.1564	81	3	6	9	12	14	17	20	23	26
9	.1564	.1593	.1622	.1650	.1679	.1708	.1736	80	3	6	9	12	14	17	20	23	26
10	.1736	.1765	.1794	.1822	.1851	.1880	.1908	79	3	6	9	12	14	17	20	23	26
11	.1908	.1937	.1965	.1994	.2022	.2051	.2079	78	3	6	8	11	14	17	20	22	25
12	.2079	.2108	.2136	.2164	.2193	.2221	.2250	77	3	6	8	11	14	17	20	22	25
13	.2250	.2278	.2306	.2334	.2363	.2391	.2419	76	3	6	8	11	14	17	20	22	25
14	.2419	.2447	.2476	.2504	.2532	.2560	.2588	75	3	6	8	11	14	17	20	22	25
15	.2588	.2616	.2644	.2672	.2700	.2728	.2756	74	3	6	8	11	14	17	20	22	25
16	.2756	.2784	.2812	.2840	.2868	.2896	.2924	73	3	6	8	11	14	17	20	22	25
17	.2924	.2952	.2979	.3007	.3035	.3062	.3090	72	3	6	8	11	14	17	20	22	25
18	.3090	.3118	.3145	.3173	.3201	.3228	.3256	71	3	6	8	11	14	17	20	22	25
19	.3256	.3283	.3311	.3338	.3365	.3393	.3420	70	3	5	8	11	14	16	19	22	24
20	.3420	.3448	.3475	.3502	.3529	.3557	.3584	69	3	5	8	11	14	16	19	22	24
21	.3584	.3611	.3638	.3665	.3692	.3719	.3746	68	3	5	8	11	14	16	19	22	24
22	.3746	.3773	.3800	.3827	.3854	.3881	.3907	67	3	5	8	11	14	16	19	22	24
23	.3907	.3934	.3961	.3987	.4014	.4041	.4067	66	3	5	8	11	14	16	19	22	24
24	.4067	.4094	.4120	.4147	.4173	.4200	.4226	65	3	5	8	11	14	16	19	22	24
25	.4226	.4253	.4279	.4305	.4331	.4358	.4384	64	3	5	8	10	13	16	18	21	23
26	.4384	.4410	.4436	.4462	.4488	.4514	.4540	63	3	5	8	10	13	16	18	21	23
27	.4540	.4566	.4592	.4617	.4643	.4669	.4695	62	3	5	8	10	13	16	18	21	23
28	.4695	.4720	.4746	.4772	.4797	.4823	.4848	61	3	5	8	10	13	16	18	21	23
29	.4848	.4874	.4899	.4924	.4950	.4975	.5000	60	3	5	8	10	13	15	18	20	23
30	.5000	.5025	.5050	.5075	.5100	.5125	.5150	59	3	5	8	10	13	15	18	20	23
31	.5150	.5175	.5200	.5225	.5250	.5275	.5299	58	3	5	8	10	13	15	18	20	23
33	.5299	.5324	.5348	.5373	.5398	.5422	.5446	57	3	5	8	10	13	15	18	20	23
32	.5446	.5471	.5495	.5519	.5544	.5568	.5592	56	3	5	7	10	12	14	17	19	22
34	.5592	.5616	.5640	.5664	.5688	.5712	.5736	55	3	5	7	10	12	14	17	19	22
35	.5736	.5760	.5783	.5807	.5831	.5854	.5878	54	2	5	7	10	12	14	17	19	22
36	.5878	.5901	.5925	.5948	.5972	.5995	.6018	53	2	5	7	9	12	14	16	18	21
37	.6018	.6041	.6065	.6088	.6111	.6134	.6157	52	2	5	7	9	12	14	16	18	21
38	.6157	.6180	.6202	.6225	.6248	.6271	.6293	51	2	5	7	9	12	14	16	18	21
39	.6293	.6316	.6338	.6361	.6383	.6406	.6428	50	2	4	7	9	11	13	15	18	20
40	.6428	.6450	.6472	.6494	.6517	.6539	.6561	49	2	4	7	9	11	13	15	18	20
41	.6561	.6583	.6604	.6626	.6648	.6670	.6691	48	2	4	7	9	11	13	15	18	20
42	.6691	.6713	.6734	.6756	.6777	.6799	.6820	47	2	4	6	9	11	13	15	17	19
43	.6820	.6841	.6862	.6884	.6905	.6926	.6947	46	2	4	6	8	11	13	15	17	19
44	.6947	.6967	.6988	.7009	.7030	.7050	.7071	45	2	4	6	8	11	13	15	17	19
°		50′	40′	30′	20′	10′	0′	°	1′	2′	3′	4′	5′	6′	7′	8′	9′

Natural Cosines 45°–90°

Mean Differences (Subtract)

TABLE V.—TRIGONOMETRIC FUNCTIONS.—*(Continued)*

		Natural Sines 45°–90°						Mean Differences (Add)					
°	0′	10′	20′	30′	40′	50′	°	1′ 2′ 3′	4′ 5′ 6′	7′ 8′ 9′
45	.7071	.7092	.7112	.7133	.7153	.7173	.7193 44	2 4 6	8 10 12	14 16 18
46	.7193	.7214	.7234	.7254	.7274	.7294	.7314 43	2 4 6	8 10 12	14 16 18
47	.7314	.7333	.7353	.7373	.7392	.7412	.7431 42	2 4 6	8 10 12	14 15 18
48	.7431	.7451	.7470	.7490	.7509	.7528	.7547 41	2 4 6	8 10 11	13 15 17
49	.7547	.7566	.7585	.7604	.7623	.7642	.7660 40	2 4 6	8 9 11	13 15 17
50	.7660	.7679	.7698	.7716	.7735	.7753	.7771 39	2 4 6	7 9 11	13 15 17
51	.7771	.7790	.7808	.7826	.7844	.7862	.7880 38	2 4 5	7 9 11	13 15 16
52	.7880	.7898	.7916	.7934	.7951	.7969	.7986 37	2 3 5	7 9 10	12 14 16
53	.7986	.8004	.8021	.8039	.8056	.8073	.8090 36	2 3 5	7 9 10	12 14 16
54	.8090	.8107	.8124	.8141	.8158	.8175	.8192 35	2 3 5	7 8 10	12 14 15
55	.8192	.8208	.8225	.8241	.8258	.8274	.8290 34	2 3 5	7 8 10	11 13 15
56	.8290	.8307	.8323	.8339	.8355	.8371	.8387 33	2 3 5	6 8 10	11 13 15
57	.8387	.8403	.8418	.8434	.8450	.8465	.8480 32	2 3 5	6 8 9	11 12 14
58	.8480	.8496	.8511	.8526	.8542	.8557	.8572 31	2 3 5	6 8 9	11 12 14
59	.8572	.8587	.8601	.8616	.8631	.8646	.8660 30	1 3 4	6 7 9	10 12 13
60	.8660	.8675	.8689	.8704	.8718	.8732	.8746 29	1 3 4	6 7 9	10 11 13
61	.8746	.8760	.8774	.8788	.8802	.8816	.8829 28	1 3 4	6 7 8	10 11 12
62	.8829	.8843	.8857	.8870	.8884	.8897	.8910 27	1 3 4	5 7 8	9 11 12
63	.8910	.8923	.8936	.8949	.8962	.8975	.8988 26	1 3 4	5 6 8	9 10 12
64	.8988	.9001	.9013	.9026	.9038	.9051	.9063 25	1 3 4	5 6 7	9 10 11
65	.9063	.9075	.9088	.9100	.9112	.9124	.9135 24	1 2 4	5 6 7	9 10 11
66	.9135	.9147	.9159	.9171	.9182	.9194	.9205 23	1 2 4	5 6 7	8 9 11
67	.9205	.9216	.9228	.9239	.9250	.9261	.9272 22	1 2 3	4 6 7	8 9 10
68	.9272	.9283	.9293	.9304	.9315	.9325	.9336 21	1 2 3	4 5 6	7 9 10
69	.9336	.9346	.9356	.9367	.9377	.9387	.9397 20	1 2 3	4 5 6	7 8 9
70	.9397	.9407	.9417	.9426	.9436	.9446	.9455 19	1 2 3	4 5 6	7 8 9
71	.9455	.9465	.9474	.9483	.9492	.9502	.9511 18	1 2 3	4 5 6	7 7 8
72	.9511	.9520	.9528	.9537	.9546	.9555	.9563 17	1 2 3	3 4 5	6 7 8
73	.9563	.9572	.9580	.9588	.9596	.9605	.9613 16	1 2 2	3 4 5	6 7 7
74	.9613	.9621	.9628	.9636	.9644	.9652	.9659 15	1 2 2	3 4 5	6 6 7
75	.9659	.9667	.9674	.9681	.9689	.9696	.9703 14	1 1 2	3 4 4	5 6 7
76	.9703	.9710	.9717	.9724	.9730	.9737	.9744 13	1 1 2	3 4 4	5 6 6
77	.9744	.9750	.9757	.9763	.9769	.9775	.9781 12	1 1 2	3 3 4	4 5 6
78	.9781	.9787	.9793	.9799	.9805	.9811	.9816 11	1 1 2	2 3 4	4 5 5
79	.9816	.9822	.9827	.9833	.9838	.9843	.9848 10	1 1 2	2 3 3	4 4 5
80	.9848	.9853	.9858	.9863	.9868	.9872	.9877 9	0 1 1	2 2 3	3 4 4
81	.9877	.9881	.9886	.9890	.9894	.9899	.9903 8	0 1 1	2 2 3	3 4 4
82	.9903	.9907	.9911	.9914	.9918	.9922	.9925 7	0 1 1	1 2 2	3 3 3
83	.9925	.9929	.9932	.9936	.9939	.9942	.9945 6	0 1 1	1 2 2	2 3 3
84	.9945	.9948	.9951	.9954	.9957	.9959	.9962 5	0 1 1	1 2 2	2 2 3
85	.9962	.9964	.9967	.9969	.9971	.9974	.9976 4	0 1 1	1 1 2	2 2 2
86	.9976	.9978	.9980	.9981	.9983	.9985	.9986 3	0 0 1	1 1 1	2 2 2
87	.9986	.9988	.9989	.9990	.9992	.9993	.9994 2	0 0 1	1 1 1	1 1 2
88	.9994	.9995	.9996	.9997	.9997	.9998	.9998 1	0 0 0	0 0 1	1 1 1
89	.9998	.9999	.9999	1.0000	1.0000	1.0000	1.0000 0	0 0 0	0 0 1	1 1 1
°	50′	40′	30′	20′	10′	0′	°	1′ 2′ 3′	4′ 5′ 6′	7′ 8′ 9′

Natural Cosines 0°–45°

Mean Differences (Subtract)

TABLE V.—TRIGONOMETRIC FUNCTIONS.—(Continued)

Natural Tangents 0°–45°

°	0'	10'	20'	30'	40'	50'		°	1'	2'	3'	4'	5'	6'	7'	8'	9'
0	.0000	.0029	.0058	.0087	.0116	.0145	.0175	89	3	6	9	12	15	17	20	23	26
1	.0175	.0204	.0233	.0262	.0291	.0320	.0349	88	3	6	9	12	15	17	20	23	26
2	.0349	.0378	.0407	.0437	.0466	.0495	.0524	87	3	6	9	12	15	17	20	23	26
3	.0524	.0553	.0582	.0612	.0641	.0670	.0699	86	3	6	9	12	15	17	20	23	26
4	.0699	.0729	.0758	.0787	.0816	.0846	.0875	85	3	6	9	12	15	18	21	24	26
5	.0875	.0904	.0934	.0963	.0992	.1022	.1051	84	3	6	9	12	15	18	21	24	26
6	.1051	.1080	.1110	.1139	.1169	.1198	.1228	83	3	6	9	12	15	18	21	24	27
7	.1228	.1257	.1287	.1317	.1346	.1376	.1405	82	3	6	9	12	15	18	21	24	27
8	.1405	.1435	.1465	.1495	.1524	.1554	.1584	81	3	6	9	12	15	18	21	24	27
9	.1584	.1614	.1644	.1673	.1703	.1733	.1763	80	3	6	9	12	15	18	21	24	27
10	.1763	.1793	.1823	.1853	.1883	.1914	.1944	79	3	6	9	12	15	18	21	24	27
11	.1944	.1974	.2004	.2035	.2065	.2095	.2126	78	3	6	9	12	15	18	21	24	27
12	.2126	.2156	.2186	.2217	.2247	.2278	.2309	77	3	6	9	12	15	18	22	25	28
13	.2309	.2339	.2370	.2401	.2432	.2462	.2493	76	3	6	9	12	15	18	22	25	28
14	.2493	.2524	.2555	.2586	.2617	.2648	.2679	75	3	6	9	12	16	19	22	25	28
15	.2679	.2711	.2742	.2773	.2805	.2836	.2867	74	3	6	9	12	16	19	22	25	28
16	.2867	.2899	.2931	.2962	.2994	.3026	.3057	73	3	6	10	13	16	19	22	26	29
17	.3057	.3089	.3121	.3153	.3185	.3217	.3249	72	3	6	10	13	16	19	22	26	29
18	.3249	.3281	.3314	.3346	.3378	.3411	.3443	71	3	6	10	13	16	19	23	26	29
19	.3443	.3476	.3508	.3541	.3574	.3607	.3640	70	3	7	10	13	16	20	23	26	30
20	.3640	.3673	.3706	.3739	.3772	.3805	.3839	69	3	7	10	13	17	20	23	26	30
21	.3839	.3872	.3906	.3939	.3973	.4006	.4040	68	3	7	10	13	17	20	23	27	30
22	.4040	.4074	.4108	.4142	.4176	.4210	.4245	67	3	7	10	14	17	21	24	27	31
23	.4245	.4279	.4314	.4348	.4383	.4417	.4452	66	3	7	10	14	17	21	24	28	31
24	.4452	.4487	.4522	.4557	.4592	.4628	.4663	65	4	7	11	14	18	21	25	28	32
25	.4663	.4699	.4734	.4770	.4806	.4841	.4877	64	4	7	11	14	18	21	25	29	32
26	.4877	.4913	.4950	.4986	.5022	.5059	.5095	63	4	7	11	15	18	22	25	29	33
27	.5095	.5132	.5169	.5206	.5243	.5280	.5317	62	4	7	11	15	19	22	26	30	33
28	.5317	.5354	.5392	.5430	.5467	.5505	.5543	61	4	8	11	15	19	23	26	30	34
29	.5543	.5581	.5619	.5658	.5696	.5735	.5774	60	4	8	12	15	19	23	27	31	35
30	.5774	.5812	.5851	.5890	.5930	.5969	.6009	59	4	8	12	16	20	23	27	31	35
31	.6009	.6048	.6088	.6128	.6168	.6208	.6249	58	4	8	12	16	20	24	28	32	36
32	.6249	.6289	.6330	.6371	.6412	.6453	.6494	57	4	8	12	16	20	24	28	33	37
33	.6494	.6536	.6577	.6619	.6661	.6703	.6745	56	4	8	13	17	21	25	29	34	38
34	.6745	.6787	.6830	.6873	.6916	.6959	.7002	55	4	9	13	17	21	26	30	34	39
35	.7002	.7046	.7089	.7133	.7177	.7221	.7265	54	4	9	13	18	22	26	31	35	40
36	.7265	.7310	.7355	.7400	.7445	.7490	.7536	53	5	9	14	18	23	27	32	36	41
37	.7536	.7581	.7627	.7673	.7720	.7766	.7813	52	5	9	14	18	23	28	32	37	42
38	.7813	.7860	.7907	.7954	.8002	.8050	.8098	51	5	10	14	19	24	29	33	38	43
39	.8098	.8146	.8195	.8243	.8292	.8342	.8391	50	5	10	15	20	24	29	34	39	44
40	.8391	.8441	.8491	.8541	.8591	.8642	.8693	49	5	10	15	20	25	30	35	40	45
41	.8693	.8744	.8796	.8847	.8899	.8952	.9004	48	5	10	16	21	26	31	36	42	47
42	.9004	.9057	.9110	.9163	.9217	.9271	.9325	47	5	11	16	21	27	32	37	43	48
43	.9325	.9380	.9435	.9490	.9545	.9601	.9657	46	6	11	17	22	28	33	39	44	50
44	.9657	.9713	.9770	.9827	.9884	.9942	1.0000	45	6	11	17	23	29	34	40	46	51
°		50'	40'	30'	20'	10'	0'	°	1'	2'	3'	4'	5'	6'	7'	8'	9'

Natural Cotangents 45°–90°

Mean Differences (Subtract)

TABLE V.—TRIGONOMETRIC FUNCTIONS.—(*Continued*)

	Natural Tangents 45°–90°							Differences					
°	0′	10′	20′	30′	40′	50′	°	0′ to 10′	10′ to 20′	20′ to 30′	30′ to 40′	40′ to 50′	50′ to 60′
45	1.0000	1.0058	1.0117	1.0176	1.0235	1.0295	1.0355	44	58	59	59	59	60	60
46	.0355	.0416	.0477	.0538	.0599	.0661	.0723	43	61	61	61	61	62	62
47	.0723	.0786	.0850	.0913	.0977	.1041	.1106	42	63	64	63	64	64	65
48	.1106	.1171	.1237	.1303	.1369	.1436	.1504	41	65	66	66	66	67	68
49	.1504	.1572	.1640	.1709	.1778	.1847	.1918	40	68	68	69	69	69	71
50	.1918	.1988	.2059	.2131	.2203	.2276	.2349	39	70	71	72	72	73	73
51	.2349	.2423	.2497	.2572	.2647	.2723	.2799	38	74	74	75	75	76	76
52	.2799	.2876	.2954	.3032	.3111	.3190	.3270	37	77	78	78	79	79	80
53	.3270	.3351	.3432	.3514	.3597	.3680	.3764	36	81	81	82	83	83	84
54	.3764	.3848	.3933	.4019	.4106	.4193	.4281	35	84	85	86	87	87	88
55	.4281	.4370	.4460	.4550	.4641	.4733	.4826	34	89	90	90	91	92	93
56	.4826	.4919	.5013	.5108	.5204	.5301	.5399	33	93	94	95	96	97	98
57	.5399	.5497	.5597	.5697	.5800	.5900	.6003	32	98	100	100	101	102	103
58	.6003	.6107	.6212	.6319	.6426	.6534	.6643	31	104	105	107	107	108	109
59	.6643	.6753	.6864	.6977	.7090	.7205	.7321	30	110	111	113	113	115	116
60	.7321	.7437	.7556	.7675	.7796	.7917	.8040	29	116	119	119	121	121	123
61	.8040	.8165	.8291	.8418	.8546	.8676	.8807	28	125	126	127	128	130	131
62	.8807	.8940	.9074	1.9210	1.9347	1.9486	1.9626	27	133	134	136	137	139	140
63	1.9626	1.9768	1.9912	2.0057	2.0204	2.0353	2.0503	26	142	144	145	147	149	150
64	2.0503	2.0655	2.0809	.0965	.1123	.1283	.1445	25	152	154	156	158	160	162
65	.1445	.1609	.1775	.1943	.2113	.2286	.2460	24	164	166	168	170	173	174
66	.2460	.2637	.2817	.2998	.3183	.3369	.3559	23	177	180	181	185	186	190
67	.3559	.3750	.3945	.4142	.4342	.4545	.4751	22	191	195	197	200	203	206
68	.4751	.4960	.5172	.5386	.5605	.5826	.6051	21	209	212	214	219	221	225
69	.6051	.6279	.6511	.6746	.6985	.7228	.7475	20	228	232	235	239	243	247
70	.7475	.7725	.7980	.8239	2.8502	2.8770	2.9042	19	250	255	259	263	268	272
71	2.9042	2.9319	2.9600	2.9887	3.0178	3.0475	3.0777	18	277	281	287	291	297	302
72	3.0777	3.1084	3.1397	3.1716	.2041	.2371	.2709	17	307	313	319	325	330	338
73	.2709	.3052	.3402	.3759	.4124	.4495	.4874	16	343	350	357	365	371	379
74	.4874	.5261	.5656	.6059	.6470	.6891	3.7321	15	387	395	403	411	421	430
75	3.7321	3.7760	3.8208	3.8667	3.9136	3.9617	4.0108	14	439	448	459	469	481	491
76	4.0108	4.0611	4.1126	4.1653	4.2193	4.2747	.3315	13	503	515	527	540	554	568
77	.3315	.3897	.4494	.5107	.5736	.6382	4.7046	12	582	597	613	629	646	664
78	4.7046	4.7729	4.8430	4.9152	4.9894	5.0658	5.1446	11	683	701	722	742	764	788
79	5.1446	5.2257	5.3093	5.3955	5.4845	5.5764	5.6713	10	811	836	862	890	919	949
80	5.6713	5.7694	5.8708	5.9758	6.0844	6.1970	6.3138	9						
81	6.3138	6.4348	6.5606	6.6912	6.8269	6.9682	7.1154	8						
82	7.1154	7.2687	7.4287	7.5958	7.7704	7.9530	8.1443	7						
83	8.1443	8.3450	8.5555	8.7769	9.0098	9.2553	9.5144	6		Differences not sufficiently accurate				
84	9.5144	9.7882	10.078	10.385	10.712	11.059	11.430	5						
85	11.430	11.826	12.251	12.706	13.197	13.727	14.301	4						
86	14.301	14.924	15.605	16.350	17.169	18.075	19.081	3						
87	19.081	20.206	21.470	22.904	24.542	26.432	28.636	2						
88	28.636	31.242	34.368	38.188	42.964	49.104	57.290	1						
89	57.290	68.750	85.940	114.59	171.89	343.77	∞	0						
°		50′	40′	30′	20′	10′	0′	°						

TABLE VI.—LOGARITHMS OF TRIGONOMETRIC FUNCTIONS

Logarithmic Sines 0°–45°

°	0'	10'	20'	30'	40'	50'		°	1'	2'	3'	4'	5'	6'	7'	8'	9'
0	∞	$\bar{3}$.4637	.7648	.9408	.0658	.1627	.2419	89									
1	$\bar{2}$.2419	.3088	.3668	.4179	.4637	.5050	.5428	88									
2	.5428	.5776	.6097	.6397	.6677	.6940	.7188	87									
3	.7188	.7423	.7645	.7857	.8059	.8251	.8436	86									
4	.8436	.8613	.8783	.8946	.9104	.9256	.9403	85									
5	$\bar{2}$.9403	.9545	.9682	.9816	.9945	.0070	.0192	84									
6	$\bar{1}$.0192	.0311	.0426	.0539	.0648	.0755	.0859	83									
7	.0859	.0961	.1060	.1157	.1252	.1345	.1436	82									
8	.1436	.1525	.1612	.1697	.1781	.1863	.1943	81									
9	.1943	.2022	.2100	.2176	.2251	.2324	.2397	80									
10	$\bar{1}$.2397	.2468	.2538	.2606	.2674	.2740	.2806	79	7	14	20	27	34	41	48	54	61
11	.2806	.2870	.2934	.2997	.3058	.3119	.3179	78	6	12	19	25	31	37	43	50	56
12	.3179	.3238	.3296	.3353	.3410	.3466	.3521	77	6	11	17	23	29	34	40	46	51
13	.3521	.3575	.3629	.3682	.3734	.3786	.3837	76	5	11	16	21	27	32	37	42	48
14	.3837	.3887	.3937	.3986	.4035	.4083	.4130	75	5	10	15	20	25	29	34	39	44
15	$\bar{1}$.4130	.4177	.4223	.4269	.4314	.4359	.4403	74	5	9	14	18	23	27	32	37	41
16	.4403	.4447	.4491	.4533	.4576	.4618	.4659	73	4	9	13	17	21	26	30	34	39
17	.4659	.4700	.4741	.4781	.4821	.4861	.4900	72	4	8	12	16	20	24	28	32	36
18	.4900	.4939	.4977	.5015	.5052	.5090	.5126	71	4	8	11	15	19	23	27	30	34
19	.5126	.5163	.5199	.5235	.5270	.5306	.5341	70	4	7	10	14	18	22	25	29	32
20	$\bar{1}$.5341	.5375	.5409	.5443	.5477	.5510	.5543	69	3	7	10	14	17	20	24	27	31
21	.5543	.5576	.5609	.5641	.5673	.5704	.5736	68	3	6	10	13	16	19	22	26	29
22	.5736	.5767	.5798	.5828	.5859	.5889	.5919	67	3	6	9	12	15	18	21	24	28
23	.5919	.5948	.5978	.6007	.6036	.6065	.6093	66	3	6	9	12	15	17	20	23	26
24	.6093	.6121	.6149	.6177	.6205	.6232	.6259	65	3	6	8	11	14	16	19	22	25
25	$\bar{1}$.6259	.6286	.6313	.6340	.6366	.6392	.6418	64	3	5	8	11	13	16	19	21	24
26	.6418	.6444	.6470	.6495	.6521	.6546	.6570	63	3	5	8	10	13	15	18	20	23
27	.6570	.6595	.6620	.6644	.6668	.6692	.6716	62	2	5	7	10	12	15	17	19	22
28	.6716	.6740	.6763	.6787	.6810	.6833	.6856	61	2	5	7	9	12	14	16	19	21
29	.6856	.6878	.6901	.6923	.6946	.6968	.6990	60	2	4	7	9	11	13	16	18	20
30	$\bar{1}$.6990	.7012	.7033	.7055	.7076	.7097	.7118	59	2	4	6	9	11	13	15	17	19
31	.7118	.7139	.7160	.7181	.7201	.7222	.7242	58	2	4	6	8	10	12	14	16	19
32	.7242	.7262	.7282	.7302	.7322	.7342	.7361	57	2	4	6	8	10	12	14	16	18
33	.7361	.7380	.7400	.7419	.7438	.7457	.7476	56	2	4	6	8	10	11	13	15	17
34	.7476	.7494	.7513	.7531	.7550	.7568	.7586	55	2	4	6	7	9	11	13	15	16
35	$\bar{1}$.7586	.7604	.7622	.7640	.7657	.7675	.7692	54	2	4	5	7	9	11	12	14	16
36	.7692	.7710	.7727	.7744	.7761	.7778	.7795	53	2	3	5	7	9	10	12	14	15
37	.7795	.7811	.7828	.7844	.7861	.7877	.7893	52	2	3	5	7	8	10	11	13	15
38	.7893	.7910	.7926	.7941	.7957	.7973	.7989	51	2	3	5	6	8	10	11	13	14
39	.7989	.8004	.8020	.8035	.8050	.8066	.8081	50	2	3	5	6	8	9	11	12	14
40	$\bar{1}$.8081	.8096	.8111	.8125	.8140	.8155	.8169	49	1	3	4	6	7	9	10	12	13
41	.8169	.8184	.8198	.8213	.8227	.8241	.8255	48	1	3	4	6	7	9	10	11	13
42	.8255	.8269	.8283	.8297	.8311	.8324	.8338	47	1	3	4	6	7	8	10	11	13
43	.8338	.8351	.8365	.8378	.8391	.8405	.8418	46	1	3	4	5	7	8	9	11	12
44	.8418	.8431	.8444	.8457	.8469	.8482	.8495	45	1	3	4	5	6	8	9	10	12
°	50'	40'	30'	20'	10'	0'		°	1'	2'	3'	4'	5'	6'	7'	8'	9'

Mean Differences (Add)

Differences {
3011–792
669–378
348–248
235–185
177–147
142–122
119–104
102–91
89–80
79–73

Logarithmic Cosines 45°–90°

Mean Differences (Subtract)

TABLE VI.—LOGARITHMS OF TRIGONOMETRIC FUNCTIONS.—*(Continued)*

Logarithmic Sines 45°–90°

°	0′	10′	20′	30′	40′	50′		°	1′	2′	3′	4′	5′	6′	7′	8′	9′
45	$\bar{1}$.8495	.8507	.8520	.8532	.8545	.8557	.8569	44	1	2	4	5	6	7	9	10	11
46	.8569	.8582	.8594	.8606	.8618	.8629	.8641	43	1	2	4	5	6	7	8	10	11
47	.8641	.8653	.8665	.8676	.8688	.8699	.8711	42	1	2	4	5	6	7	8	9	11
48	.8711	.8722	.8733	.8745	.8756	.8767	.8778	41	1	2	3	4	6	7	8	9	10
49	.8778	.8789	.8800	.8810	.8821	.8832	.8843	40	1	2	3	4	5	7	8	8	10
50	$\bar{1}$.8843	.8853	.8864	.8874	.8884	.8895	.8905	39	1	2	3	4	5	6	7	9	10
51	.8905	.8915	.8925	.8935	.8945	.8955	.8965	38	1	2	3	4	5	6	7	8	9
52	.8965	.8975	.8985	.8995	.9004	.9014	.9023	37	1	2	3	4	5	6	7	8	9
53	.9023	.9033	.9042	.9052	.9061	.9070	.9080	36	1	2	3	4	5	6	7	8	9
54	.9080	.9089	.9098	.9107	.9116	.9125	.9134	35	1	2	3	4	4	5	6	7	8
55	$\bar{1}$.9134	.9142	.9151	.9160	.9169	.9177	.9186	34	1	2	3	3	4	5	6	7	8
56	.9186	.9194	.9203	.9211	.9219	.9228	.9236	33	1	2	2	3	4	5	6	7	7
57	.9236	.9244	.9252	.9260	.9268	.9276	.9284	32	1	2	2	3	4	5	6	6	7
58	.9284	.9292	.9300	.9308	.9315	.9323	.9331	31	1	2	2	3	4	5	6	6	7
59	.9331	.9338	.9346	.9353	.9361	.9368	.9375	30	1	2	2	3	4	5	5	6	7
60	$\bar{1}$.9375	.9383	.9390	.9397	.9404	.9411	.9418	29	1	1	2	3	4	4	5	6	6
61	.9418	.9425	.9432	.9439	.9446	.9453	.9459	28	1	1	2	3	3	4	5	5	6
62	.9459	.9466	.9473	.9479	.9486	.9492	.9499	27	1	1	2	3	3	4	5	5	6
63	.9499	.9505	.9512	.9518	.9524	.9530	.9537	26	1	1	2	3	3	4	4	5	6
64	.9537	.9543	.9549	.9555	.9561	.9567	.9573	25	1	1	2	2	3	4	4	5	5
65	$\bar{1}$.9573	.9579	.9584	.9590	.9596	.9602	.9607	24	1	1	2	2	3	3	4	5	5
66	.9607	.9613	.9618	.9624	.9629	.9635	.9640	23	1	1	2	2	3	3	4	4	5
67	.9640	.9646	.9651	.9656	.9661	.9667	.9672	22	1	1	2	2	3	3	4	4	5
68	.9672	.9677	.9682	.9687	.9692	.9697	.9702	21	1	1	2	2	3	3	4	4	5
69	.9702	.9706	.9711	.9716	.9721	.9725	.9730	20	0	1	1	2	2	3	3	4	4
70	$\bar{1}$.9730	.9734	.9739	.9743	.9748	.9752	.9757	19	0	1	1	2	2	3	4	4	4
71	.9757	.9761	.9765	.9770	.9774	.9778	.9782	18	0	1	1	2	2	3	3	3	4
72	.9782	.9786	.9790	.9794	.9798	.9802	.9806	17	0	1	1	2	2	3	3	3	4
73	.9806	.9810	.9814	.9817	.9821	.9825	.9828	16	0	1	1	1	2	2	3	3	3
74	.9828	.9832	.9836	.9839	.9843	.9846	.9849	15	0	1	1	1	2	2	2	3	3
75	$\bar{1}$.9849	.9853	.9856	.9859	.9863	.9866	.9869	14	0	1	1	1	2	2	2	3	3
76	.9869	.9872	.9875	.9878	.9881	.9884	.9887	13	0	1	1	1	2	2	2	2	3
77	.9887	.9890	.9893	.9896	.9899	.9901	.9904	12	0	1	1	1	1	2	2	2	3
78	.9904	.9907	.9909	.9912	.9914	.9917	.9919	11	0	1	1	1	1	2	2	2	3
79	.9919	.9922	.9924	.9927	.9929	.9931	.9934	10	0	1	1	1	1	2	2	2	3
80	$\bar{1}$.9934	.9936	.9938	.9940	.9942	.9944	.9946	9									2
81	.9946	.9948	.9950	.9952	.9954	.9956	.9958	8									2
82	.9958	.9959	.9961	.9963	.9964	.9966	.9968	7									1–2
83	.9968	.9969	.9971	.9972	.9973	.9975	.9976	6									1–2
84	.9976	.9977	.9979	.9980	.9981	.9982	.9983	5			Differences						1–2
85	$\bar{1}$.9983	.9985	.9986	.9987	.9988	.9989	.9989	4									0–2
86	.9989	.9990	.9991	.9992	.9993	.9993	.9994	3									0–1
87	.9994	.9995	.9995	.9996	.9996	.9997	.9997	2									0–1
88	.9997	.9998	.9998	.9999	.9999	.9999	.9999	1									0–1
89	.9999	.0000	.0000	.0000	.0000	.0000	.0000	0									0–1
°		50′	40′	30′	20′	10′	0′	°	1′	2′	3′	4′	5′	6′	7′	8′	9′

Mean Differences (Subtract)

Logarithmic Cosines 0°–45°

Table VI.—Logarithms of Trigonometric Functions.—(Continued)

Logarithmic Tangents 0°–45°

°	0′	10′	20′	30′	40′	50′	°	1′	2′	3′	4′	5′	6′	7′	8′	9′
0	$-\infty$	$\bar{3}$.4637	.7648	.9409	*.0658*	*.1627*	*.2419*	89									
1	$\bar{2}$.2419	.3089	.3669	.4181	.4638	.5053	.5431	88									
2	.5431	.5779	.6101	.6401	.6682	.6945	.7194	87									
3	.7194	.7429	.7652	.7865	.8067	.8261	.8446	86									
4	.8446	.8624	.8795	.8960	.9118	.9272	.9420	85									
5	$\bar{2}$.9420	.9563	.9701	.9836	.9966	*.0093*	*.0216*	84									
6	$\bar{1}$.0216	.0336	.0453	.0567	.0678	.0786	.0891	83									
7	.0891	.0995	.1096	.1194	.1291	.1385	.1478	82									
8	.1478	.1569	.1658	.1745	.1831	.1915	.1997	81									
9	.1997	.2078	.2158	.2236	.2313	.2389	.2463	80									
10	$\bar{1}$.2463	.2536	.2609	.2680	.2750	.2819	.2887	79	7	14	21	28	36	43	50	57	64
11	.2887	.2954	.3020	.3085	.3149	.3212	.3275	78	7	13	20	26	33	39	46	52	59
12	.3275	.3336	.3397	.3458	.3517	.3576	.3634	77	6	12	18	24	30	36	42	48	54
13	.3634	.3691	.3748	.3804	.3859	.3914	.3968	76	6	11	17	22	28	33	39	44	50
14	.3968	.4021	.4074	.4127	.4178	.4230	.4281	75	5	10	16	21	26	31	36	42	47
15	$\bar{1}$.4281	.4331	.4381	.4430	.4479	.4527	.4575	74	5	10	15	20	25	29	34	39	44
16	.4575	.4622	.4669	.4716	.4762	.4808	.4853	73	5	9	14	19	24	28	33	38	42
17	.4853	.4898	.4943	.4987	.5031	.5075	.5118	72	4	9	13	18	22	27	31	35	40
18	.5118	.5161	.5203	.5245	.5287	.5329	.5370	71	4	8	13	17	21	25	29	34	38
19	.5370	.5411	.5451	.5491	.5531	.5571	.5611	70	4	8	12	16	20	24	28	32	36
20	$\bar{1}$.5611	.5650	.5689	.5727	.5766	.5804	.5842	69	4	8	12	15	19	23	27	31	35
21	.5842	.5879	.5917	.5954	.5991	.6028	.6064	68	4	7	11	15	18	22	26	30	33
22	.6064	.6100	.6136	.6172	.6208	.6243	.6279	67	4	7	11	14	18	22	25	29	32
23	.6279	.6314	.6348	.6383	.6417	.6452	.6486	66	3	7	10	14	17	21	24	28	31
24	.6486	.6520	.6553	.6587	.6620	.6654	.6687	65	3	7	10	13	17	20	23	27	30
25	$\bar{1}$.6687	.6720	.6752	.6785	.6817	.6850	.6882	64	3	7	10	13	16	20	23	26	29
26	.6882	.6914	.6946	.6977	.7009	.7040	.7072	63	3	6	10	13	16	19	22	26	29
27	.7072	.7103	.7134	.7165	.7196	.7226	.7257	62	3	6	9	12	15	18	21	25	28
28	.7257	.7287	.7317	.7348	.7378	.7408	.7438	61	3	6	9	12	15	18	21	24	27
29	.7438	.7467	.7497	.7526	.7556	.7585	.7614	60	3	6	9	12	15	18	21	23	26
30	$\bar{1}$.7614	.7644	.7673	.7701	.7730	.7759	.7788	59	3	6	9	12	14	17	20	23	26
31	.7788	.7816	.7845	.7873	.7902	.7930	.7958	58	3	6	9	11	14	17	20	23	25
32	.7958	.7986	.8014	.8042	.8070	.8097	.8125	57	3	6	8	11	14	17	20	22	25
33	.8125	.8153	.8180	.8208	.8235	.8263	.8290	56	3	6	8	11	14	17	19	22	25
34	.8290	.8317	.8344	.8371	.8398	.8425	.8452	55	3	5	8	11	13	16	19	22	24
35	$\bar{1}$.8452	.8479	.8506	.8533	.8559	.8586	.8613	54	3	5	8	11	13	16	19	21	24
36	.8613	.8639	.8666	.8692	.8718	.8745	.8771	53	3	5	8	11	13	16	18	21	24
37	.8771	.8797	.8824	.8850	.8876	.8902	.8928	52	3	5	8	10	13	16	18	21	24
38	.8928	.8954	.8980	.9006	.9032	.9058	.9084	51	3	5	8	10	13	16	18	21	23
39	.9084	.9110	.9135	.9161	.9187	.9212	.9238	50	3	5	8	10	13	15	18	21	23
40	$\bar{1}$.9238	.9264	.9289	.9315	.9341	.9366	.9392	49	3	5	8	10	13	15	18	21	23
41	.9392	.9417	.9443	.9468	.9494	.9519	.9544	48	3	5	8	10	13	15	18	20	23
42	.9544	.9570	.9595	.9621	.9646	.9671	.9697	47	3	⋆5	8	10	13	15	18	20	23
43	.9697	.9722	.9747	.9772	.9798	.9823	.9848	46	3	5	8	10	13	15	18	20	23
44	.9848	.9874	.9899	.9924	.9949	.9975	.0000	45	3	5	8	10	13	15	18	20	23
°	50′	40′	30′	20′	10′	0′	°	1′	2′	3′	4′	5′	6′	7′	8′	9′

Mean Differences (Add) — for degrees 0–9:

Differences {
3011–792
670–378
348–249
235–185
170–148
143–124
120–105
104–93
91–82
81–74
}

Logarithmic Cotangents 45°–90°

Mean Differences (Subtract)

TABLE VI.—LOGARITHMS OF TRIGONOMETRIC FUNCTIONS.—*(Continued)*

Logarithmic Tangents 45°–90°

°	0'	10'	20'	30'	40'	50'		°	1'	2'	3'	4'	5'	6'	7'	8'	9'
45	0.0000	.0025	.0051	.0076	.0101	.0126	.0152	44	3	5	8	10	13	15	18	20	23
46	.0152	.0177	.0202	.0228	.0253	.0278	.0303	43	3	5	8	10	13	15	18	20	23
47	.0303	.0329	.0354	.0379	.0405	.0430	.0456	42	3	5	8	10	13	15	18	20	23
48	.0456	.0481	.0506	.0532	.0557	.0583	.0608	41	3	5	8	10	13	15	18	20	23
49	.0608	.0634	.0659	.0685	.0711	.0736	.0762	40	3	5	8	10	13	15	18	20	23
50	0.0762	.0788	.0813	.0839	.0865	.0890	.0916	39	3	5	8	10	13	15	18	20	23
51	.0916	.0942	.0968	.0994	.1020	.1046	.1072	38	3	5	8	10	13	16	18	21	23
52	.1072	.1098	.1124	.1150	.1176	.1203	.1229	37	3	5	8	10	13	16	18	21	23
53	.1229	.1255	.1282	.1308	.1334	.1361	.1387	36	3	5	8	11	13	16	18	21	24
54	.1387	.1414	.1441	.1467	.1494	.1521	.1548	35	3	5	8	11	13	16	19	21	24
55	0.1548	.1575	.1602	.1629	.1656	.1683	.1710	34	3	5	8	11	14	16	19	22	24
56	.1710	.1737	.1765	.1792	.1820	.1847	.1875	33	3	6	8	11	14	17	19	22	25
57	.1875	.1903	.1930	.1958	.1986	.2014	.2042	32	3	6	8	11	14	17	20	22	25
58	.2042	.2070	.2098	.2127	.2155	.2184	.2212	31	3	6	9	11	14	17	20	23	35
59	.2212	.2241	.2270	.2299	.2327	.2356	.2386	30	3	6	9	12	15	17	20	23	26
60	0.2386	.2415	.2444	.2474	.2503	.2533	.2562	29	3	6	9	12	15	18	21	23	26
61	.2562	.2592	.2622	.2652	.2683	.2713	.2743	28	3	6	9	12	15	18	21	24	27
62	.2743	.2774	.2804	.2835	.2866	.2897	.2928	27	3	6	9	12	15	19	22	25	28
63	.2928	.2960	.2991	.3023	.3054	.3086	.3118	26	3	6	10	13	16	19	22	25	29
64	.3118	.3150	.3183	.3215	.3248	.3280	.3313	25	3	7	10	13	16	20	23	26	29
65	0.3313	.3346	.3380	.3413	.3447	.3480	.3514	24	3	7	10	13	17	20	23	27	30
66	.3514	.3548	.3583	.3617	.3652	.3686	.3721	23	3	7	10	14	17	21	24	28	31
67	.3721	.3757	.3792	.3828	.3864	.3900	.3936	22	4	7	11	14	18	22	25	29	32
68	.3936	.3972	.4009	.4046	.4083	.4121	.4158	21	4	7	11	15	19	22	26	30	33
69	.4158	.4196	.4234	.4273	.4311	.4350	.4389	20	4	8	12	15	19	23	27	31	35
70	0.4389	.4429	.4469	.4509	.4549	.4589	.4630	19	4	8	12	16	20	24	28	32	36
71	.4630	.4671	.4713	.4755	.4797	.4839	.4882	18	4	8	13	17	21	25	29	34	38
72	.4882	.4925	.4969	.5013	.5057	.5102	.5147	17	4	9	13	18	22	26	31	35	40
73	.5147	.5192	.5238	.5284	.5331	.5378	.5425	16	5	9	14	19	23	28	32	37	42
74	.5425	.5473	.5521	.5570	.5619	.5669	.5719	15	5	10	15	20	25	29	34	39	44
75	0.5719	.5770	.5822	.5873	.5926	.5979	.6032	14	5	10	16	21	26	31	37	42	47
76	.6032	.6086	.6141	.6196	.6252	.6309	.6366	13	6	11	17	22	28	33	39	45	50
77	.6366	.6424	.6483	.6542	.6603	.6664	.6725	12	6	12	18	24	30	36	42	48	54
78	.6725	.6788	.6851	.6915	.6981	.7047	.7113	11	7	13	20	26	33	39	46	52	59
79	.7113	.7181	.7250	.7320	.7391	.7464	.7537	10	7	14	21	28	35	42	49	57	64
80	0.7537	.7611	.7687	.7764	.7842	.7922	.8003	9									
81	.8003	.8085	.8169	.8255	.8342	.8431	.8522	8						74–81			
82	.8522	.8615	.8709	.8806	.8904	.9005	.9109	7						82–91			
83	.9109	.9214	.9322	.9433	.9547	.9664	.9784	6						93–104			
84	.9784	.9907	*.0034*	*.0164*	*.0299*	*.0437*	*.0580*	5						105–120			
85	1.0580	.0728	.0882	.1040	.1205	.1376	.1554	4		Differences				123–143			
86	.1554	.1739	.1933	.2135	.2348	.2571	.2806	3						148–178			
87	.2806	.3055	.3318	.3599	.3899	.4221	.4569	2						185–235			
88	.4569	.4947	.5362	.5819	.6331	.6911	.7581	1						249–348			
89	.7581	.8373	.9342	2.0591	.2352	.5363	∞	0						378–670			
														792–3011			
°	50'	40'	30'	20'	10'	0'		°	1'	2'	3'	4'	5'	6'	7'	8'	9'

Logarithmic Cotangents 0°–45°

ANSWERS TO PROBLEMS

Answers are included only for those problems requiring a numerical solution

Chapter II, page 17

1. $x' = -6.67$; $y' = -5.0$. **2.** $x' = -8$; $y' = +1$.

3. For a real image, 62.5 cm. away; for a virtual image, 37.5 cm. away.

4. 72.25 cm. toward the mirror.

5. 5. **6.** 60 deg.

7. 1.5 cm. from surface; diameter $= 0.80$ mm.; $\alpha = -1.04$.

8. $n = 2$.

9. 13.9 from the side; $\beta = +1.235$; $\alpha = +1.15$.

10. About 54 ft.

12. 78.9 from the emergent nodal point.

Chapter III, page 29

2. $f = f' = +15$; $p = p' = -10$; P and P' coincide at middle of sphere.

3. $f = f' = +20$; $p = 0$; $p' = -6.67$.

4. $f = +15.9$; $f' = +21.2$; $\Delta = -136$; $p = -\frac{5}{17}$.

5. $f_1 = +23.266$; $f_1' = +31.095$; $f_2 = +132.85$; $f_2' = +142.85$;
$f_3 = +85.712$; $f_3' = +79.712$; $f = +15.497$; $f' = +20.712$.

7. $f_2 = -66.67$ cm.

8. $f = +20$; at principal focal point F'; 10 cm. outside of bowl.

9. If the index of glycerin is taken as 1.48, $f = -1.04$ mm.

10. If only one side of the cylinder is used, and considering $r_1 = +500$ cm. and $r_2 = +498$ cm., $f = -373,500$ cm. Considering $r_1 = r_2 = +500$ cm., $f = +750,000$ cm.

Chapter IV, page 34

1. Less than 1 cm.

2. Exit pupil is 4.8 cm. toward eye from ocular and has a diameter of 1 cm.

3. HINT: find β for the entrance and exit pupils and use eq. 2-7. Image is 20.9 cm. to right of exit pupil and is 1.31 cm. in height.

4. If stop in front, $f/15$; if behind, $f/13.5$.

5. $f/5.3$.

Chapter V, page 44

1. One point 135 cm. from 20-candle-power lamp toward 30-candle-power lamp; another point -1335 cm. on side of 20-candle-power lamp.

2. 1386.

3. Brightness $= 5.83 \times 10^{-4}$ candles per cm.^{2}

Chapter VI, page 70

3. Distance of primary image from mirror vertex = 25.1 cm.; of secondary image = 36.2 cm. Length of primary image = 3.06 cm.; length of secondary image = 4.4 cm.; astigmatic difference = 11.1 cm.

5. 8.31 and 12.85 along axis from vertex.

6. $f_C = 50.0179$ cm., $f_D = 50.000$ cm., $f_F = 49.9645$ cm., $f_G = 50.0178$ cm.

Chapter VII, page 86

1. $\beta = 22.2$.

2. 0.67 mm.

3. 4.16 cm. from glass.

4. $\gamma = 12$; $f_2 = 1.67$.

5. 1 in.

7. $f_2 = 7.79$ cm.; $\beta_\infty = 3.08$.

Chapter VIII, page 99

2. Assuming minimum deviation in each case, dispersion at 4000 angstroms is 3.11×10^3 radians per cm., at 7000 angstroms is 5.66×10^2 radians per cm. Sodium doublet just resolved if $t = 1.7$ cm.

4. About 65 deg.

5. $n = 1.18$.

Chapter X, page 135

1. 5.86×10^{-5} cm.

2. $n = 1.00029$.

3. About $14° 17'$.

4. 5461 angstroms.

5. 5.76×10^{-4} cm.

Chapter XI, page 162

2. About 50 cm.   **3.** 0.0145 cm.   **4.** 5.945 mm.

5. For $R = 0.75$, resolving power = 520,000; for $R = 0.90$, resolving power = 1,475,000.

Chapter XII, page 206

1. 1.22×10^{-3} cm.

2. For visual observations, about 51 sec. of arc or 3.5 mm. from center; for photographic observations, a larger distance.

3. About 5.8×10^{-5} cm.   **4.** $b = 2a$.

5. $R = 150,000$ in first order; about 113 cm. on a side; 3.567 mm.

Chapter XIII, page 249

1. $t = 0.015$ times an odd integer; parallel to the optic axis.

2. $n = 1.5869$.   **3.** About 1 deg.   **4.** 0.016π.

5. Slightly elliptical, direction of major axis parallel to original plane of vibration.

6. 1.99.

Chapter XIV, page 271

1. 9875.02, 15239.22, 18473.69, 20572.95, 22012.21, all cm^{-1}.

2. $\tilde{\nu}_\infty = 27419.42$ cm.$^{-1}$· $\lambda_\infty = 3647$ angstroms; $V = 3.4$ volts.

3. Total radiation per year $= 1.42 \times 10^{41}$ ergs; of which 6.56×10^{31} strikes the earth.
4. $a_1 = 0.53 \times 10^{-8}$ cm.; $v = 2.182 \times 10^8$ cm. per sec.; $W = 2.15 \times 10^{-4}$ ergs.
5. Separations may be calculated from $R_H/R_D = 8.9952/8.9976$.
6. $T = 5786$ deg. abs.; $E = 2.285 \times 10^{14}$ ergs.

Chapter XVI, page 322

1. About 15,000 gauss.
2. Yes, at 2150 angstroms in first order, 4300 angstroms in second order, etc.
4. About 20,000 gauss; $R = 0.03$.

Chapter XVII, page 339

1. Numerical aperture $= 0.1503$, assuming f' for eye is 2.07 cm.
2. About 30 cm.   3. Magnification is about 3.33.

INDEX